Modern Combat Aircraft Design

Modern Combat Aircraft Design

Klaus Huenecke

Naval Institute Press
Annapolis, Maryland

Published and distributed in the United States of America and Canada, and The
Republic of the Philippines by the Naval Institute Press, Annapolis, Maryland 21402

Modern Combat Aircraft Design is translated from the German language work Das
Kampfflugzeug von Heute first published in 1984 by Motorbuch Verlag.
Translated from German by Dermot McElholm.

Original German text © Klaus Huenecke 1984 & 1987.

This English translation © Airlife Publishing Ltd. 1987.

First English language edition published in England
by Airlife Publishing Ltd. 1987, reprinted 1990, 1994.

Library of Congress Catalog Card No. 87-61280

ISBN 0-87021-426-8

Printed in England.

Contents

Foreword

Flying has always had a special grip on the public imagination. The faster planes became, the more the fascination with these technological miracles grew. This is especially true of combat aircraft: on the one hand because of their superiority in speed and manoeuvrability to all other aircraft; and on the other hand however because – as military equipment – they permitted little insight into their inner secrets. An additional difficulty is that combat aircraft technology is relatively complicated and difficult to explain.

It should not be surprising therefore that the available literature, in spite of widespread interest in aeronautics in general and in combat aircraft in particular, is in the main a superficial compilation of types or the history of their development.

In this book an attempt has been made for the first time to describe the modern combat aircraft as the product of a highly developed technology; in doing so it was important to find a technically sound way of representation yet at the same time use clearly understood descriptions.

Jet-propelled combat aircraft, known popularly as "jet fighters", first appeared towards the end of the Second World War. They were the result of extensive research activity, particularly in the area of high-speed aerodynamics, which had been carried out systematically since the thirties. After the war the work done under the pressure of wartime events formed the basis for rapid further de-velopment. In 1947 a research plane broke the 'sound barrier' for the first time. Only a few years later the leading nations in the world had operational combat aircraft which could fly at more than twice the speed of sound. After the introduction of the complicated swing-wing came a return to the less costly manoeuvrable combat aircraft. The types F-16 and F-18 embody the culmination of this develop-ment; which is by no means at an end.

The process by which a combat air-craft comes into being normally begins with a military requirement. The task of the **aircraft design** is to fulfil this as well as possible. First, questions regarding range and military payload are dealt with in the **mission analysis.** Here we have the aircraft in rough outline, but not how-ever in its final form. This takes shape more and more through contributions from other fields. Above all **aero-dynamics** must be mentioned here be-cause it occupies a central position in the design. As a special area of flow theory it deals with the aerial forces on the air-craft, such as lift and drag; as well as their effect on the design of the wing, fuselage and tail.

The behaviour of the aircraft at high angles-of-attack, which is a particularly important criterion for combat aircraft, is above all an aerodynamic problem.

The notions of **stability** and **control** are closely bound up with aerodynamics. Under these terms are to be understood the ability of the aircraft to return to the original flight situation automatically, or to alter the flight situation arbitrarily through the pilot's actions.

The performance of modern combat aircraft would, however, be unthinkable without corresponding advances in **pro-pulsion technology.** Particularly notice-able is the substantially increased thrust/ weight ratio of modern engines, and re-duced fuel consumption through better cooling, new materials and the use of turbofan engines.

Great attention is devoted to the inte-gration of the propulsion system with the airframe. In order to exploit fully the performance potential of the combat air-craft, optimal flow conditions in the engine area have to be ensured. In particular the characteristic requirement for combat aircraft of high manoeuvra-bility has led to special solutions for the air intake and tail.

Using engine and aerodynamic data the expected **flight performance** can be estimated. Elements of performance are, for example, turning, climb, pull-out and specific excess power, which are at the same time essential characteristics of manoeuvrability.

The airframe and engine are the exter-nal attributes of an aeroplane from which one can to a certain extent tell their function. Apart from them there are how-ever numerous 'black boxes' inside the aircraft whose function is not recognis-able, but which are, nevertheless, of decisive importance for combat effectiveness. Terms such as radar, infra-red, lasers, and navigational/attack systems are grouped together here under **avionics.**

It is the human being, however, above all, who must operate this complicated technology. The point of contact between human being and technology is represented by the cockpit. Its design is an important factor.

In spite of all the emphasis laid on modern technologies for the combat aircraft, its development is by no means over. New concepts of control, together with improved aerodynamics and other technologies, are opening up a potential for manoeuvrability which has, up to now, been considered unattainable. This brief general survey is intended to provide the first prerequisites of the organization and contents of this book. The selected topics characterize the latest technology.

The presentation has been kept comprehensible and selected in such a way that little previous knowledge is required. However mathematical formulae of a simple kind were unavoidable in some cases. In the Appendix some ideas taken from aircraft technology are mentioned which are referred to in the text. Numerical data are basically given in the International System of Units.

The author has endeavoured to ensure a high standard of text and illustrations.

This book is based on practical experience. It is intended for those readers who wish to acquire a sound knowledge of modern combat aircraft technology, or must acquire this knowledge for professional reasons. The book is also suitable for: the technically interested layman; for the engineer in his field; for members of the armed forces as well as for students in aeronautical as well as other areas of technology.

1 Development of the modern combat aircraft

When, on 14th October 1947, the US Air Force Major Charles Yeager, in his XS-1, reached a speed corresponding to Mach 1.06 he was the first human being to succeed in breaking the sound barrier. This heralded a new era in the history of air travel. Today this first step into the world beyond the sound barrier appears comparatively clumsy.

The rocket-powered XS-1 (the initials stand for 'Experimental Supersonic') first had to be carried to a height of 7 kilometres (23000 ft), where its engine was ignited to provide the necessary thrust for a brief period. It became clear however that the United States had taken over the technological lead from a Europe scarred by war.

The fact that Europe, and especially Germany, possessed a vast technological lead towards the end of the war is undisputed. At that time the Germans had already been working for 20 years in the high-speed field. Towards the end of the 20s scientists and engineers were researching streamlined bodies at high speeds. In 1933 Adolf Busemann investigated the behaviour of wing profiles in the high-speed tunnel at the Kaiser-Wilhelm Institute for Flow Research in Göttingen. Through the use of Laval nozzles he succeeded in producing flow speeds one and a half times the speed of sound. Two years later, on the occasion of a symposium in Rome on high-speed aerodynamics, he was able, using his results, to point to the importance of thin

1-1 **The best propeller-driven combat aircraft of the forties could, at best, only reach half the speed of sound (Spitfire, in the background a Hurricane).**

11

1-2 **The flight performance of the Me 163 rocket interceptor was limited by compressibility effects at transonic speeds.**

1-3 **The 262 had a sweptback wing and could reach 860 km/h (464 knots) in level flight.**

profiles which postponed the rise in transonic drag to higher Mach numbers.

At this time rocket technology was also making enormous progress, and the use of rocket engines in combat aircraft was also considered. In 1934 Eugen Sänger considered that a rocket-powered fighter that would fly at supersonic speeds was feasible.

In 1939 Albert Betz, also in Göttingen, pointed out the advantages of the swept-back wing, which enabled the transonic rise in drag to be displaced to higher Mach numbers. Two essential criteria were thereby recognised as determining factors for favourable transonic drag behaviour, i.e. thin profiles and a swept-back leading edge.

The combat aircraft of that time, in Germany the Bf 109 and in Great Britain the Spitfire, were however incapable of advancing into these speed ranges (Fig. 1-1). At best, they could reach half the speed of sound. Even if they had succeeded in extracting the performance from the piston engines of that time necessary to penetrate into the transonic speed range, a speed of more than 800 km/h (430 knots) would nevertheless not have been possible with the propeller as a means of propulsion. The rapid decrease in efficiency, caused by air compressibility phenomena at the propeller blades, prevents the propeller from 'gripping' sufficiently at these speeds.

Only the introduction of jet propulsion opened up the possibility of increasing flight speeds further. The fastest combat aircraft of that time was the well-known Me 163 "Komet" whose sweptback wing had a twist to ensure longitudinal stability and to improve low-speed behaviour (Fig. 1-2). From the combination of revolutionary aerodynamics (for its time) and rocket propulsion emerged an extremely small all-wing type, whose prototype reached a speed of 1000 km/h (M = 0.82) on 2nd October 1941.

The flight Mach number of the production-line machines were M = 0.8. Above M = 0.84 the aircraft showed a dangerous nose-down tendency, because of the displacement of the wing centre of pressure to the rear, which could not be compensated for by control measures. Thorough research of this behaviour, which would have been necessary with the introduction of new technology, could not take place because of wartime events. Nevertheless a speed of 1130 km/h (610 knots) was successfully attained at low altitude with an experimental aircraft in June 1944.

The Me 262 was the first 'fully-developed' combat aircraft which possessed a sweptback wing (Fig. 1-3). Although the leading edge exhibited a relatively slight sweep angle of 18.5 degrees, the two Jumo 004B engines could thrust it to 860 km/h (465 knots) in level flight; 130 km/h (70 knots) faster than the Allies' best propeller-driven fighters. The Me 262 had slats which automatically extended in order to improve the low-speed characteristics. The final speed was as high as 1000 km/h (540 knots). At Messerschmitt designs with larger sweep angles were also investigated, but were not realized, in light of the still unresearched stability problems. In contrast, the first British jet fighter, the "Meteor", did not have a sweptback wing. At a speed of 765 km/h (413 knots) it was scarcely faster than the fastest British propeller fighter, the Spitfire Mk. XIX. All the same the significance of compressibility phenomena for the future development of combat aircraft had been recognized in Britain. The RAF's original wish to adopt the American P-38 "Lightning" fighter was dropped, because this aircraft, although it was very fast, exhibited considerable transonic problems. Instead the British started their own investigations to explore the high-speed range. Thus a Spitfire Mk. XI reached a speed equivalent to Mach 0.92 in a dive in 1944; this must, surely, have been the highest ever achieved by a propeller aircraft. In spite of its elliptical wing plan the Spitfire was already distinguished by a very thin profile.

In the USA, just as in the UK, designers were advancing into the Jet Age at a conservative pace. The first American jet-propelled aircraft, the Bell "Aira-

1-4 The first operational combat aircraft able to fly just above the speed of sound in a dive was North American's F-86.

comet", just reached 665 km/h (359 knots). This rather poor performance was not only due to the low thrust of engines at that time, but was above all due to the complete lack of any research in the high-speed field. In fact in the USA such research had been practically left untouched. In order to regain a position at the forefront of technology and to gather experience in the higher Mach-number range as quickly as possible, the USAAF in 1946 decided to use rocket motors in their research aircraft as propulsion units. On 8th December 1946 the Bell XS-1 was flown. This was to be the first aircraft in the world to fly faster than Mach 1. This aircraft had a straight wing with a profile thickness of only 10%. With the low cruising power of the engines, the initially intended speed of 2700 km/h (1457 knots) could not be reached by a long way. Its successor, the Bell X-1A, reached Mach 2.5 on 16th December 1953. The rivalry in the American services led to the Douglas "Skyrocket", a parallel development financed by the US Navy.

This aircraft possessed mixed turbine and rocket propulsion and could fly unaided at transonic speeds in level flight. On 21st November 1953 the "Skyrocket" was the first manned aircraft in the world to fly at more than twice the speed of sound and reached Mach 2.01. For this record flight the turbine engine had been removed and the thrust was generated by the rocket motor alone. However the "Skyrocket" first had to be carried to a high altitude, suspended under the wing of a Superfortress bomber.

Despite the fact that this record was short-lived, the performance achieved is remarkable, because the aircraft was designed for a maximum Mach number of only 1.4.

Combat aircraft designs from the period immediately after the war largely reflect the technological level of the USA and Great Britain during the last war years. They all had turbine engines and were equipped with wings which were not sweptback. The British types, the Gloster "Meteor", Hawker "Sea Hawk" and Supermarine "Attacker", as well as

1-5 **Turbojet-engined Fighter Ta 183 from the Focke-Wulf works, designed by Hans Multhopp in 1944; here seen as a model in a makeshift wind tunnel near Bad Eilsen. It was usual to suspend the model upside down on wires which transmitted the aerodynamic forces to measuring scales. Because of the approaching end of the war the project never got beyond the wind tunnel stage.**

the American models, the Republic F-84 "Thunderjet" and Lockheed F-80 "Shooting Star", are examples of this. It seemed that the advantages of the sweptback wing were being completely ignored outside Germany: and this in spite of the fact that even before the end of the war mission reports on the Me 262 had been available; and Busemann's published work had been known about for some time. When the Allies were able to look through the research papers after the occupation of Germany, only North American's design team reacted promptly to the newly acquired technology. Their XP-86 project was started again with a wing swept back at 35° based on German research data.

This wing was 11 per cent thick and had automatically operated slats. In October 1947 the famous F-86 "Sabre" was developed from the XP-86: the F-86 was the first operational combat aircraft to break the sound barrier, although only in a dive (Fig. 1-4).

The Me 262 did not however remain the only project of importance for future developments. At the Focke-Wulf works in Bremen, under Professor Tank's direction, a combat aircraft was developed

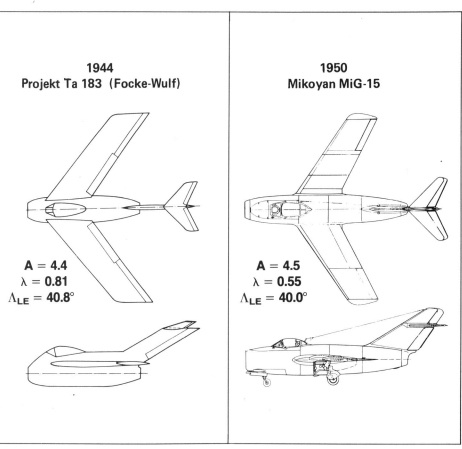

1944 Projekt Ta 183 (Focke-Wulf)	1950 Mikoyan MiG-15
$A = 4.4$ $\lambda = 0.81$ $\Lambda_{LE} = 40.8°$	$A = 4.5$ $\lambda = 0.55$ $\Lambda_{LE} = 40.0°$

1-6 **The German Ta 183 fighter project served as a model for the Soviet MiG-15.**

1-7   **The first Western supersonic 'jet fighter' was North American's F-100, here seen as the F-100F two-seater version.**

which was designated as the Ta 183 (Fig. 1-5). Because of its unusual shape it was nicknamed the "Huckebein", which roughly translated means "Crow". The construction contract for this aircraft, which was to be equipped with Heinkel's HeS 011 turbojet engine, was placed in March 1945 by the German Air Ministry, but prototypes could no longer be completed. What is noteworthy is the wing sweepback angle of 40.8° ($\Lambda_{25} = 40°$) and the extremely sweptback vertical tail at 60°.

The construction documents for this aircraft fell into the hands of Soviet troops in Berlin, and when the British sold Rolls-Royce "Nene" turbine engines to the Soviet Union, the Eastern bloc was also able to join the Jet Age. The result of this unexpected German-British co-operation was the famous MiG-15, which gave the Americans considerable trouble in the Korean War (Fig. 1-6). The F-80 with its

straight wings proved to be hopelessly inferior in aerial combat, and even the F-86 could scarcely keep up with the combat performance of the MiG-15. It was solely due to the Americans' better combat training that the F-86 was finally able to achieve a shoot-down ratio of at least 3:1 in its favour.

The experiences of the Korean War served as a basis for the next generation of combat aircraft. In the USA North American built the F-100 "Super Sabre", and the Soviet Union developed the MiG-17 and MiG-19 models from the MiG-15.

The F-100 (maiden flight 1953) was the first production-line aircraft in the West to exceed Mach 1 in level flight (Fig. 1-7). This aeroplane was thus the first 'supersonic fighter'. In contrast to its predecessor, the F-86, the F-100 had greater wing sweepback and a wing

thickness of 7 per cent. In order to reduce the twisting moments of the extremely tapered wing, the ailerons were grouped near the fuselage. The elevator, as a so-called flying stabilizer, was completely adjustable. In order to accelerate to high speeds the aeroplane was equipped with afterburning.

The Soviet MiG-17 was a revised design of the MiG-15 and, apart from an extended tail cone, had above all a completely redesigned wing. However even with afterburning (MiG-17F) this aeroplane was not able to break the sound barrier either. Its highest Mach number was about M = 0.98. Only the twin-jet MiG-19 was able to reach Mach 1.35 in level flight and thus keep pace with the F-100.

As Mach numbers increased, aircraft designs increasingly departed from the World War II models. There was however **one** wing shape from that time

15

1-8 **Mirage 5 with delta wing.**

which has lost none of its attractiveness even today. This is the delta wing developed by Alexander Lippisch, which was taken up by France, the UK and the Soviet Union in particular.

The French aircraft industry, which had risen again after the war, pursued ambitious delta wing projects which indicated future trends. It was able to score a considerable success with the Nord "Griffon 2" in 1957. This aeroplane had a delta wing with a thickness of 4.8 per cent and a leading-edge sweepback of 60°, as well as a delta-shaped foreplane. A turbo-ramjet engine imparted a speed of more than twice the speed of sound. France also developed its famous "Mirage" combat aircraft, based on the Mirage 1 of 1955, which became a worldwide success (Fig. 1-8).

The secret of the delta wing lies in its geometry: the large profile chord in the wing root area permits the proportionally

thin profile thicknesses, necessary for high-speed flight; on the other hand the relatively deep chord permits lighter structures. In addition there is a favourable flow behaviour at high angles-of-attack and an acceptable drag at supersonic speeds.

While France with its delta wing aeroplanes was going for all-wing types, the Soviet Union was exclusively pursuing configurations with tails. The most famous example is the MiG-21, which as with the Mirage has a delta wing with an aspect ratio of about 2 (Fig. 1-9). This aircraft was built in numbers which no other "jet fighter" in the world ever reached (over 10,000 is the suggested number). The MiG-21 was until recently the 'standard opponent' for NATO. It has small dimensions and good manoeuvrability.

In the West the endeavours to reach increasingly higher operational speeds,

as well as a changing military doctrine, led to the development of the F-104 "Starfighter", which made its maiden flight on 7th February 1954. In comparison with the total dimensions of the aeroplane the wing is extremely small, straight and only 3.4 per cent thick (Fig. 1-10).

It had been known for a long time that a straight wing is more favourable for low speeds than a sweptback one. The high wing loading necessitated special measures for low-speed flight to keep the flow attached to the wing, in this case by blowing air into the boundary layer.

The F-104 was a useful interceptor in the skies of California, but its adaptation to European requirements led to a less happy solution. In addition the T-tail, combined with the 'stickpusher', which automatically generates pitchdown moments when the angle-of-attack is too large, often turned out to be a deathtrap

16

1-9 **MiG-21 with delta wing and conventional empennage.**

for pilot and aircraft near the ground (see chapter 5). Nevertheless the manufacture under licence of the F-104 offered an opportunity for the European aircraft industry, and especially the German and Italian aircraft industry, to regain a position at the forefront of technological progress.

The F-4 "Phantom" (Fig. 1-11) became the United States Air Force's most important combat aircraft (and later that of numerous other airforces) in the sixties and seventies. On its maiden flight on 27th May 1958 the F-4 was only intended as a defensive aircraft for the US Navy operated from aircraft carriers. The armament consisted predominantly of guided missiles: an aircraft cannon was not part of the original design. The successes of this naval fighter led the USAF afterwards to adopt the F-4 in large numbers. The F-4 employed by the German Air Force had wing slats to improve the ma-

noeuvrability at high angles-of-attack. Since 1967 the F-4E has had an inbuilt cannon, after operational experience had highlighted the ineffectiveness of an all-missile armament.

The Lockheed YF-12A constituted a milestone in combat aircraft construction. It was planned originally as an interceptor, but has been employed as a strategic high altitude reconnaisance plane with the designation SR-71 (Fig. 1-12). This aircraft can fly 5000 km (2698 nm) at Mach 3 at an altitude of 24 km (80000 ft). Its unusual shape is characterized by a fuselage extended far to the front with laterally arranged strakes, and a delta-like wing which blends into the fuselage. Titanium is used on a large scale to reduce the weight. The heating-up of the airframe by the air flowing past at high speed posed a new problem for the first time in manned air travel; the so-called thermal barrier. Later the Americans

undertook numerous experiments with the X-15 research plane, of which three were built. On 3rd October 1967 one of these succeeded in reaching a speed of 7300 km/h (Mach 6.72).

This is the highest speed ever reached by an aircraft to which the name is still applicable. With this aircraft the dividing line between air travel and space travel becomes blurred.

An aircraft comparable in performance with the SR-71 is the Soviet MiG-25, originally intended as an interceptor against the planned American XB-70 supersonic bomber, but which has since been operated as a strategic high-altitude reconnaisance aircraft.

A particular characteristic of the classic combat aircraft, compared with a transport aircraft, is the variation in its flight regimes. This is characterized by large changes in height and Mach numbers. In order to achieve good flight performance

17

1-10 **The Starfighter was the first operational combat aircraft to fly at more than twice the speed of sound: here on a test flight with MBB Kormoran missiles.**

1-11 **The standard NATO combat aircraft in the seventies: the F-4 Phantom.**

it is therefore desirable to adjust the wing to the given flight configuration. This thought led to the idea of the swing-wing aircraft. In 1964 General Dynamics presented the F-111, the first mass-produced combat aircraft with a swing wing. Bell had already experimented in this area in 1951 with the X-5, based on the Messerschmitt P.1101 design of 1944. In 1953 Grumman investigated the possibilities of a swing wing using its Jaguar experimental aircraft. It was only in 1969 however, after numerous setbacks with the F-111, that Grumman presented the F-14, an efficient fighter with swing wings which is operated from aircraft carriers and can reach more than double the speed of sound (Fig. 1-13). The advanced avionics permit combat with six hostile aircraft at the same time. For this purpose it carries "Phoenix" long-range missiles.

The idea of the swing-wing aircraft also appealed to the German, British and Italian aircraft industries, who have since been working together on the Tornado. The Soviet Union has several operational models with swing wings.

The jet-supported vertical take-off aircraft represents a special development in combat aircraft construction; it is capable of operating independently of conventional airfields, which are particularly vulnerable in war. A promising position which the German aircraft industry had won in the 60s with the VAK-191B and VJ-101 models was unfortunately not taken advantage of. Up to now the only operational aircraft in the West with vertical take-off characteristics is the British Aerospace Harrier (Fig. 1-14).

The wars in Vietnam and the Middle East emphasised that combat aircraft developed in the West were almost exclusively designed for high speed, not for manoeuvrability. As a consequence in 1972 McDonnell Douglas presented the F-15, an air superiority fighter which had never before been realized in this form (Fig. 1-15). The maximum flight Mach number is about 2.5, which is indeed hardly more than that of which the F-104 and F-4 are capable. However the two

1-12   **The SR-71 flies at more than three times the speed of sound.**

1-13 **F-14 with swing wing which can be adjusted to any given Mach number.**

engines provide a previously unattainable thrust-weight ratio, which is an important prerequisite for high manoeuvrability in aerial combat. The relatively large sweepback, combined with a wing loading which is not too small, also makes the F-15 eminently suitable for high-speed, low-level flight.

In 1972 the American aircraft industry brought out the F-16 and YF-17/F-18, the so-called lightweight fighters, which were originally developed as simple low-cost, air-superiority fighters to complement the F-15 (Fig. 1-16). Strake wings, used on these aircraft for the first time, made it possible to fly at unprecedented angles-of-attack. The manoeuvre limits are no longer decided by the aircraft, but by the pilot.

In this brief outline the development of the jet-propelled combat aircraft has been sketched from its beginnings during the Second World War up to the present day. In the following chapters modern combat aircraft technology will be described.

1-14 **The only operational combat aircraft in the West with vertical take-off capability is the British "Harrier".**

1-15 **McDonnell Douglas F-15 – the most efficient all-weather fighter at the present time.**

1-16 **F-16 and YF-17/F-18 lightweight fighters, designed for air superiority use.**

2 Tasks of Combat Aircraft

2.1 **Combat Tasks**

One of the functions of a combat aircraft is the accomplishment of a combat task. Essentially this means that the aircraft takes off, carries out its combat task and returns to its operational base. This sequence, including take-off and landing, is called a **mission.** The mission analysis, i.e. the quantitative breakdown of the mission sequence, forms the indispensable basis of the aircraft design.

The form the combat task takes depends on the **mission requirements.** In this context one has to differentiate between two main groups. With one group a military payload has to be conveyed over a certain distance. This includes all support for the ground forces, strikes on other targets on the ground (aircraft, ships and so on), and aerial reconnaissance. The other group's target is hostile aircraft in the air. This includes air superiority and interception.

The following missions are of particular relevance for combat aircraft:

– air superiority (AS)
– interception (air defence – AD)
– battlefield interdiction (ID)
– interdiction/strike (IDS)
– close air support (CAS)
– tactical reconnaissance
– counter-air
– naval strike

Every mission requires for its successful execution particular prerequisites with respect to aerodynamics, propulsion, armament, avionics and so on. The better the aircraft fulfils the combat task, the greater the probability of success. Accordingly, the greatest effectiveness is to be expected from an aircraft which is specially designed for one single mission. However, this would lead to a diversity of models, the realization of which is already prohibited on grounds of cost. Every model would require its own research and development programme as well as its own production procedure. In addition, there would be type-dependent ground installations and separate pilot training.

Therefore, in practice the procedure is such that, according to military necessity, tactics and geographical position, several missions can be carried out by one and the same aircraft type. In this case allowance is made for the requirements of the particular operation by means of different armament and avionics equipment.

The alternative method, designing a combat aircraft for as many missions as possible (multi-role), leads in general to a situation where ultimately none of the intended missions can be carried out with maximum effectiveness.

A mission consists of a number of phases. Each phase is characterized by length or duration, as well as by typical flight conditions (altitude, Mach number) or engine power settings. For an air superiority mission, a classification might look like this (Fig. 2-1):

1. Take-off and acceleration to optimum climbing speed.
2. Subsonic cruise in the direction of the combat zone at an optimum altitude for range, and Mach number.
3. Descending flight and acceleration to maximum supersonic flight at low altitude.
4. High-speed, low-altitude flight as far as the combat zone.
5. Aerial combat (a period of two minutes with maximum afterburning thrust at a particular altitude and flight Mach number is often allowed for this, e.g. H = 5 km, M = 1.6).
6. Leaving the combat zone in climbing flight and acceleration to maximum Mach number.
7. Withdrawal from combat area with maximum Mach number and at maximum altitude.
8. After reaching a safe distance, continuation of the return flight at an optimum altitude for range and Mach number.

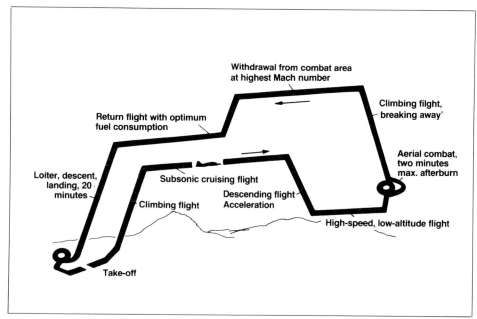

2-1 **Example of an air superiority mission.**

9. Return to the point of departure and landing with fuel reserve for loiter.

In practice, operations of the kind described are hardly likely to proceed in this desirable chronological order. However, they form the indispensable basis for aircraft design and therefore determine to a large extent the design criteria, such as aircraft size, engine, wing type.

To simplify matters, essential phases of the mission are used to characterize the mission profile, with the flight altitude being stated in qualitative form as a characteristic (high = hi, low = lo).

In this case one would consequently speak of a hi-lo profile. In the following, some missions and their reactions on designing and equipping aircraft will be explained.

2.1.1 Air Superiority (AS)

Among all types of mission the air superiority mission (AS mission) has the greatest value. Military missions over own territory, on water and in the air can only be carried out safely if the opponent's airforce is prevented from intervening. The combat aircraft needed for this are specially designed for this task and are called **air superiority fighters.**

The main task of the air superiority fighter consists of attaining air supremacy, or at least of controlling the airspace within a limited area and for a limited length of time. The targets are primarily hostile aircraft operating in the airspace laid claim to. The real military operation targets can then be reached under the protective umbrella of one's own airforces and without interference from hostile aircraft.

The character of the AS mission determines the special properties of the air superiority fighter. What counts here is not the highest speed, but the capacity to manoeuvre whilst withstanding the greatest loads. **Manoeuvrability** is expressed in climbing performance, acceleration capacity and turning speed.

AERODYNAMICS

The properties required for manoeuvring air combat are attained by means of special measures in the design of the aircraft. In this connection the wing takes on the greatest importance; it must be able to absorb the high loads arising in turning flight due to the action of centrifugal force, without the flow separating uncontrollably. The present state of aerodynamics and strength, related to wing design for combat aircraft, permits **load factors** which correspond to almost ten times the aircraft weight (by load factor is meant the number of times the normal weight is multiplied in a particular manoeuvre). Such high values are only possible if the wing in normal flight is not excessively loaded, and has the capacity to absorb further loads. The characteristic measurement of this is **wing loading,** which is defined as aircraft weight divided by wing area and is one of the most important design parameters of all.

As a further characteristic, a wing suitable for aerial combat has a more or less sharply sweptback leading edge, which permits controlled separation in the form of vortex flows (see Ch. 4).

Typical features of the air superiority fighter, according to this, are a relatively large wing and a modest aircraft weight, which together lead to a low wing loading. These design criteria were convincingly realized in the American F-16 and YF-17/F-18 lightweight fighters (Fig. 2-2).

2-2 **Typical air superiority fighters of the new generation are the American aircraft F-16 and YF-17/F-18.**

ENGINES

The second important requirement for an air superiority fighter concerns the engine. The fundamental requirements for every engine, namely:
- high thrust
- favourable fuel consumption
- low-smoke combustion

have particular importance for aerial combat.

High thrust is necessary to be able to accelerate to high speed in the shortest time, whether it is to obtain a favourable firing position or to build up a higher-energy flight state. Those engines suitable for this are all equipped with afterburning; they permit a brief thrust increase of over 50 per cent (see chapter 6). In conjunction with a low total aircraft weight a high **thrust-to-weight ratio** results, which, next to low wing loading, is seen as vital for a highly manoeuvrable air superiority aircraft. The highest known thrust-to-weight ratios are about 1.4, the thrust force thus exceeding the aircraft weight by 40 per cent.

With thrust-to-weight ratios above 1, the aircraft could in theory be borne by its own jet. In practice, this **excess power** can be converted into high accelerations and climbing speeds, which are indispensable for aerial combat.

Although in the design of an air superiority fighter the emphasis is put on manoeuvrability, it cannot be overlooked that an actual aerial combat, compared with the total duration of a mission, may only take a relatively short time. In project studies two minutes is taken as being typical. By far the greatest part is spent in take-off, outward and return flight, loiter and landing (see Fig. 2-1). In these secondary phases of the air superiority mission, the fuel reserve must be used extremely economically, which means doing without afterburn as well as maintaining optimum-range flight speeds and altitudes.

In order to attain favourable fuel consumption, modern propulsion units are designed, without exception, as **by-pass** engines. The air flowing in is divided in the compressor, the greater part – 50 to 70% – flowing through the gas generator, while the lower pressure remainder is conducted along the outside of the engine (by-pass configuration), and mixes with hot gas aft of the turbines. The **by-pass ratio** indicates how large the proportion of the air conducted along outside is, in relation to that air quantity flowing through the gas generator. For combat aircraft engines, by-pass ratios between 0.2:1 and 1:1 are typical. Thus General Electric's F404 engine (for the F-18) has a by-pass ratio of 0.34:1, while Pratt & Whitney's F100 engine (for the F-15 and F-16), which is twice as powerful, has a by-pass ratio of 0.71:1 (see Table 6.1).

The requirement of low-smoke combustion had existed for civil engine construction for a long time, as a consequence of increasing environmental awareness. In military engine construction, low-smoke afterburning is aimed at for other reasons, primarily tactical ones. A smoke trail visible from a distance is a tell-tale sign which can ruin the element of surprise, an important element of aerial combat.

ARMAMENT

The third important condition for the execution of the combat task relates to kind and quantity of combat equipment on board and the electronics employed (called 'avionics' in aviation). In the case of the highly manoeuvrable air superiority fighter, experience has shown that the most effective armament consists of a permanently built-in gun and two or four target-seeking, air-to-air missiles. The weapons must be easy to operate, reliable, and should not be susceptible to neutralization by countermeasures. These requirements are best fulfilled by the gun.

Criteria for the assessment of its combat value are:
- high accuracy
- small recoil forces
- high rate of fire
- reliability

In spite of the special conditions of aircraft installation (small installation space and restricted weight), modern weapons technology has led to solutions which permit effective target strike. The high rate of fire necessary for aerial combat can be attained today with 'revolver' guns, such as the 27-mm Mauser or the 30-mm Oerlikon KCA. Considerably higher rates of fire are possible with the multi-barrelled Gatling guns, such as General Electric's M-61A, the standard gun in US fighters. However, the increase in fire performance must be purchased at the expense of higher ammunition consumption.

The relatively small range of guns – they are considered a close range weapon – makes it necessary to carry target-seeking, air-to-air missiles. These can either be equipped with an infra-red, target-seeking head, which responds to the hot parts of the aircraft (nozzle, exhaust gases), or with a semi-active, radar target-seeking head which uses the emission of a radar beam[1] reflected by the target.

AVIONICS

Aerial combat is predominantly flown under visual flight conditions. Nevertheless, a limited all-weather capability is required, so that radar and a head-up display are part of the avionics equipment.

The following are examples of air superiority aircraft (Fig. 2-3):

F-4E	Viggen	MiG-21
F-5E	Mirage III E	MiG-23
F-14	Mirage 2000	
F-15		
F-16		
F-18		

----
[1] This method is subject to increasing criticism

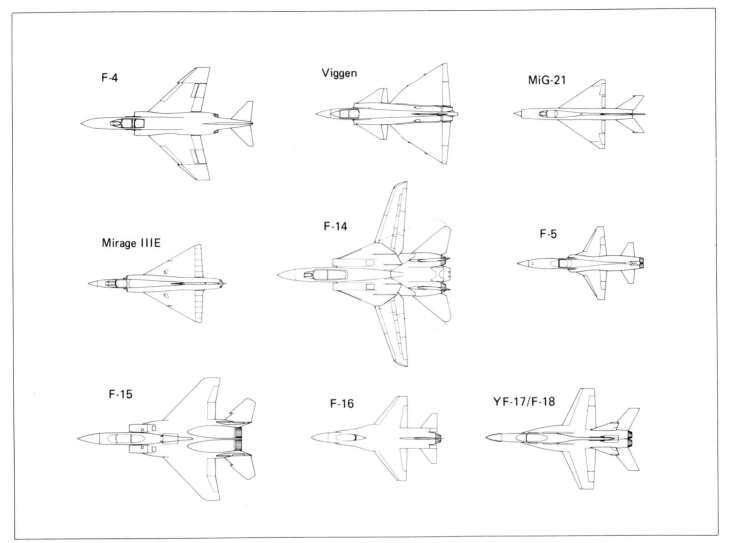

2-3 **Examples of air superiority fighters.**

2.1.2 Interception

The task of the interceptor takes place within the framework of air defence (AD), as a reaction to the intrusion of an opponent who has been detected by airborne radar or ground radar. Corresponding to this set task, operations must be possible in any weather and at any time of day. Hostile aircraft flying in at very high and very low altitudes require particular attention. Therefore the following requirements are needed for an interceptor:

- maximum climb performance
- high acceleration capacity
- cruise at supersonic speed
- ability to fly low at high speeds
- avionic equipment for target acquisition
- identification friend or foe (IFF)
- effective air-to-air armament with missiles.

A less urgent requirement, though desirable, is that of adequate manoeuvrability. Large ranges are also not absolutely necessary, as above all it is the intrusion of enemy aircraft into one's own airspace which has to be repulsed.

These requirements postulate a high wing loading. The delta wing with an aspect ratio of 2 to 2.5 is one example which meets the aerodynamic requirements.

For this type of operation a high specific thrust is required from the engine; obtaining a favourable specific

27

fuel consumption is less urgent. The most suitable are pure turbojet engines with relatively low compression ratios, e.g. J79, M53 (see Chapter 6).

Examples of AD aircraft are:

	Mirage III E	Su-11
F-106	Lightning	Su-15
F-4E	Tornado	Su-27
F-15	Mirage F.1E	MiG-25
F-14		Tu-28P
	Mirage 2000	
	JA 37 Viggen	MiG-31

The foregoing examples of AS and AD aircraft show that a sharp division is scarcely possible in practice. Very often the same types of aircraft are concerned being equipped for a particular task through the choice of armament and avionics. Moreover, it becomes apparent that aircraft which control air superiority, the most difficult of missions, are also capable of interception, battlefield interdiction and ground combat support.

2.1.3 Battlefield interdiction

Battlefield interdiction is directed at the area behind the forward line of battle. The object is to restrict the opponent's operative freedom of movement, to stop his supply lines and to eliminate his reserves. The operation must be possible in all weathers and at any time of day.

The target area is considered to be the space between 25 nm and 50 nm behind the front. Preferred are moving targets and stationary pin-point and area targets, such as:
- junctions (railway stations, bridges, roads)
- supply installations (transshipment points for fuel, munitions, material, repair facilities)
- anti-aircraft and radar positions
- armoured units
- assembly areas.

The following combat aircraft properties can be derived from this list of tasks:
- all-weather operation, also from temporary airfields
- transonic speed in low-altitude flight
- capacity for low-level attack (precision navigation and fire-control in all weather conditions)
- high offensive armament load
- medium to long range
- good manoeuvrability.

Examples of ID aircraft are:

F-4E	Mirage 5	Su-17/-20
F-104G		Su-24
F-111	Mirage 2000	MiG-21
A-6	Buccaneer	MiG-27
A-7	Harrier	YAK-28P
F/A-18	Tornado IDS	
A-4	Jaguar	

The following armament types can be considered.
- bombs (conventional, salvo, scatter, incendiary bombs)
- guns
- unguided missiles (rockets)
- target-seeking, guided missiles

2.1.4 Close air support (CAS)

Operations within the framework of close air support serve to support directly land forces involved in combat at the front line. The targets attacked lie in the actual battlefield, i.e. in a strip which extends up to 25 nm on either side of the front. In this area one's own troops are engaged in combat with the enemy. Due to the small distance between friendly and enemy troops an aircraft guidance system must be available. Moreover, minimum visibility conditions must assume to prevail over the operations area.

Preferred targets are:
- infantry and artillery positions
- tanks
- columns of vehicles.

The following requirements for the aircraft result:
- low flight plus low-level attack properties
- high manoeuvrability
- medium offensive armament load
- short to medium range.

The operational speed is relatively low and usually lies in the subsonic range. In any case, a head-up display unit should be part of the avionic equipment.

As CAS aircraft come into particularly close contact with the opposition, it is necessary to armour vital components.

In order to simplify the weapons system, variable geometry can be dispensed with at the intakes and thrust nozzle (example: MiG-27, which was developed from the MiG-23 and has fixed intakes instead of adjustable intakes, as well as a shortened and simplified adjustable nozzle).

The weapons carried consist of:
- guns
- bombs of all kinds
- unguided missiles
- target-seeking guided missiles.

Examples of CAS aircraft (Fig. 2-4):

A-10	Buccaneer	Su-17
		Su-20
A-6	Harrier	Su-20
A-4	Tornado	Su-25
		YAK-38
A-7	Jaguar	MiG-27

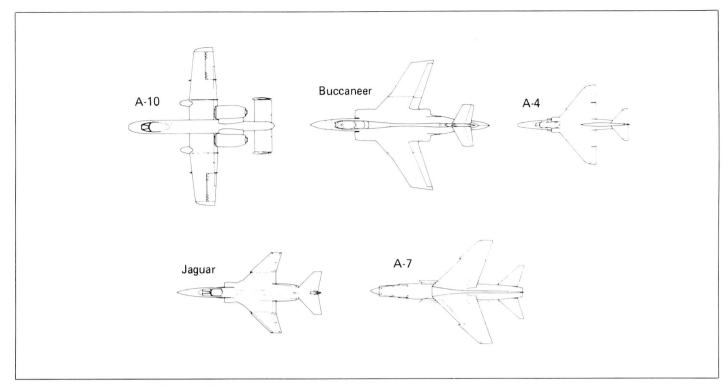

2-4   **Combat aircraft for close air support.**

2.2 **Properties of a Combat Aircraft**

The probability of success of a combat task depends on certain design-specific properties of the aircraft, among them:
– manoeuvrability
– handling qualities
– range
– visibility for the pilot
– fire-power
– unobtrusiveness

Apart from these there are operational characteristics, such as number of aircraft operating, tactics and frequency of operations.

MANOEUVRABILITY

The most important requirement for an air superiority fighter is **manoeuvrability.**
The criteria for assessing this are climb performance, acceleration capacity and turn rate.

HANDLING QUALITIES

An aircraft has good **handling qualities** if the pilot can carry out all manoeuvres easily and safely. Good handling qualities are the basic condition for a successful operation; unfavourable handling qualities strain the pilot and distract him dangerously from his combat task. Tendencies of the aircraft to pitch, yaw, spin, as well as flow separation and buffeting phenomena at the wing in the fringe areas of the operational spectrum can be kept in check or completely
avoided by means of suitable measures. If they do not succeed, the operational value of the aircraft is flawed.

RANGE

By range is meant the ability of the aircraft to reach the combat zone and to cover it. Range is determined by the quantity of fuel carried and the operational profile flown. Half of the value of the combat range is called the **radius of action.**

Determination of the necessary fuel quantity must take into account in large measure the kind of combat. An aerial combat consists primarily of acceleration and turning flight. The aircraft which is

2-5 **Visibility as an important criterion for an air superiority fighter (General Dynamics F-16).**

most suitable for this is the one which, for a given radius of action, can carry out most of the given flight manoeuvres: or, for a given number and type of combat manoeuvres, has the greatest radius of action. In designing a combat aircraft, the procedure is often as follows: within the overall concept of the aircraft a 'trade-off' is made among the parameters of:-

– thrust/weight ratio
– wing loading
– wing aspect ratio
– fuel as a proportion of total weight

The range potentials for a given quantity of fuel are then compared with each other.

VISIBILITY

By **visibility** is meant the possibility of keeping the opponent in view continu-

ously during all flight manoeuvres. This decisive factor was largely disregarded after the Korean War. In the new American combat aircraft of the types F-14, F-15, F-16 and F-18, the cockpit canopies are 'correctly' designed in this respect (Fig. 2-5). 'Correctly' means that the pilot has all-round visibility from an eye-point above the aircraft. In constructional terms this results in a relatively large cockpit canopy within a small fuselage breadth. Aerodynamically, however, this solution is unfavourable. The unavoidably higher drag has to be offset by thrust and thus makes sufficiently powerful engines necessary.

FIRE-POWER

Fire-power is determined by the kind and quantity of combat equipment car-

ried and by the extent to which they can be employed. Combat equipment must be easy to operate and should not be vulnerable to counter-measures.

One of the most effective items of combat equipment is the **gun.** A 20-mm gun suffices to destroy hostile aircraft. A 30-mm weapon is even suitable for the elimination of tanks.

For an air superiority fighter, air-to-air missiles with infra-red or radar target-seeking heads complement the gun. They make it possible to extend the range of action of the combat equipment carried. Guided missiles are used when a hostile aircraft lies outside the range of the gun and when there is a chance of a hit.

Advances in missile technology make it increasingly unlikely in future that an aircraft will get caught in the range of action of the hostile ground defence.

'Thinking' missiles seek their target automatically after being launched, while the launching aircraft can get safely away (fire and forget).

The fire control system, part of the navigation and attack system, is designed for effective weapon operation while making minimum demands on the pilot. To increase accuracy, gyro-stabilized gun sights are installed in which a computer, using elementary ballistic equations, provides information on the hit successes of the bullets. This then decides on the firing of the gun, as soon as the calculated target mark, which is displayed on the combining glass of the sight, coincides with the target (see Chapter 11). The aiming system can also be used for guided-missile operation by simply switching over.

Target-seeking glide bombs have been specially developed for striking ground targets; these have high accuracy.

The weapon actuators should be as small in number as possible, but clearly arranged and simple to operate. Where the mission requires, search and tracking radar must be carried.

UNOBTRUSIVENESS

By unobtrusiveness is meant the ability to attack the opponent without being detected. This significant property for a combat aircraft is achieved by:
- keeping the overall dimensions small
- applying the right camouflage
- having engines with low-smoke combustion, and
- carrying only passive sensors.

As a rule, smaller aircraft have better chances of identifying their opponent visually before being identified by him. In Vietnam the American pilots had extreme difficulties in spotting the MiG-21, whose small design was outstandingly successful, over long distances.

It is important for all sensors to be largely passive. Radiated energy makes it possible to be detected by an opponent and attracts radiation-seeking missiles.

OPERATIONAL FREQUENCY

Complex and highly-developed aircraft are expensive and can only be kept operational at great expense and effort. Simple aircraft, in contrast, attain the highest frequency of operations. There is a simple relation between simplicity of construction and equipment on the one hand, and its repairability on the other hand. An item of equipment which is not taken along cannot break down either, and thus never be the cause of the aircraft not being able to take off.

Increasing complication is likely to reduce the combat value. This circumstance is scarcely noticeable in peace, because an intact industry can always repair defective equipment. However, in war, a technology which is difficult to control can have disastrous consequences.

3 Aircraft Design

3.1 **Significance of the Design**

A newly developed combat aircraft should normally be better than the best type in current use for a comparable range of tasks. This means that the latest technology flows into every type of aircraft in large quantities. As development advances rapidly, a combat aircraft, on being put into service, can expect a service life of 20 years at most. After that time it is usually considered obsolete.

The need to replace obsolete equipment leads to considerations among the military planning staff and in the aircraft industry as to how a new aircraft should be designed which
a) comes up to the most modern state of engineering,
b) meets the military requirements and,
c) can be acquired at a price which is reasonable for the users (airforces).

The solution of this task is crucially dependent on the **aircraft design.** Its connection it is basically irrelevant whether the aircraft is civil or military.

role can be best compared with architecture in the construction industry. The design thus represents a period of time in which the future properties of the aircraft are to a large extent determined, and the most important technical decisions for the project are reached. The more thorough and farsighted the execution of this work is, the more the final aircraft will come up to the original expectations.

3.2 **Design Phases**

The fact that modern high-performance aircraft are complicated systems composed of numerous components imposes the need to ensure that the necessary design process to build such equipment proceeds in a meaningfully ordered scheme. Such a plan is based on experiences with projects already carried out, and taking into account the experiences of other manufacturers.

In the design process a distinction is made between the individual phases which follow one another chronologically and which identify the corresponding degree of progress of the project. In this

3.2.1 **Pre-phase activities**

The so-called **pre-phase activities** are indispensable for decision-making at the beginning of a project; they take place in the early but still requirement-orientated run-up. Consequently these still come **before** those activities which are concerned with the real concept phases which form the central concept of the material formation process. By pre-phase activities are meant technical and operations-analytical studies, component and experimental developments. These serve to prepare new technologies in such a way that they become ready for use and are assessable with respect to their military use and the amount of time available. It is here, above all, that it is necessary to create a sound foundation. Experience shows that the biggest mistakes are usually made at the beginning.

3.2.2 Initial configuration estimates

The real development process begins with considerations of a general kind. These serve the preparation of the future project and determine the design target. In this **initial configuration estimate** important parameters are investigated which have an influence on the flight performances; such as payload, range or radius of action, flight speed, spectrum of tactical air operations (Fig. 3-1).

In addition to this, various possibilities of aircraft design are considered by the project department. These are put down as a first design on the drawing-board. In co-operation with the various departments recognizable advantages and disadvantages are discussed and weighed against each other.

For this task only relatively few personnel are involved. The data produced is, for the time being, only provisional. Nevertheless, it is possible to make a first statement about whether the planned aircraft will be suitable for the fulfilment of the initial performance requirements.

3.2.3 Feasibility Study

The initial configuration estimate is followed by the feasibility study. The aim of the latter is to look for ways, on the basis of the work already done, in which the desired configuration can be realized as effectively as possible. And this means above all at minimum cost. This task is particularly difficult when development risks are present in the design process which up to then cannot be mastered with the experience gained by the personnel. Because new aircraft development projects cost thousands of millions, it is essential to reduce any risks step by step. What matters in this case is

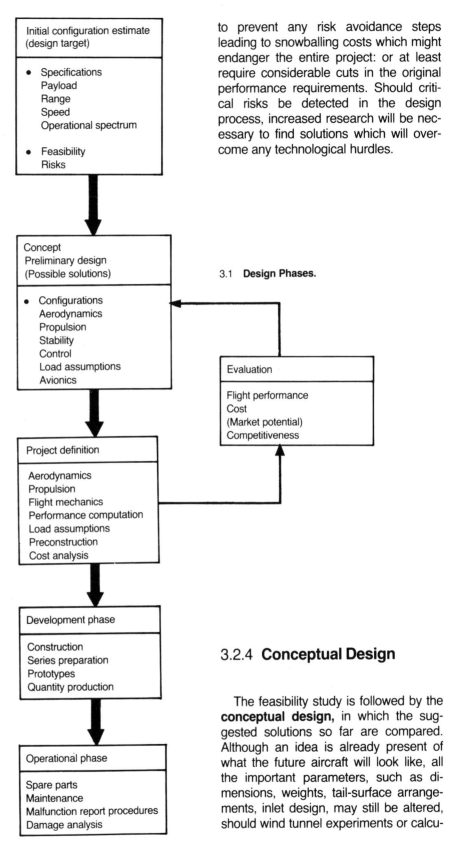

3.1 **Design Phases.**

to prevent any risk avoidance steps leading to snowballing costs which might endanger the entire project: or at least require considerable cuts in the original performance requirements. Should critical risks be detected in the design process, increased research will be necessary to find solutions which will overcome any technological hurdles.

3.2.4 Conceptual Design

The feasibility study is followed by the **conceptual design,** in which the suggested solutions so far are compared. Although an idea is already present of what the future aircraft will look like, all the important parameters, such as dimensions, weights, tail-surface arrangements, inlet design, may still be altered, should wind tunnel experiments or calcu-

33

lation results make it necessary. As a rule an attempt will be made to determine the properties of the aircraft by means of computer studies which are as simple as possible and not too expensive. The results obtained, which may always contain an uncertainty factor, are frequently supported by means of wind tunnel experiments. Often the wind tunnel is the only means of arriving at results. Thus, for example, the effect of so-called strakes on the wing flow cannot be determined so far by mathematical methods, so that all that remains is recourse to experiment.

The conceptual design proceeds in an iterative loop: aerodynamics requires a series of input parameters for predesign considerations; aerodynamic data thus obtained flow back to the project department to determine performance, from which new input parameters for the aerodynamics result, and so on. In theory the iterations could be continued without interruption, if the conceptual design itself were not under great deadline pressure.

The result of this phase is the **point design,** which confirms the feasibility of the design target in a certain dispersion range.

The point performances of an air superiority fighter could, for example, run as follows:

maximum Mach number at optimum altitude	$M = 2.5$
maximum Mach number at sea level	$M = 1.2$
specific excess power (SEP)	220 m/s (722 ft/s)
load factor, sustained turn	6 g in 3000 m
load factor, instantaneous turn	4 g at 280 km/h
take-off run over 50 ft obstacle	2700 ft
landing run from 50 ft	1500 feet

Each of these points involves a certain armament and fuel load.

3.2.5 Project Definition

After concluding the conceptual design the project definition begins. The most important task is the determination of the external dimensions of the aircraft on the basis of the preceding parameter studies. By using the most modern computation procedures, the behaviour of the aircraft can be predetermined at this stage – as far as this is at all possible – long before its first flight. In addition the entire flight range is investigated in the wind tunnel on scale models. Costly fatigue experiments on critical structural components, even the destruction of an airworthy airframe (static test cell), are intended to give information on strength and life.

These measures are necessary in order to keep to the guarantees required by the customer, and to exclude risks as far as possible.

The results of the project definition are continually compared with the desired values of the point design and the predictions of the time involved. In the past it often became apparent that the data in the point design were too optimistic, so that work on the design had to be stopped.

3.2.6 Development Phase

The actual design phase concludes with project definition. This requires a period of at least a year. The conversion of the work done so far into a finished aircraft (hardware) is carried out in the subsequent **development phase,** in which detailed design specifications are created and the construction of prototypes begins. During the test flying it becomes apparent whether the aircraft meets the requirements. Any changes

which may be necessary can have a fatal effect on the project because they increase the cost.

After successfully concluding the development flying the way is free for quantity production. This is characterized by the production of construction drawings, equipment, and so on. To carry out **quantity production,** extensive organisation is necessary for supervising and controlling production from material acquisition to final assembly.

3.2.7 Acquisition and Operational Phase

In the **acquisition phase,** the aircraft coming off quantity production are handed over to the armed forces. At the same time inspection procedures are worked out.

Finally comes the **operational phase,** which is primarily characterized by maintenance and spare-part acquisition for operational aircraft. Among the features of this phase are repair and servicing, extending the operational spectrum, as well as remedying possible design faults, which only become apparent at this stage. For example, with aircraft of the RAF and the Royal Navy there are, on average, 500,000 malfunctions, both major and minor, a year. This number may be regarded as representative of a modern airforce and as an indication of the complexity of modern weapons systems. To reduce the tendency to malfunction it is of utmost importance to record all malfunction reports at a terminal equipped with a computer.

In the operational phase the further development of the aircraft into variants usually takes place. That is if the airforces have a corresponding need.

The sequence of phases described here corresponds to a large extent to the scheme applied in the aircraft industry today.

4 Aerodynamics

Aerodynamics, as a special area of flow dynamics, is concerned with aerodynamic forces which affect the entire aircraft or its parts while it is moving through the atmosphere. These forces are dependent on the geometrical form of the aircraft, the speed of flight and the physical properties of the air; often in a complicated manner. It is the task of aerodynamics to describe these relations both qualitatively and quantitatively.

Moreover, aerodynamics forms an indispensable basis for assessment of flight performance (see chapter 9). Topics such as: investigating the inlet flow, designing the aircraft tail, and the influence of external loads on the flow around the aircraft. All these require primarily an aerodynamic solution.

As well as the general principles of aerodynamics this chapter describes in particular the aerodynamics of combat aircraft.

4.1 Wings for combat aircraft

The wing is the most important major component of an aircraft. It gives the aircraft its characteristic external appearance and determines its flight characteristics.

The numerous, variously configured wing shapes available emphasise that the ideal wing, to all intents and purposes, does not exist, but rather that every wing possesses specific properties which can only be attained with that particular type, while the other performance requirements are fulfilled to a greater or lesser extent. The preference for a particular property is laid down in the design requirements.

As with other areas of aviation technology, the wing has also been progressively developed, and this development is by no means over.

In the early 1940s the appearance of combat aircraft was determined by elliptical and trapezoidal wing planforms of relatively high aspect ratios. The British Spitfire provides a typical example of an elliptical wing, while the other fighters of that period (Me 109, Hurricane, Mustang) had trapezoidal wings with straight leading and trailing edges (Fig. 4-1).

These wing shapes proved to be optimal for the speeds attainable at that time, around 700 km/h (corresponding to M = 0.55), because of their favourable drag characteristics. However the introduction of the turbojet engine, and the greater speeds it made possible, revealed the limitations of this wing planform. The transition to the sweptback wing proved to be an aerodynamic necessity, and its first application was in 1943 on the Me 262. The slight leading edge sweepback of 18.5° made it clear that new ground was being broken only gradually. The risks involved in the sweptback wing were too great, and the time, no doubt, too short for a thorough research of its behaviour. From 1950 on, the USA's F-86 and the USSR's MiG-15 confirmed the principle of the sweptback wing (see Fig. 4-1.). With the F-86 at least it became possible for the first time to just exceed the speed of sound in a dive. Ten years later (1960) the operational speed of combat aircraft had exceeded twice the speed of sound. Other wing shapes were found to be more suitable, such as the delta wing on the MiG-21 and Mirage, a delta-like sweptback wing on the F-4 and the trapezoidal wing on the Starfighter.

In 1970 came the introduction of the swing wing, which could adapt better to different flight speeds; for example on the F-14 and F-111. Also for the first time, combat aircraft appeared which could fly considerable distances at more than three times the speed of sound, i.e. the MiG-25 and the SR-71. While the MiG-25 possesses a conservative swept back

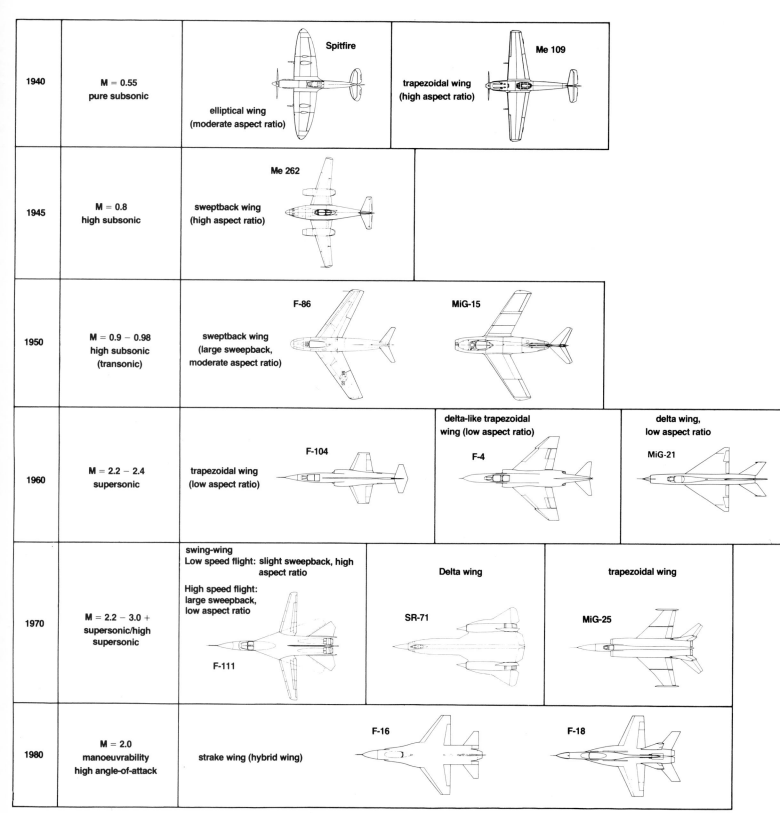

1940	$M = 0.55$ pure subsonic	Spitfire — elliptical wing (moderate aspect ratio)	Me 109 — trapezoidal wing (high aspect ratio)	
1945	$M = 0.8$ high subsonic	Me 262 — sweptback wing (high aspect ratio)		
1950	$M = 0.9 - 0.98$ high subsonic (transonic)	F-86 sweptback wing (large sweepback, moderate aspect ratio)	MiG-15	
1960	$M = 2.2 - 2.4$ supersonic	F-104 trapezoidal wing (low aspect ratio)	F-4 delta-like trapezoidal wing (low aspect ratio)	MiG-21 delta wing, low aspect ratio
1970	$M = 2.2 - 3.0 +$ supersonic/high supersonic	F-111 swing-wing Low speed flight: slight sweepback, high aspect ratio — High speed flight: large sweepback, low aspect ratio	SR-71 Delta wing	MiG-25 trapezoidal wing
1980	$M = 2.0$ manoeuvrability high angle-of-attack	strake wing (hybrid wing)	F-16	F-18

4-1   Historical development of the modern combat aircraft wing.

wing which is clearly separated from the body, the SR-71 displays a delta-like wing which blends into the body.

The demand for greater manoeuvrability for the combat aircraft of the 80s led to the development of hybrid wings composed of several simple planforms. The main wing is trapezoidal with a leading edge sweepback of between 30 and 40 degrees and with a very slim delta portion installed in front as, for example, a strake or leading edge extension (LEX).

4.2 **Geometry of the Wing**

The geometrical shape of the wing is determined essentially by:
– planform
– wing section, profile
– twist
– dihedral, anhedral

In order to describe the geometry a wing-based system of coordinates is used which defines **longitudinal axis, lateral axis** and **normal axis** (Fig. 4-2 and Fig. 5-4).

PLAN FORM

The dimension in the direction of the lateral axis (y-axis) is the **wing span** b. The dimension in the direction of the longitudinal axis (x-axis) is the wing chord, c, which depends on the given y-coordinate. The inner **wing chord** (y = 0) is referred to as c_i; the outer wing chord (y = b/2) is referred to as c_t. The **wing area** S is the projection of the wing on the x - y plane.

From the stated quantities we can derive the two most important parameters for the classification of wings, i.e. aspect ratio and taper ratio.

The **aspect ratio** A is a measure of the slenderness of the wing in the wing span direction and is defined as the quotient of the square of the wing span and the wing area:

$$\text{aspect ratio } A = \frac{b^2}{S}$$

Typical aspect ratio values for combat aircraft wings lie between 2 and 5 (see table 4.1 on page 58). For purposes of comparison, the aspect ratio of commercial aircraft is in the range of 7 to 10 (Airbus: A = 9.39, Boeing 747: A = 6.96) and for gliders between 16 and 20.

The **taper ratio** λ is given by the ratio of the outer and inner wing chords:

$$\text{taper ratio} = \frac{c_t}{c_i}$$

Usual taper ratio values lie between 0 and 0.5. A wing with a constant profile chord has a taper ratio of 1, a typical delta wing has a ratio of 0 because of its non-existent wing tip chord.

By means of the taper ratio the load distribution of the wing outwards can be influenced and a quasi-elliptical lift distribution produced.

A further important parameter is the sweep. It is represented as the angle formed by the leading edge and the lateral axis. In connection with non-dimensional aerodynamic coefficients the mean aerodynamic chord $\bar{\bar{c}}$ (abbreviated to m.a.c., MAC, AMC) is used as reference length (Fig. 4-2). This quantity is of particular importance in stability considerations. By means of the mean aerodynamic chord an equivalent imaginary rectangular wing with the same area is described which has the same longitudinal moment as the actual wing.

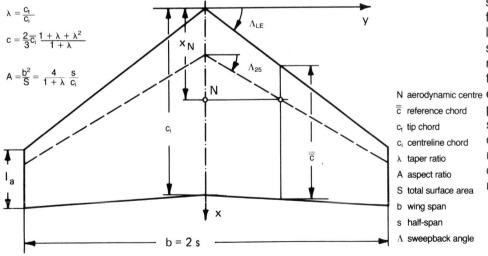

$$\lambda = \frac{c_t}{c_i}$$

$$c = \frac{2}{3}\bar{c_i}\frac{1 + \lambda + \lambda^2}{1 + \lambda}$$

$$A = \frac{b^2}{S} = \frac{4}{1 + \lambda}\frac{s}{c_i}$$

N aerodynamic centre
$\bar{\bar{c}}$ reference chord
c_t tip chord
c_i centreline chord
λ taper ratio
A aspect ratio
S total surface area
b wing span
s half-span
Λ sweepback angle

4-2 **Geometry of the wing.**

The significance of this value lies in the fact that with their aid aerodynamic coefficients and centre of gravity positions of different aircraft may be easily compared with one another.

The significance of the mean aerodynamic chord may become clearer when it is considered that one can conceive of the entire lift of the semi-wing as acting on one point on this line by taking 25% of the distance from the foremost point (see Fig. 4-2). This point is the centre-of-gravity of the wing surface; it is referred to as the (geometrical) **aerodynamic centre.**

The angle of incidence refers to the angle between the profile chord of the wing root section and the fuselage axis. Its value, if it exists at all, lies in the order of magnitude of one degree.

WING SECTIONS (PROFILES)

By a wing section or profile we mean a section running perpendicular to the y-axis through the wing. The geometry of a classic profile is characterized by the following quantities (Fig. 4-3):

1. Mean line
This is a reference line of the profile and runs in the middle between the upper surface and the lower surface. The mean line can be straight or curved. Its shape determines essentially the aerodynamic properties of the section, especially the load distribution, the pitching moment coefficient and the angle-of-attack at zero lift.

2. Profile chord
The profile chord is the decisive reference line of the section. The **angle-of-attack** is also defined by it as the angle between the chord and the direction of the airflow.

3. Camber
The quantitative description of the curvature of the mean line is termed the camber. In general it suffices if the maximum departure of the mean line from the chord as well as the distance between it and the profile leading edge is stated. This is usually done in terms of percentage of the profile chord.

4. Thickness distribution
This is constructed perpendicular to the mean line. The coordinates of the upper and lower surface of the uncambered section must therefore be known. The profile thickness increases until it reaches its maximum. Only the magnitude of the maximum thickness and its position relative to the leading edge are stated, referring in each case to the profile chord. The nose of the profile is part of a circle whose radius also relates to the profile chord. There is a connection between the profile thickness, maximum thickness position and the radius of the nose. The trailing edge is sharpened.

CLASSIFICATION OF WING SECTIONS

The various requirements of flight have brought about the development of a large number of wing sections. The first systematic investigations took place in the "Aerodynamische Versuchsanstalt" (Aerodynamic Experimental Laboratory) in Göttingen between 1923 and 1927. The most extensive and still most widely used classification of wing sections was developed in the NACA[4] Research Laboratory in the USA beginning in 1933 and further developed over the years.

This classifies the wing sections according to numbers which at the same time give information about the geometry. For combat aircraft, but also for commercial aircraft, the sections from the NACA-6 series are preferred, which are mostly used by manufacturers as modified wing sections after minimal changes. For example, the F-16 has the NACA 64A204 modified profile (see Fig. 4-3, below). This means that a profile of the NACA-6 series was used as a basis for the modification (first digit = 6). The second digit (4) gives the position of minimum pressure (maximum speed) in tenths of the profile chord, which in this case lies at 40% of the chord.

The letter A (instead of the otherwise usual hyphen in this series) already represents a modification of the original profile and in such a way that from 80%

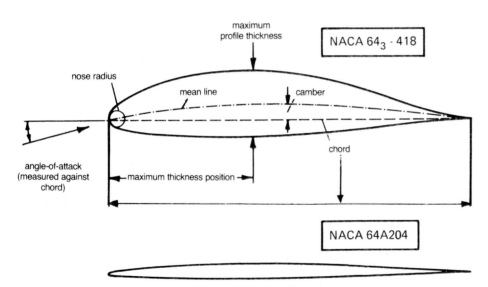

maximum profile thickness

NACA 64₃ - 418

nose radius

mean line

camber

chord

angle-of-attack (measured against chord)

maximum thickness position

NACA 64A204

4-3 **Explanation of wing profile: using the 4% thick profile of the F-16.**

[4] National Advisory Committee for Aeronautics, today NASA

of the chord the upper surface and the lower surface run in a straight line to the trailing edge (no contour curvature).

The third from last number identifies the lift coefficient at which minimum drag is to be expected. The number has to be multiplied by 0.1 to obtain the design lift coefficient ($C_L = 0.1 \times 2 = 0.2$). The last two digits give the profile thickness, which in this example is 4%.

Thus the range of profiles available for combat aircraft is defined. The thickness lies generally between 3 and 7%: with subsonic combat aircraft 10% or more can be reached (the A-10 even has a profile of 16% thickness). The manufacturers use either their own profile designs or, as in the case of the F-16, NACA profiles, which are adapted to the special needs of the aircraft. The coordinates of these profiles are however military secrets and are not published.

SPECIAL PROFILES

Alongside the classic profiles, which were originally only intended for subsonic speeds, there are further types which have been developed especially for transonic and supersonic speeds. Among these is the double-wedge profile, found for example on the Starfighter, and the parabolic profile (Fig. 4-4). Their common characteristic is a sharp leading edge which serves to fix the shock positions of supersonic flow. However the sharp leading edge proves to be a disadvantage in subsonic flow. Separation appears there even at low angles-of-attack, which increases drag. On the other hand only a slight drag-reducing suction can form at cruising speed.

4-4 **Special profiles.**

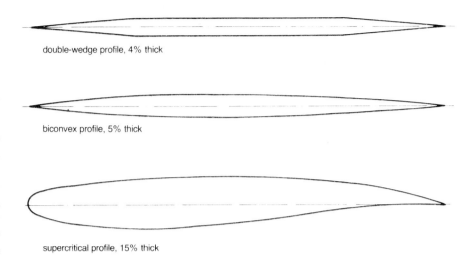

double-wedge profile, 4% thick

biconvex profile, 5% thick

supercritical profile, 15% thick

Repeated attempts have been made to apply the newly developed supercritical profiles in combat aircraft design. Supercritical profiles provide high lift at low drag, although only in a narrow Mach range around $M = 0.8$. At higher Mach number, especially in the supersonic range, a considerably greater drag is to be expected than with the conventional profiles. This is particularly dependent on the large nose radius of supercritical types (see Fig. 4-4, below). However, the extensive range of speeds which combat aircraft must cover makes this type rather unattractive for combat aircraft. Its principal application is rather to be seen with transport aircraft, which possess a single design point (Mach number, flight altitude).

TWIST

Twist refers to the twisting of the profiles in relation to one another. Twist always increases outwards in such a way that the outer wing has a smaller (geometrical) angle-of-attack than the inner wing (Fig. 4-5).

In general twist represents an aero-

[5] There is a cheap paperback on the NACA classification of wing sections; Abbott/Doenhoff: Theory of Wing Sections, Dover Press, New York.

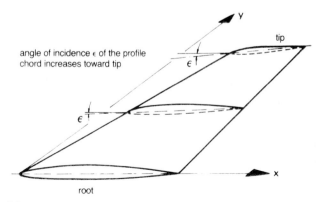

angle of incidence ϵ of the profile chord increases toward tip

tip

root

4-5 **Wing twist**

dynamic aid for approaching the elliptical and, thereby, particularly low-drag distribution, if this cannot be attained by alterations to the plan form. In particular, flow separation over the outer wing area can be prevented in the case of wings with sweptback leading edges.

DIHEDRAL (ANHEDRAL)

The inclination of the wing halves with respect to the x - y plane is called the dihedral (Fig. 4-6). With positive dihedral the wing (or a part of it) is inclined upwards (example: F-4), with negative dihedral (anhedral) downwards (example: F-104). The dihedral or anhedral improves the lateral stability of the aircraft (see Chapter 5).

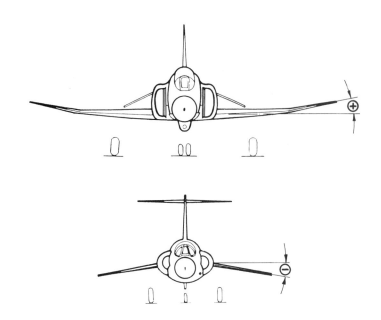

4-6 **Positive dihedral (F-4, top) and negative dihedral (anhedral) (F-104).**

4.3 **Forces on the Wing**

The loads on the wing have a number of different origins. The correct determination of this load is needed for efficient wing construction so as to obtain the necessary strength with maximum weight-saving.

The following forces operate on the aircraft during flight as well as during take-off and landing:
1) aerodynamic forces which are caused by the flow over and around the wing (distributed load);
2) weight of wing construction (distributed load);
3) inertial forces caused by the aircraft mass during manoeuvres (distributed and point loads);
4) concentrated loads (point loads), caused by components or items of equipment attached to the wing, such as the fuselage, engines, suspended

weapons, auxiliary fuel tanks, other external stores;
5) concentrated loads which are not linked to the mass, e.g. engine thrust, if the engines are mounted on the wing (which is seldom the case for combat aircraft); aerodynamic forces which are transmitted by the external forces to the wing by interference effects; undercarriage forces during take-off and landing as well as rolling along the ground.

This account will restrict itself to the aerodynamic forces.

As the aircraft moves through the air the flow produces pressures of various intensities which act on the wing upper surface primarily as negative pressure and on the lower surface primarily as positive pressure. The upper surface is therefore also referred to as the suction

surface and the lower surface as the pressure surface. Together the different pressures on the wing form a pressure distribution. The sum of all contributions from this distribution acting perpendicularly to the airflow provides the lift (Fig. 4-7).

The second important component is drag. By definition drag comprises all forces parallel to the airflow. The component of this from the pressure distribution is slight, so that the drag cannot be derived from it alone. The actual drag force is the result of the friction which the viscous air produces on the surfaces in contact with the airflow.

Lift L and drag D combine to give the resulting aerodynamic force R. To assess the forces acting on the wing's structure a different set of coordinates is more meaningful. Namely the perpen-

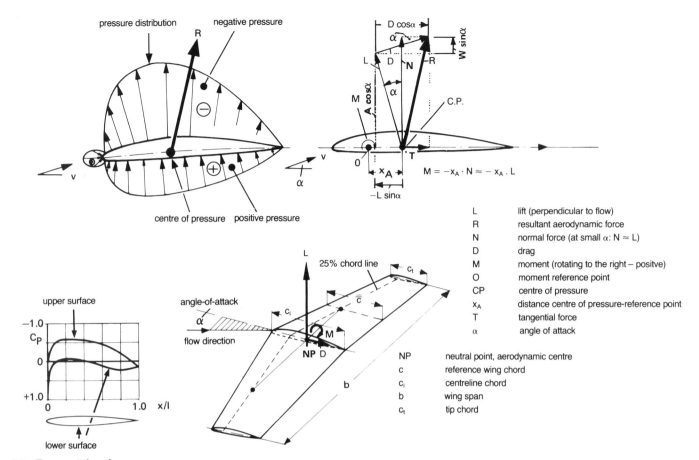

$D\cos\alpha$

α

$W\sin\alpha$

L   D   N   R

$A\cos\alpha$

α

M   C.P.

0

x_A T

$M = -x_A \cdot N \approx -x_A \cdot L$

$-L\sin\alpha$

v

α

L	lift (perpendicular to flow)
R	resultant aerodynamic force
N	normal force (at small α: $N \approx L$)
D	drag
M	moment (rotating to the right – positve)
O	moment reference point
CP	centre of pressure
x_A	distance centre of pressure-reference point
T	tangential force
α	angle of attack

upper surface

-1.0

C_P

0

$+1.0$

0   1.0 x/l

lower surface

L

25% chord line c_t

angle-of-attack

α

flow direction

c_i $\overline{\overline{c}}$

M

NP D

b

NP	neutral point, aerodynamic centre
c	reference wing chord
c_i	centreline chord
b	wing span
c_t	tip chord

4-7   Forces at the wing.

dicular and tangential coordinates of the wing chord. From this the normal force N and the tangential force T (see Fig. 4-7) can be obtained. Note however that we are only dealing with a different division of one and the same resulting aerodynamic force R.

In the first case this is resolved in the direction of flow and perpendicular to it (drag and lift). In the second case the resolution is made in the direction of the chord (tangential force) and perpendicular to it (normal force).

With the aid of the angle-of-attack the following relations can be derived from the distribution of forces (see Fig. 4-7), above right):

normal force
$$N = L \times \cos\alpha + D \times \sin\alpha$$
tangential force
$$T = -L \times \sin\alpha + D \times \cos\alpha$$

For small angles-of-attack $\sin\alpha \approx 0$ and $\cos\alpha \approx 1$, so that in this case the normal force is almost equal to the lift.

The longitudinal moment, which we will deal with later, can, in particular, be represented simply by this means.

For stability considerations, as well as to prove the structural strength, not only the size of the resulting aerodynamic force must be known, but we need to know its point of contact. Behind the simplifying concept of a resulting aerodynamic force is the idea that the aerodynamic forces distributed on the surface of the wing can be reduced to a single force acting as a point.

This point of contact, which may for example lie on the profile chord, can be determined experimentally if the moment is measured around a randomly fixed centre of rotation in a wind tunnel. The moment is known to be the product of lift

and lever arm (moment = lift times leve arm), so that the point of contact of the resulting aerodynamic force results from the simple relation of moment divided by lift. This position is referred to as the **centre of pressure.** As the standard measurements of force include lift, drag and longitudinal moment, the corresponding locations of the centres of pressure can be determined easily.

If the lifts measured in the wind tunnel are entered in the corresponding positions of the centres of pressure –for this purpose the reference wing-chord $\overline{c}$ is taken – the points of the lift arrows ideally describe a hyperbola (Fig. 4-8, bottom left).

At large angles-of-attack the centre of pressure moves forward, at small angles backward. This is the result of flow conditions on the wing, which take different forms according to the angle-of-

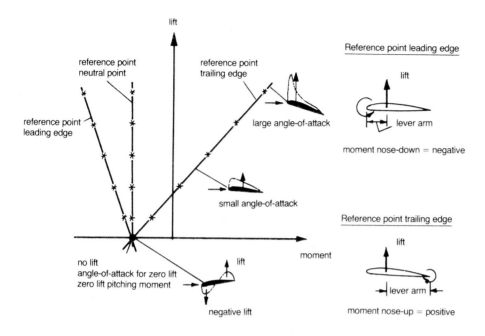

reference point
neutral point

reference point
leading edge

reference point
trailing edge

large angle-of-attack

small angle-of-attack

lift

moment

no lift
angle-of-attack for zero lift
zero lift pitching moment

negative lift

Reference point leading edge

lift

lever arm

moment nose-down = negative

Reference point trailing edge

lift

lever arm

moment nose-up = positive

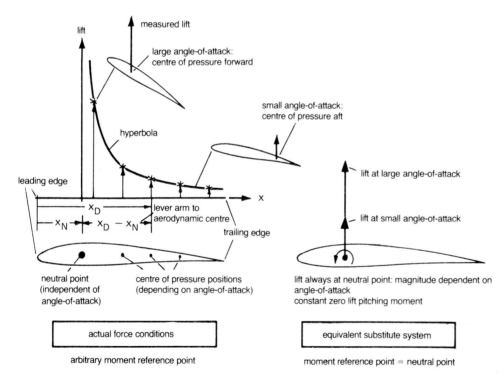

lift

measured lift

large angle-of-attack:
centre of pressure forward

hyperbola

small angle-of-attack:
centre of pressure aft

leading edge

x_D

x_N $x_D - x_N$

lever arm to
aerodynamic centre

trailing edge

x

neutral point
(independent of
angle-of-attack)

centre of pressure positions
(depending on angle-of-attack)

lift at large angle-of-attack

lift at small angle-of-attack

lift always at neutral point: magnitude dependent on
angle-of-attack
constant zero lift pitching moment

actual force conditions

arbitrary moment reference point

equivalent substitute system

moment reference point = neutral point

4-8 **Centre of pressure and neutral point.**

attack (see types of pressure distribution, Fig. 4-8, above left).

At large angles-of-attack the lift is concentrated well forward, while at the, so-called, zero angle-of-attack the negative lift in the forward area of the profile is exactly as large as the positive lift in the rear area. So that, although there is no lift, there is however a moment, the so-called zero lift pitching moment.

The centre of pressure is mainly used in strength calculations, because the point of contact of the resultant aerodynamic force is critical for the dimensioning of components. However for stability considerations an aerodynamic force whose point of application is not fixed is impractical. For this reason the **aerodynamic centre** (neutral point) is always used, whose position is independent of the angle-of-attack.

Because centre of pressure and aerodynamic centre are often confused with each other, here are some explanations: if the leading edge of the profile is chosen as reference point for the longitudinal moment, then the representation of the lift as a curve versus the pitching moment results in a straight line with negative slope (see Fig. 4-8, above left). This also makes sense if one visualises the interrelation of forces at the profile (see Fig. 4-8, above right).

If the trailing edge is chosen as reference point this now yields a straight line with positive slope at the same angles-of-attack (see Fig. 4-8). Through the choice of a reference point the slope of the curve can be controlled.

What is desired is a curve where the moment is not dependent on the angle-of-attack. This condition is obviously fulfilled when the straight line has a vertical slope. This behaviour is attained by choosing the aerodynamic centre as reference point. In this case the longitudinal moment is of same value for every angle-of-attack. It corresponds in value to the zero lift pitching moment (see Fig. 4-8, the curve in the middle). The moment is also said to behave neutrally with regard to the angle-of-attack (hence neutral point).

With the aid of the neutral point it is possible to reduce the actual interrelation of forces to an equivalent but simpler alternative system (see Fig. 4-8, below right).

The lift which is dependent on the angle-of-attack and its point of contact, which is also dependent on this angle, must be given if the centre of pressure is used. It is enough when using the aerodynamic centre to state only the lift and the constant zero lift pitching moment.

In the case of the most frequently occurring **unsymmetrical** (cambered) profiles the centre of pressure always lies behind the aerodynamic centre at positive angles-of-attack (see Fig. 4-8, below left).

When the lift becomes very small then from the definition of the centre of pressure (moment divided by lift), centre of pressure positions outside the profile can easily result. For zero lift the centre of pressure can be at infinity!

On the contrary with **symmetrical** profiles the centre of pressure does not alter its position with the angle-of-attack. This can be explained by the formation of the flow on this type of profile. Only in this case are the centre of pressure and the aerodynamic centre identical.

The aerodynamic centre lies at around 25% of the chord with all profiles. With sweptback wings the local aerodynamic centre positions are superimposed on one another to form the total aerodynamic centre of the wing which, for example in the case of the F-4, lies at 31% of the mean aerodynamic chord (MAC).

The above considerations apply to the **linear** angle-of-attack range, i.e. as long as the lift increases linearly with the angle-of-attack. As we will see the aerodynamic centre alters its position with Mach number (see Fig. 5-6).

4.3.1 Aerodynamic Coefficients

At a particular angle-of-attack the magnitude of the forces depends mainly on the wing surface S, the atmospheric

lift force	=	lift coefficient	×	dynamic pressure	×	wing surface
L	=	C_L	×	½ ρv^2	×	S
drag force	=	drag coefficient	×	dynamic pressure	×	wing surface
D	=	C_D	×	½ ρv^2	×	S

density ρ and the square of the flight speed v:

C_L and C_D are dimensionless quantities which are termed respectively the **lift coefficient** and the **drag coefficient**. The equation $q = ½ \rho v^2$ gives the **dynamic pressure.**

It is usual to employ the non-dimensional coefficients C_L and C_D instead of the forces L and D, which have dimension. The advantage is that the coefficients are independent of the wing size and have the same numerical values for the wind tunnel model as for the large-scale model. The following expressions result:

$$\text{lift coefficient } C_L = \frac{L}{q\,S}$$

$$\text{drag coefficient } C_D = \frac{D}{q\,S}$$

Lift and drag alone are not sufficient for a full understanding of the action of the aerodynamic forces on the wing, as they only determine the magnitude of the resulting aerodynamic force, but not however its point of application. For this the **moment** is used, produced by the aerodynamic force resultant around an arbitrary point. The position of the randomly chosen moment reference point is stated in percentages of the reference wing chord $\bar{c}$. The moment coefficient is defined by analogy to the lift and drag coefficients:

$$\text{moment coefficient } C_m = \frac{M}{q S \bar{c}}$$

M is the moment of the aerodynamic force L, which forms M together with the lever arm x_A: $M = - L \times x_A$ (see Fig. 4-7).

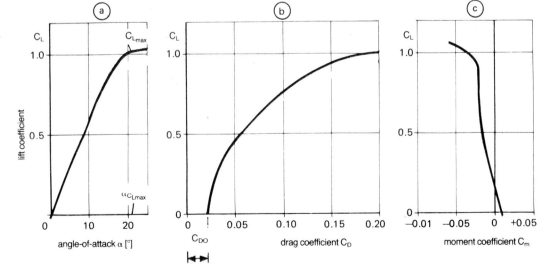

4-9 **Aerodynamic coefficients of lift, drag and pitching moment of the F-4E (clean configuration, Mach 0.7, position of centre of gravity 31% $\bar{c}$, altitude 300m).**

4.3.2 Representation of the Aerodynamic Coefficients

Lift and drag depend on the angle-of-attack in a precise way. This behaviour is expressed in the representation of the aerodynamic coefficients (Fig. 4-9). The lift coefficient is usually represented as being dependent on:-
- the angle of attack $C_L = f(\alpha)$,
- the drag coefficient $C_L = f(C_D)$ and
- the moment coefficient $C_L = f(C_m)$

A wind tunnel investigation which provides the coefficients C_L, C_D and C_m is termed a three-component measurement.

In the following we will explain what is to be learnt from these curves.

LIFT

The increase of lift with angle-of-attack is at first linear; an increase in the angle-of-attack thus corresponds to a proportional increase in the lift coefficient. This range is characterized by attached flow on the entire wing (Fig. 4-10, for $\alpha = 6°$).

After exceeding a particular angle-of-attack the curve changes direction and follows an increasingly flatter path, until finally the lift reaches its maximum. The flow on the upper surface thereby increasingly separates, accompanied by an increase in drag.

A further rise in angle-of-attack leads to a decline in lift and to an increase in drag. This is the stall.

Characteristic magnitudes of the lift curve are (see Fig. 4-10):
1. the lift curve slope C_{L_α}

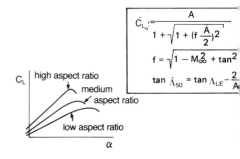

$$C_{L_\alpha}' = \frac{A}{1 + \sqrt{1 + (f\frac{A}{2})^2}}$$

$$f = \sqrt{1 - M_\infty^2 + \tan^2}$$

$$\tan \bar{\Lambda}_{50} = \tan \Lambda_{LE} - \frac{2}{A}$$

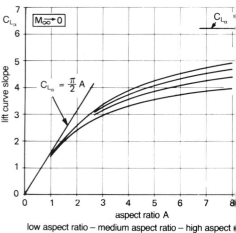

low aspect ratio – medium aspect ratio – high aspect

4-11 Influence of wing aspect ratio on the lift curve slope.

2. the maximum lift $C_{L_{max}}$

The lift curve slope is one of the most important characteristics of the wing. It represents the tangents to the lift curve and describes its linear range. In general wings with large aspect ratio have relatively steep lift curves with clearly defined maximum values. The lift maximum appears at low angles-of-attack and is characterised by a subsequent steep decline.

In contrast, wings with a low aspect ratio show the opposite behaviour, i.e. a slight lift curve slope and an indistinct or barely perceptible maximum lift at high angles-of-attack. Wings with a low aspect ratio therefore require higher angles-of-attack to produce a particular lift than wings with a high aspect ratio.

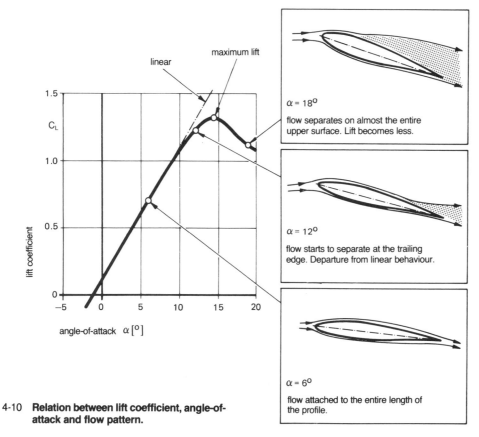

4-10 Relation between lift coefficient, angle-of-attack and flow pattern.

$\alpha = 18°$

flow separates on almost the entire upper surface. Lift becomes less.

$\alpha = 12°$

flow starts to separate at the trailing edge. Departure from linear behaviour.

$\alpha = 6°$

flow attached to the entire length of the profile.

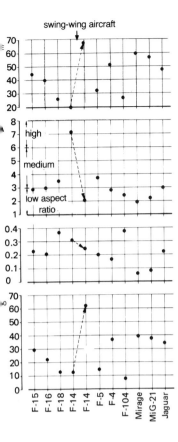

swing-wing aircraft

high

medium

low aspect ratio

F-15 F-16 F-18 F-14 F-14 F-5 F-4 F-104 Mirage MiG-21 Jaguar

To assess the lift curve slope there are simple relations as a function of aspect ratio and Mach number (Fig. 4-11). The equations represent the conditions for Mach numbers up to M = 0.7 relatively well.

The lift curve slopes of typical combat aircraft wings lie between 2.5 and 3.5 in the low-speed range. They rise with increasing Mach number and at Mach 1 reach their maxima with values around 5 (see also Fig. 4-66).

The linear part of the lift curve represents the normal operating range of the wing; the non-linear range is avoided in normal flight because of its dangerous flow conditions. However in manoeuvring flight penetration of the non-linear area is unavoidable, and therefore is part of the compulsory demonstrations in the training of all pilots.

DRAG

Drag has many causes. We differentiate between drag components which are practically independent of lift and those which take effect only when lift is produced.

The drag which is independent of the lift is termed **profile drag** and includes friction drag, pressure drag and roughness drag (Fig. 4-12).

Friction drag is primarily the result of the viscosity of the air. Experiments have shown that the flow adheres to a surface and only at a certain distance away behaves as if there were no friction.

Frictionless flow is termed **potential flow.** The decrease in speed of the external flow to the value zero at the surface of a solid (e.g. wing surface) takes place within a thin layer termed the **boundary layer.** Shear stresses arise at a tangent to the surface which together make up the friction drag. The magnitude of the friction drag is dependent on the surface involved.

4-12 **Drag components of the wing.**

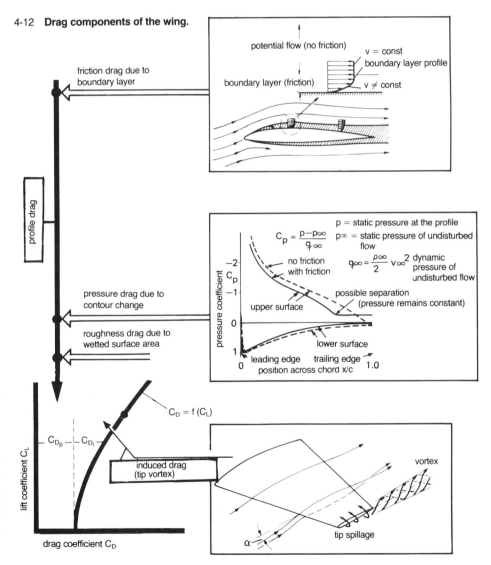

An alteration of the streamline form results from the existing boundary layer. On the external flow (potential flow), the boundary layer acts almost as if it were a part of the solid in the airflow; the solid is thus, in effect, made thicker. A contour which is altered in this way leads to a pressure distribution which is less favourable than in the case of frictionless flow, hence the term **pressure flow.**

Roughness drag is due to rough areas on the surface resulting from the manufacturing process. Among these are: protruding or too deeply countersunk rivet heads; attached aerials; measuring probes and outlets. Another important cause is the microstructure of the metal surface and the protective coating of camouflage paint.

The reduction of roughness drag should begin during the development phase of the aircraft. Close co-operation among the aerodynamics, design and manufacturing departments should en-sure high quality, so that efficiency is not reduced by flaws.

It is possible to affect the friction drag by interfering with the boundary layer. The measures applied will be dealt with in the section on high-lift devices.

The above-mentioned drag components are always present, even when the wing is not providing any lift, for example in a dive. Therefore the drag is characterised as **lift-independent.** This must be distinguished from **lift-dependent drag,** which is caused by pressure equalisation between the upper and lower surfaces of the wing (Fig. 4-13, see also Fig. 4-12). As a consequence of the negative pressure on the upper wing surface and of the positive pressure on the lower surface an equalisation flow is produced at the wing tips which is super-imposed on the main flow. The stream-lines are thereby so deflected that on the upper surface they point towards the fuselage while on the lower surface they point away from the fuselage. When these flows in different directions flow together at the trailing edge, a number of small vortices arise whose strength is relatively small in the fuselage area but is very large at the wing tips.

Together these individual vortices form a vortex sheet. Because of its unstable nature the vortex sheet coils up in a spiral shape immediately behind the wingtips and then merges into a pair of oppositely rotating vortices. These vortices can be clearly observed on large or manoeuvr-ing aircraft; particularly their gradual decay. The continual production of such vortices represents a loss, which has to be offset by additional thrust from the engines.

This component of wing drag, which is dependent on lift, is termed **induced drag** (drag due to lift, vortex drag).

Induced drag is at its lowest when the lift is distributed elliptically over the wing span. With this elliptical lift distribution the

4-13 **Formation of induced drag due to different pressures between the upper and lower surface of the wing.**

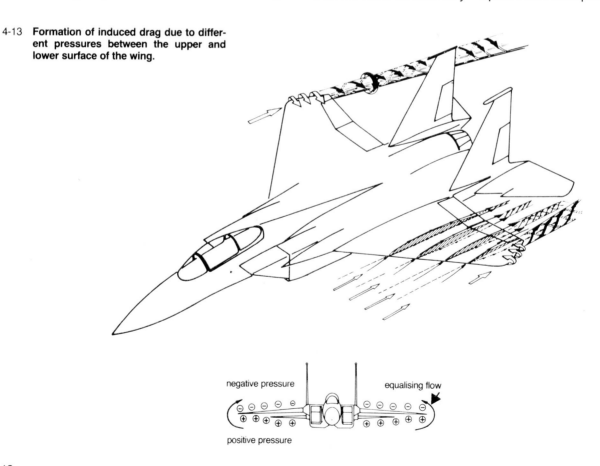

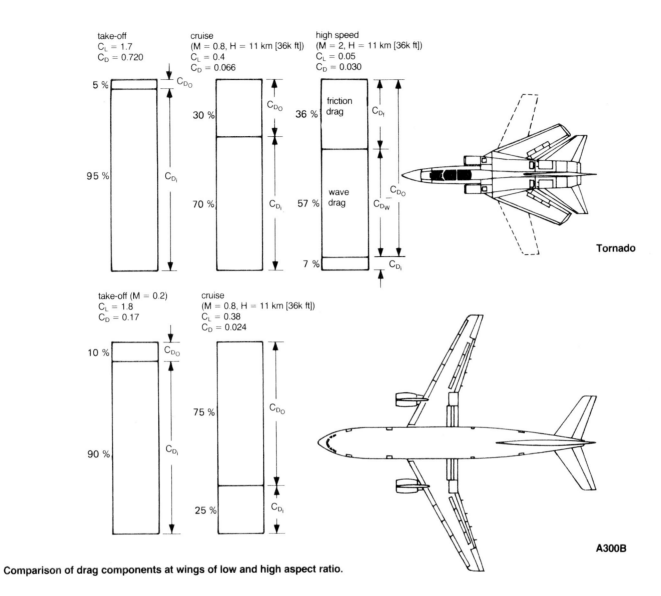

take-off
$C_L = 1.7$
$C_D = 0.720$

cruise
(M = 0.8, H = 11 km [36k ft])
$C_L = 0.4$
$C_D = 0.066$

high speed
(M = 2, H = 11 km [36k ft])
$C_L = 0.05$
$C_D = 0.030$

5 % C_{D_O}

30 % C_{D_O}

36 % friction drag C_{D_f}

95 % C_{D_i}

70 % C_{D_i}

57 % wave drag C_{D_W} C_{D_O}

7 % C_{D_i}

Tornado

take-off (M = 0.2)
$C_L = 1.8$
$C_D = 0.17$

cruise
(M = 0.8, H = 11 km [36k ft])
$C_L = 0.38$
$C_D = 0.024$

10 % C_{D_O}

75 % C_{D_O}

90 % C_{D_i}

25 % C_{D_i}

A300B

4-14 **Comparison of drag components at wings of low and high aspect ratio.**

induced drag depends only on the lift coefficient C_L and the wing aspect ratio A. The following simple relation applies for this:

$$\text{induced drag } C_{D_i} = \frac{C_L{}^2}{\Pi A}$$

As drag increases with decreasing aspect ratio (as the equation shows), the small aspect ratio of combat aircraft wings means a high proportion of induced drag in the total drag (Fig. 4-14).

For this reason an effort is made to influence the drag favourably by means of special measures, such as manoeuvring flaps and variable camber wings.

The assumption of elliptical load distribution is only approximately correct in the lowest angle-of-attack range (up to about $\alpha = 2°$). At higher angles-of-attack considerably higher induced drag has to be expected.

MOMENT

The action of aerodynamic forces on the wing simultaneously produces a moment, which in the linear range of lift also follows a largely linear path, and exhibits non-linear behaviour only when flow separations appear.

The moment path is termed **stable** if a nose-heavy (negative) moment is produced with increasing angle-of-attack which attempts to rotate the wing back

47

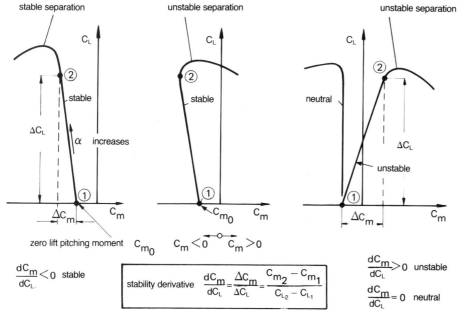

4-15 **Explanation of longitudinal stability.**

again to the original angle-of-attack, such as in the case of a vertical gust. In this case the tangents to the moment curve have negative slope, and the stability derivative dC_m/dC_L, which is applicable here, is negative (Fig. 4-15, see also chapter 5).

If the curve has positive slope $(dC_m/dC_L > 0)$, then the wing, and thereby the aircraft, is unstable. The moment in this case has a nose-up (positive) effect which attempts to rotate the aircraft further from its equilibrium position (see Fig. 4-15, right).

The moment behaviour when flow separation starts is of great significance.

Almost all wing plan-forms are characterised by the fact that the centre of pressure[6] moves forward when separation begins, whereby a destabilising moment results. This undesirable behaviour has no consequences with straight and slightly tapered wings, such as of the A-10 type, because this type of wing stalls first in the area of the wing root so that at high angles-of-attack it automatically does a 'nose over'.

However in the case of delta wings and sweptback wings the flow first separates in the outer area, because the local lift coefficients on the outer wing are greater than on the inner wing. The

attached flow in the inner area produces, together with the flow breakdown in the inner area, a nose-up moment which is strengthened by the action of the downwash on the horizontal tail.

Vortices coming from the leading edge or from the strake have an additional adverse effect on the moment conditions.

The potential interference influences of the wing flow have to be taken into account when the horizontal tail is being designed. A horizontal tail located high up turns out to be unfavourable (F-104). At high angles-of-attack it gets into the separated flow of the wing and is ineffective in attaining the moment equilibrium. Thus there is no way of counteracting the upward pitching movements, which usually results in the loss of the aircraft. One solution to this problem, which is unsatisfactory from an aerodynamic point of view, is the Starfighter's artificial limitation of the angle-of-attack by means of a so-called 'stick pusher', a control which forces a nose-down moment when a particular angle-of-attack is exceeded.

The majority of present day combat aircraft were designed for natural stability. The linear part of their moment curve thus follows a slightly negative path $(dC_m/dC_L < 0)$. In contrast, an unstable design offers the advantage of much greater manoeuvrability and a smaller horizontal tail. However this predicates a control system with sufficient redundancy to meet the failure case because otherwise the aircraft would be lost. The related problems of artificial stability will be dealt with in Chapter 13.

---

[6] The centre of pressure is an imaginary point at which the resultant aerodynamic force acts (see Fig. 4-8).

4.4 The Wing in Subsonic Airflow

In this section the behaviour of the flow at high angles of attack in particular will be shown. As the flow process in the non-linear range is very complicated, the mechanism of separation will first of all be made clear by considering profile behaviour while omitting span influences. Finally the various planform influences will be considered and thereby the transition to the modern wing for combat aircraft.

4.4.1 Flow Separations at the Wing Section (Profile)

At low angles-of-attack the flow is attached to the entire length of the profile (see Fig. 4-10). This flow condition is characteristic of the linear portion of the lift curve. However at higher angles-of-attack flow separations take place and so there is a deviation from the linear lift path. This behaviour is therefore also termed **non-linear**. Systematic wind tunnel investigations on wing profiles have revealed that in this higher angle-of-attack range three basic types of flow separation can be distinguished, i.e.
- trailing-edge separation
- leading-edge separation with short separation 'bubble', and
- leading-edge separation with long separation 'bubble'. (Fig.4-16).

The classic separation process is the **trailing-edge separation**, which appears at profiles with more than 12% relative thickness. The separation begins at a particular angle-of-attack at the trailing edge, and moves forward with increasing angle-of-attack. Maximum lift is reached when the separation position has advanced roughly to the middle of the profile.

This form of separation proceeds relatively 'good-naturedly', because the suction peak at the leading edge remains for a long time (see pressure distribution, profile A, Fig. 4-16). Profiles with trailing-edge separation therefore have a rounded lift curve in the area of their maximum lift. Thick profiles are used in commercial aircraft, sports planes, and gliders, but also for special subsonic

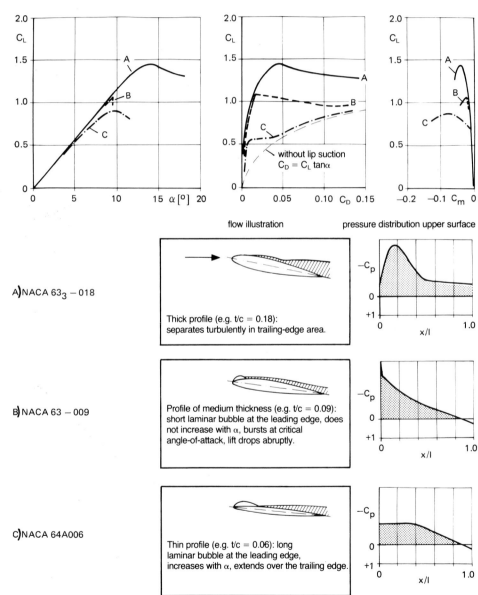

A) NACA 63₃ − 018

B) NACA 63 − 009

C) NACA 64A006

flow illustration

pressure distribution upper surface

Thick profile (e.g. t/c = 0.18): separates turbulently in trailing-edge area.

Profile of medium thickness (e.g. t/c = 0.09): short laminar bubble at the leading edge, does not increase with α, bursts at critical angle-of-attack, lift drops abruptly.

Thin profile (e.g. t/c = 0.06): long laminar bubble at the leading edge, increases with α, extends over the trailing edge.

4-16 **Separation shapes for different wing profiles.**

combat aircraft like the A-10, for example.

Profiles of medium thickness (9-12%) have high suction peaks at the leading edge even at relatively low angles-of-attack (see pressure distribution profile B, Fig. 4-16). Separation takes place immediately after the pressure minimum; the laminar boundary layer changing abruptly into a turbulent state. If the angle-of-attack is not too large, the air flows again along the surface to the trailing edge. In the narrowly defined area of sudden change, which amounts of about 1% of the profile, a **short 'bubble'** bursts, causing a momentary lift breakdown. One of the characteristics of this profile is therefore a practically linear path up to maximum lift, then a sudden decline in lift with an abrupt increase in drag (see lift and drag curves, profile B, Fig. 4-16).

The undesirable properties of such profiles have led to various modifications of the wing leading edge, which is usually thickened; even when greater drag has to be put up with at higher speeds.

For combat aircraft thin profiles with relative thicknesses of 4 to 8% are common, and having a very small leading edge radius. These profiles show linear behaviour only up to angles-of-attack of 4 to 5° (see lift curve, profile C,

Fig. 4-16). Afterwards laminar separation and the formation of a short 'bubble' also appear.

This 'bubble' changes into a **long 'bubble'** before the maximum lift angle-of-attack is reached. This is indicated by a kink in the lift curve. The long 'bubble' becomes larger with increasing angle-of-attack until it reaches the trailing edge when the wing achieves its maximum lift. For this reason thin profiles, as with thick profiles with trailing-edge separation, have a rounded lift curve. However the maximum lift is considerably less because of the separation at the trailing edge. Linked with this is the reduction of the suction peak, which leads to decline of lip suction and increases the drag (see pressure distribution, profile C, Fig. 4-16).

The separation characteristics described should not only be seen in connection with profile thickness. Pressure distribution is the decisive factor. Moreover the three basic types of flow separation cannot always be accurately differentiated one from another.

Thus it is possible for leading-edge and trailing-edge separations to appear simultaneously. It can also happen that, for example, thick profiles show laminar separation with subsequent laminar re-attachment, even at the trailing edge. In other words, the flow does not become

turbulent. This often appears in the wind tunnel because of insufficiently large Reynolds numbers[7], resulting from the limited dimensions of the test section.

This can cause expensive misinterpretation of the results, as the boundary layer on the wind tunnel model appears to have lower drag than the full-scale model possesses with its actual turbulent boundary layer.

The investigation of profiles has been one of the dominant topics since the earliest days of aerodynamics. Nevertheless no one has succeeded in solving the problems of maximum lift with theoretical models.

The reason for this lies, above all, in the fact that for the time being there are still no procedures for reliably describing the behaviour of the boundary layer. The methods of predicting the maximum lift are therefore based mainly on the systematic evaluation of a large number of measurements.

---

[7] See Appendix, page 248

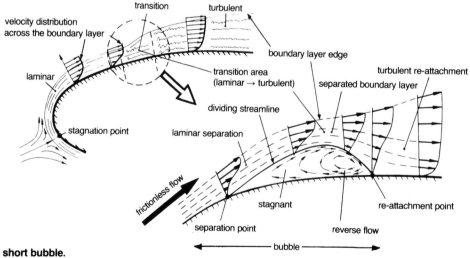

velocity distribution across the boundary layer

transition

turbulent

boundary layer edge

laminar

transition area (laminar → turbulent)

turbulent re-attachment

separated boundary layer

stagnation point

dividing streamline

laminar separation

frictionless flow

stagnant

re-attachment point

separation point

reverse flow

bubble

4-17 **Flow model of the short bubble.**

4.4.2 Flow Separation at Wings

The properties of wing profiles can only be found in a wing of infinitely large aspect ratio. The small aspect ratio of combat aircraft causes the profile properties to recede into the background. The wing plan-form becomes of decisive importance. For purposes of comparison the lift characteristics of the wing of high and low aspect ratio will be considered (Fig. 4-18). The linear path of lift reaches its limit, in the case of a wing with a large aspect ratio, at the onset of the flow separations which appear at the larger angles-of-attack. These non-linear[8] influences cause a decrease of lift and finally lead to flow break-down. The behaviour of a wing with a large aspect ratio is to a large extent determined by the properties of its profile, whose predomi-

---

[8] The linear, i.e. straight, curve path is theoretically simpler to describe. Deviations from the straight line are referred to as non-linear effects, which theoretically can only be approximately accounted for, or not at all.

---

nant parameter is the thickness. The quasi two-dimensional properties of this wing still remain if the leading edge is moderately swept, as in the case of commercial aircraft.

In contrast is the behaviour of wings with a low aspect ratio.

A slender delta wing will be chosen as an example (see Fig. 4-18). The lift curve runs noticeably flatter than in the case of the wing with a high aspect ratio and already shows a non-linear **increase** in lift at small angles-of-attack. The cause of this behaviour is equally attributable to friction influences. However these are of a completely different kind from the flow separations at the wing with a high aspect ratio. In the case of a significantly swept wing with a low aspect ratio the flow separates at the leading edge even at low angles-of-attack and coils up into a stable vortex, which increases downstream and assumes the typical conical shape.

Because of its position and the characteristics of its origin, this separation shape is called a **leading-edge vortex**.

The conical vortex induces considerable negative pressures on the upper wing surface, which explains the additional non-linear lift. As a consequence of the negative pressure the flow passing directly over the vortex is captured by the latter and becomes itself part of the vortex. The suction force of the vortex centre, which decreases outwards, defines a boundary flow surface which, although it lies in the sphere of the vortex's influence, can still be freed from this influence by the centrifugal forces which are sufficient for this purpose. This flow surface reattaches itself behind the vortex and flows to the trailing edge (Fig. 4-19). A **re-attachment line** can be defined on the wing. It is also called a **dividing streamline** because the generating flow surface divides the adjacent flow in the inner area of the wing from the sphere of influence of the leading-edge vortex.

The essential difference between the two types of wing lies in the fact that the flow on a wing with a high aspect ratio has the following characteristics:-

a) it separates only in the maximum lift range, and –

b) the separation is of an unstable nature: whereas with the low aspect ratio wing –

c) the flow separates at low angles-of-attack, and –

d) the separation is itself stable.

In combat aircraft design the delta wing represents a successful means of generating lift (examples: MiG-21, Mirage). Nevertheless this type of wing represents only **one** of many possibilities. Other wing shapes are more common. These have less sweep and have a larger aspect ratio than comparable delta wings (see wing types, table 4-1). A wing of this type with moderate leading-edge sweepback (about 30-40°) bears a marked resemblance in its flow characteristics to a delta wing at medium angles-of-attack (α = 6 to 10°). A leading edge vortex also comes into existence here. This does not run along the entire leading edge at high angles-of-attack, but turns inwards as a free vortex in the direction of

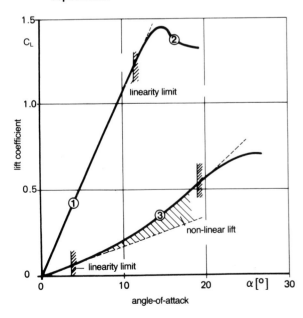

4-18 **Lift behaviour of wings of high and low aspect ratio.**

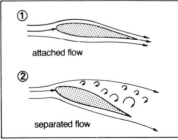

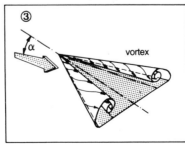

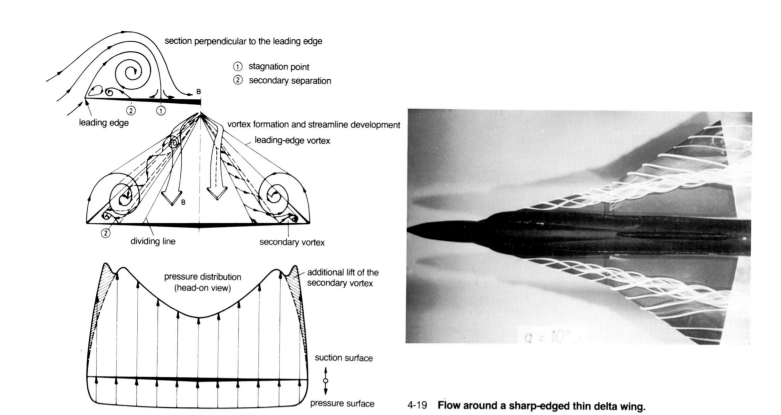

section perpendicular to the leading edge

① stagnation point
② secondary separation

leading edge

vortex formation and streamline development

leading-edge vortex

dividing line

secondary vortex

pressure distribution
(head-on view)

additional lift of the
secondary vortex

suction surface

pressure surface

4-19　**Flow around a sharp-edged thin delta wing.**

the main flow and persistently influences the flow field of the outer wing (Fig. 4-20). Reverse flow and stagnant zones have particularly damaging effects. They arise as a consequence of the vortex turning away in the outer area of the wing so as to prevent effective lift generation.

To reactivate the outer areas endangered by separation various measures are applied, such as a sawtooth (dogtooth) leading edge, slats and cambering.

One of the essential disadvantages of trapezoidal and sweptback wings is the poor stall behaviour of the flow at higher angles-of-attack, while the more strongly sweptback delta wing causes the least problems in this respect.

The cause of this behaviour is the progressive flow stall from the wing tip to the fuselage with increasing angles-of-attack. As an alternative, wing shapes were developed which also showed a controlled separation in the form of vortices in the higher angle-of-attack range, in spite of a little sweepback. Thus the advantages of the less sweptback wing (better low-speed properties, greater flap

4.4.3 **Wings with Strakes**

For the demanding requirements of manoeuvrability, particularly during turns in aerial combat, the current classical wing types have proved unsuitable. This applies to the trapezoidal wing (F-104, F-5), as well as to the sweptback wing (F-4), and to a certain extent to the delta wing (Mirage, MiG-21).

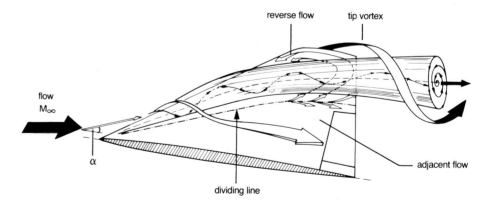

reverse flow

tip vortex

flow
M_∞

α

dividing line

adjacent flow

4-20　**Simplified model of the upper surface flow of a low-aspect ratio sweptback wing at angle-of-attack.**

effectiveness) can be combined with the advantages of the delta wing (better stall characteristics). These wing shapes are termed strake wings or hybrid wings (Fig. 4-21).

A strake (or leading-edge extension, LEX) has a strongly sweptback leading edge running well forward alongside the fuselage. This gives the impression of a very slender delta wing installed immediately in front of the main wing. The strake leading edge can be straight or curved and is always designed with a sharp leading edge.

The action of the strake becomes clear if the behaviour of a trapezoidal wing with or without a strake is considered (Fig. 4-22). At an angle-of-attack of 6° the simple trapezoidal wing shows the leading-edge vortex typical of wings with a low aspect ratio and moderate sweepback; this arises from the separated flow and runs practically to the tip. At 12° angle-of-attack the vortex is already to a large extent turned into the direction of the main flow. This causes a reverse-flow zone on the outer wing, while attached flow is to be found only in the inner area. This process is the cause of the nonlinear behaviour of the wing, which reaches its maximum lift at relatively low angles-of-attack (here at 18°). In this case only reverse-flow and stagnant zones are perceptible on the wing, which mean high drag.

However the addition of a strake permits considerable improvement of flow quality. At 6° angle-of-attack the strake influence is slight, because the main area of the wing is still functioning in the linear range and shows healthy flow. At an angle-of-attack of 12°, however, the strake wing reveals a marked gain in lift.

The vortex generated at the strake continues its path over the main wing, while the main wing vortex, which is twisting downwards, is deflected further outwards. At an even greater angle of attack (α = 18°) the influence of the wing vortex has disappeared. However the strake vortex is in a position to suppress significantly the development of the stagnant zone on the main wing (without

4-21 **Strake wing (Northrop YF-17, predecessor of McDonnell Douglas F/A-18).**

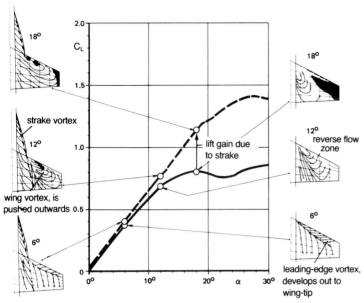

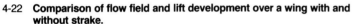

4-22 **Comparison of flow field and lift development over a wing with and without strake.**

4-24 **F-16 in high angle-of-attack flight with humidity condensing because of the negative pressure in the core of the strake vortex, rendering it visible.**

strake) so that only a small proportion of the outer wing is not generating lift.

The dominant influence in the lift behaviour of the hybrid wing comes from the strake vortex, which obtains its energy from the separated flow of the strake leading edge and is able to extend itself over the entire chord of the downstream main wing (Fig. 4-23). The strake vortex does not develop further out of the separated flow after reaching the main wing, but continues its movement using its own energy. The displacement effect of the strake vortex leads to the stabilising of the leading edge vortex of the main wing, which tends to separate. Thus two vortex systems exist side by side which influence each other positively and support each other. Because of the same direction of rotation which both vortices have on one wing half, the flow between the vortices is characterised by strong turbulence.

In the core of the vortex high negative pressures can arise, which, in suitable atmospheric conditions, cause suspended moisture to condense, so that the core zone of the strake vortex becomes visible during flight manoeuvres at high angle-of-attack (Fig. 4.24).

4-23 **Explanation of observed flow development at the strake wing at 12° angle-of-attack.**

4.5 High-lift Devices

The design of combat aircraft wings is primarily related to the requirements of high speed flight. These dictate outstanding performance and manoeuvrability at high subsonic and transonic speeds. A projected wing design must exhibit acceptable drag characteristics over the complete range of Mach number; including that of supersonic flight. A wing design with the following parameters will meet these requirements:-

- moderate wing loading (3000-4000 N/m^2) (63-84 lb/ft^2)
- low aspect ratio (A = 3-4)
- medium sweepback (Λ_{LE} = 35°-50°), and
- minimum thickness/chord ratio (t/c = 0.04-0.07).

However, the additional needs of low speed flight, to permit operations from short runways, impose conditions which are difficult to fulfil.

The lift curve for the F-4 exemplifies the problems which arise when the flight speed is reduced. Assuming a wing loading of 3545 N/m^2 (74 lb/ft^2) and an air density at sea level[9] of ρ = 1.225 kg/m^3 (0.0023 slugs/ft^3), a particular speed can be assigned to every lift coefficient with the aid of the lift equation (Fig. 4-25). A continual increase in the angle-of-attack is necessary during deceleration to maintain lift. The lowest possible speed, the so-called **stalling speed** v_s, is reached at maximum lift. The aircraft is already out of control as a consequence of flow separations at the wing; and uncontrollable roll and yaw oscillations arise which can no longer be overcome, due to the detached flow. As a safety precaution against stalling, a minimum permissible flight speed v_{min} is prescribed, which is about 20% above the stalling speed:

$$v_{min} = 1.2 \, v_s$$

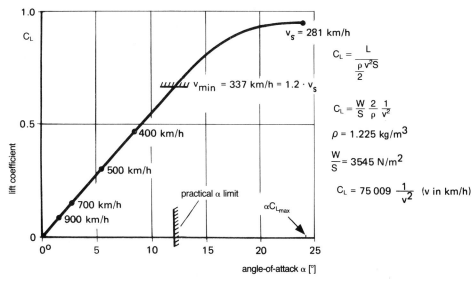

$$C_L = \frac{L}{\frac{\rho \, v^2 S}{2}}$$

$$C_L = \frac{W}{S} \frac{2}{\rho} \frac{1}{v^2}$$

$$\rho = 1.225 \text{ kg/m}^3$$

$$\frac{W}{S} = 3545 \text{ N/m}^2$$

$$C_L = 75\,009 \, \frac{1}{v^2} \quad \text{(v in km/h)}$$

4-25   **During low-speed flight the angle-of-attack must be increased to maintain lift. The minimum permissible flight speed V_{min} limits the usable lift and angle-of-attack range (example: F-4 without flaps). W = weight, S = wing area.**

From this a maximum effective lift coefficient can be derived, which amounts to about 70% of maximum lift[10]. In the above example a minimum flight speed of 337 km/h (180 knots) results for the F-4's 'clean' wing (i.e. for the wing without flap deflection): but this would lead to unacceptably long runways. Nevertheless, in order to obtain the maximum lift at low speeds which cannot be supplied by the 'clean' wing, **high-lift devices** in the form of leading-edge and trailing-edge flaps are necessary.

The **plain trailing-edge flap** represents a simple form of flap which is created by rotating the rear part of the profile around one point within the profile contour (Fig. 4-26, top). The flap deflection increases the camber, so that a greater lift arises at the same angle-of-attack. At deflections of 10° to 15°, the

flow on the upper surface of the flap begins to separate, but the separation zone remains restricted to the flap for the time being. The lift increases with increasing flap deflection and reaches its maximum just before the flow on the entire wing breaks down. In this case the separation jumps forward from the flap onto the wing.

With the plain trailing-edge flap a lift increase of around ΔC_L = 1.0 is possible, provided that the initial profile is only slightly curved or not at all. These conditions are always fulfilled in the case of combat aircraft, so that the plain trailing-edge has found widespread use as an effective and low-priced high-lift device in combat aircraft design.

A further increase in lift is possible by adopting slotted flaps, and these are also frequently encountered on modern combat aircraft. This type of flap is characterised by a slot between the main segment of the profile and the deflected flap. The lift increase is due to increased camber

9) See standard atmosphere, Appendix

10) $\dfrac{C_L}{C_{L_{max}}} = \dfrac{v_s^2}{v_{min}^2} = \dfrac{v_s^2}{(1.2 v_s)^2} = 0.7$

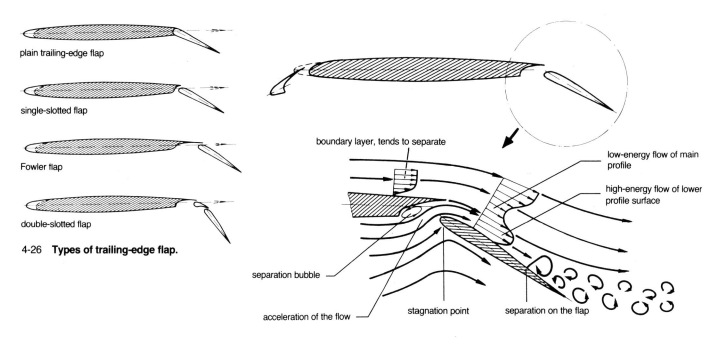

plain trailing-edge flap

single-slotted flap

Fowler flap

double-slotted flap

4-26 **Types of trailing-edge flap.**

boundary layer, tends to separate

low-energy flow of main profile

high-energy flow of lower profile surface

separation bubble

acceleration of the flow

stagnation point

separation on the flap

4-27 **Mode of operation of the slot flow with a trailing-edge flap.**

and, in some cases, to enlargement of the wing surface by extending the flap rearwards.

The slot ensures that the high energy flow moves from the lower wing surface into the 'tired' boundary layer of the upper surface, thereby preventing any tendency for flow separation at large flap deflection angles (Fig. 4-27). It is important to ensure that when the slotted flap is operated the separation bubble arising at the lower surface of the main segment does not burst. This is achieved by means of a suitable slot geometry, and in addition, the slot is so designed that:

a) the slot cross-section decreases in the flow direction (jet effect); and

b) the flow emerging from the slot crosses into the slower wing boundary layer tangentially.

The numerous versions of slotted flaps are classified according to their geometry. The classification usually relates to the number of slots. The **single-slotted flap** (see Fig. 4-26, second from top) is the simplest in construction and therefore the most widespread. The **Fowler flap** functions with greater effect because the flap is extended rearwards as well as deflecting downwards (see

Fig. 4-26, second from bottom). The possible kinematics of flap adjustment range from simple rotation about a fixed point, outside the profile, to the combined rotation and translation movements, in which the leading edge of the flap moves near the trailing edge of the original profile. In the example of the Fowler flap, the upper surface of the main segment is

drawn to the rear so that the flow is adequately channelled and the necessary slot effect is maintained throughout the range of settings.

A further boost of effectiveness is attained with the **double-slotted** type of flap. This is used, for example, on the F-111 and the Tornado (see Fig. 4-26, bottom). Apart from its greater complexity

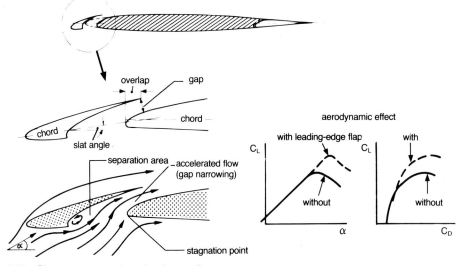

4-28 **Slat geometry and mode of operation.**

56

4-29 **Leading-edge devices to improve high-lift behaviour: slat on the F-4; plain leading-edge and trailing-edge flap on the F-5; fixed leading edge camber on the F-15.**

from the lower wing surface to move into the boundary layer of the upper surface (Fig. 4-28), which is 'tired' and thereby prone to separate. The separation risk arises from the high suction point in the nose area of the wing and the subsequent strong pressure rise against which the boundary layer has to move. With the aid of a slat, the suction point can be largely uncoupled from the main wing and displaced to the slat, to which high loads are thereby allocated. At the same time the load distribution of the main wing is improved, which in turn means that the wing is overall more efficient.

However, the effectiveness of a slat has to be measured against the relatively high construction costs of the operating mechanism and designing for high aerodynamic loads. For this reason also, slats are relatively rare (Fig. 4-29, top left as well as Table 4.1 overleaf).

A further, frequently encountered, leading-edge device is the plain flap. The front part of the flap is rotated around a point within the wing profile. The plain leading-edge flap is simple and robust,

there is the penalty of the higher construction cost and weight, which together lead to higher costs for the total flap system.

By extending trailing-edge flaps rearwards a considerable increase in lift can be attained, depending on the type of flap, over the entire angle-of-attack range. However at all times a greater or lesser increase in drag has to be accepted. In contrast, wing lift can be increased with **leading-edge devices** without an unacceptable increase in

drag. However their effectiveness begins only at high angles-of-attack in the maximum lift range.

Leading edge devices contribute to a reduction in the high negative pressure peaks. Separation appears only at high angles-of-attack, so that the effective angle-of-attack range becomes greater.

The most effective leading-edge device on a not too sharply sweptback wing is the **slat,** which permits increases in maximum lift of up to $\Delta C_L = 0.2$.

The slat causes the high-energy flow

type	wing							
	span	wing area	aspect ratio A	taper ratio λ	sweepback leading-edge Λ_{LE}	thickness (inner/outer) %	wing loading	high-lift and manoeuvre devices, spoilers, airbrakes.
F-15	13,04 m	59,3 m²	2,88	0,23	45°	6,6%/ 3%	3556 N/m² (74 lb/ft²)	inner trailing-edge flap, plain trailing-edge flap type, outer aileron. No movable leading-edge devices, however increasing camber of the profile towards the tip. One-piece airbrake behind cockpit canopy.
F-16	9,14 m	27,87 m²	3,0	0,21	40°	4%	3449 N/m² (72 lb/ft²)	plain trailing-edge flap, undivided, operates simultaneously as aileron (flaperon). One-piece leading-edge flap. Airbrakes on both sides of the fuselage close to the jet nozzle.
F-18	11,43 m	37,2 m²	3,52	0,37	26°	5%/ 3,5%	3250 N/m² (68 lb/ft²)	plain trailing-edge flap, outboard ailerons. Continuous leading-edge flap (plain) with straight leading-edge. Airbrake between vertical tail surfaces.
F-14	19.54 m or 11.72 m (at the minimum or maximum sweepback position of the wing respectively)	53.3 m² or 66.3 m²	7.16 or 2.07	0.31 or 0.25	20° or 68°	10%/ 5%	4787 N/m² (98 lb/ft²) or 3847 N/m² (80 lb/ft²)	three section trailing-edge flap over full span at 10° flap deflection (manoeuvre) as plain trailing-edge flap, during take-off and landing (35°) as single-slotted flap. Leading-edge device: two section slat over full span. Deflection of slat and trailing-edge flap only possible at sweepback position under 50°, four spoilers above each wing.
F-5	7,7 m	15,79 m	3,75	0,2	31,5°	4,8%	3989 N/m² (83 lb/ft²)	single-slotted, trailing-edge flaps with ailerons outboard. One-piece leading-edge flaps (plain), two airbrakes below fuselage in front of main landing gear.
F-4	11,8 m	49,26 m²	2,82	0,17	51,4°	6,4%/ 3%	3545 N/m² (74 lb/ft²)	plain trailing-edge blown flaps with ailerons outboard; only movable downwards; necessary upward aileron deflection via spoilers on the wing. Leading-edge devices: two-section slats. Brake parachute in afterbody cone.
F-104	6,68 m	18,2 m²	2,45	0,376	27°	3,4%	4856 N/m² (101 lb/ft²)	plain trailing-edge flaps, blown during landing, ailerons outboard. Leading-edge device: plain leading-edge flaps, one-piece, over full span.
Mirage	8,22 m	34,85 m²	1,94	0,062	60°	4,5%/ 3,5%	2220 N/m² (46 lb/ft²)	plain trailing-edge surface in two sections, combining function of ailerons and elevators. No leading-edge devices. Airbrakes on the upper and lower surface of the wing near the leading-edge. Brake parachute in afterbody cone.
MiG-21	7,15 m	23,2 m²	2,2	0,083	57°	4,3%	3463 N/m² (72 lb/ft²)	plain trailing-edge flap, in the case of MiG-21SPS blown outboard ailerons. No leading-edge devices.
Jaguar	8,49 m	24,0 m²	3,0	0,228	48°	6%/ 5%	4263 N/m² (89 lb/ft²)	trailing-edge: one-piece double-slotted flaps. Control of lateral motion by means of two-section spoilers in front of the trailing-edge flaps, in combination with differential elevators. Leading-edge device: slats in the outer area of the wing. Brake parachute in afterbody cone.
MiG-25	14,0 m	56,0 m²	3,07	0,32	40° anhedral −6°	3,5%	4764 N/m² (100 lb/ft²)	plain inner trailing-edge flaps inboard, ailerons outboard. No leading-edge devices.

horizontal tail				vertical tail			
$\frac{l_H}{\bar{c}}$	$\frac{S_H}{S}\left(\frac{S_{HN}}{S}\right)$	V_H (V_{HN})	type	$\frac{l_v}{s}$	$\frac{S_v}{S}$	V_v	type
1,17	0,46 (0,18)	0,54 (0,21)	all-moving tail, differential, sweepback 50°	0,83	0,19	0,16	twin tail fins, sloped at 2° outwards, sweepback 37°
1,39	0,34 (0,21)	0,47 (0,29)	all-moving tail, differential, sweepback 40°	1,01	0,20	0,20	single tail fin, sweepback 48°, two ventral fins
1,65	0,36 (0,24)	0,60 (0,39)	all-moving tail, differential, sweepback 41°	0,61	0,28	0,17	twin tail fins, sloped 15° outwards, sweepback 43°
1.88 or 0.91	0.67 (0.24) or 0.54 (0.19)	1.26 (0.45) or 0.49 (0.17)	all-moving tail, differential, sweepback 51°	0.58 or 1.19	0.31 or 0.31	0.18 or 0.37	twin tail fins, sweepback 47°, two ventral fins
1,65	0,32 (0,18)	0,52 (0,29)	all-moving tail, sweepback 3.25°	0,87	0,20	0,17	single tail fin, sweepback 35.5°
1,52	0,17 (0,15)	0,25 (0,22)	all-moving tail, sweepback 42.5°, negative dihedral 23°	1,05	0,13	0,13	single tail fin, sweepback 65°
1,98	0,25 (0,23)	0,49 (0,46)	all-moving tail, sweepback 19.3°	1,39	0,21	0,30	single tail fin, T-tail, sweepback 44°
–	–	–	–	0,97	0,14	0,14	single tail fin, sweepback 63°
1,35	0,31 (0,19)	0,41 (0,26)	all-moving tail, sweepback 59°	1,22	0,21	0,26	single tail fin, sweepback 48°, one ventral fin
1,68	0,33 (0,26)	0,55 (0,44)	all-moving tail, sweepback 45°	1,35	0,17	0,23	single tail fin, sweepback 48°, two ventral fins
1,29	0,34 (0,18)	0,44 (0,23)	all-moving tail, sweepback 52°	0,88	0,21	0,19	twin tail fins, sweepback 51.5°, two ventral fins

Table 4.1

and requires little servicing. This type of slat is employed for example on the F-5 (see Fig. 4-29, top right).

If we want to do without movable flaps – which is occasionally necessary for a variety of reasons – the leading edge can be modified by increasing its curvature towards the tip. This step was taken with the F-15, which has no leading-edge devices (see Fig. 4-29, bottom). Nevertheless this makes higher drag inevitable in the supersonic range, so that high-performance engines with adequate excess thrust are necessary.

Another way of improving the high-lift properties of the wing is by adding a so-called **saw-tooth leading edge** (Fig. 4-30). The saw-tooth leading edge generates a strong leading-edge vortex whose flow at high angles-of-attack is intended to re-energise the outer area of the wing flow, which otherwise tends to separate. The saw-tooth leading edge is used, among others, on the Crusader (LTV F-8), the F-4, and the horizontal tail of the F-15.

The saw-tooth leading edge is a sure sign that the aircraft builder has not got the wing flow under control and therefore has had to resort to this makeshift solution. However the necessity for this usually emerges only in wind tunnel or flight experiments when the configuration is already to a large extent 'frozen' and changes to the wing structure are no longer possible.

A fence is a very easy means of influencing the boundary layer. At one time this was frequently employed, but because of advances in wing design it has largely disappeared from combat aircraft.

By means of a boundary layer fence a virtual division of a sweptback wing into discrete areas occurs, so that undesirable spanwise boundary layer effects

4-30 'Saw-tooth leading edge' high-lift device (Vought A-7D).

cannot spread, except to a limited extent, to neighbouring areas. In particular the object is to prevent the drifting of the boundary layer into the outer areas which are endangered by separation anyway. A disadvantage of the boundary layer fence is its high friction and interference drag in high-speed flight.

As an additional measure to reduce leading-edge separation in the outer area of the wing, differential deflection of the trailing-edge flap can be used. That is, provided the flap is partitioned, such as in the F-15 (see Fig. 8-27). This design exploits the fact that, when the flap is deflected, not only are loads transferred to the flap, but also the entire pressure distribution of the profile is influenced. That is, the greater the flap deflection, the higher the suction points at the leading edge (Fig. 4-31). In order to reduce excessively high negative pressure peaks, which always appear in the outer area and promote flow separation, the outer flap must therefore be less extended than the inner flap. This method is all the

4-31 **Load distribution as a result of flap deflection (profile NACA 63A 015, flap deflection 10°, variation angle-of-attack α).**

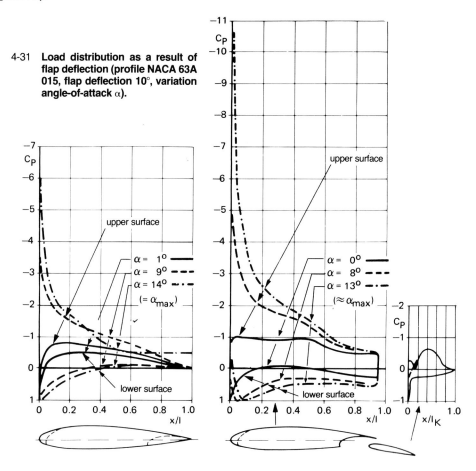

60

more effective the further the flap extends in the spanwise direction.

Finally it will be shown how the various high-lift devices influence the lift curve. The sole practical use of leading-edge devices (movable or fixed) is to lengthen the lift curve of the 'clean' wing and displace the maximum value to higher angles-of-attack (Fig. 4-32). The extension of the trailing-edge flap alone displaces the lift curve of the 'clean' wing almost parallel upwards, the maximum lift frequently lying at a lower angle-of-attack than that of the 'clean' wing. Together with leading-edge devices, the transferred curve is lengthened, so that higher maximum lifts are possible. The combined application of leading-edge and trailing-edge devices leads, as a rule, to higher flap effectiveness than through the deflection of a flap alone. Table 4.1 shows a selection of the high-lift devices applied in some modern combat aircraft design.

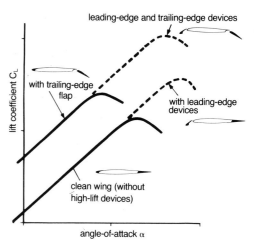

4-32 **Influence of various high-lift devices on C_L development.**

4.6 **Wing/Fuselage Interference**

The essential aerodynamic properties of an aircraft are determined by the wing, which must generate the necessary lift. The **fuselage** of a combat aircraft, in contrast, has the function of making room for engines, fuel, electronic equipment, guns, landing gear, and the pilot's 'workplace' (Fig. 4-33).

The design of combat aircraft fuselages is more complicated than that of commercial aircraft and is determined by two essential factors:

a) in order to reduce drag, in particular wave drag, there has to be a particular distribution of the cross sections in order to fulfil the conditions most effectively (area rule, Sears-Haack body);

b) the initial fuselage design must provide room for subsequent modifi-

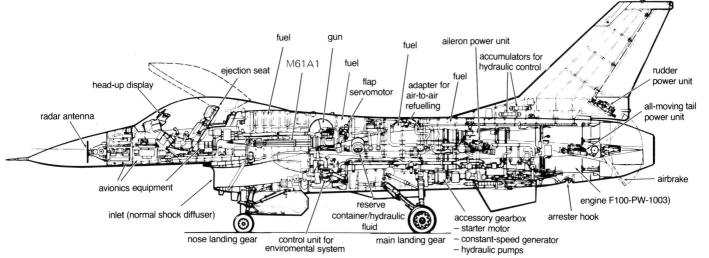

4-33 **The fuselage has to contain engines, fuel, avionics equipment, guns, landing gear, cockpit and much more (General Dynamics F-16).**

cations and additional equipment during the life of the aircraft.

In general the fuselage has a plane of symmetry which coincides with that of the aircraft. Moreover the fuselage acts as a connecting element for wings and tail surfaces, and therefore needs sufficient structural strength to absorb and transmit all forces which arise. Nevertheless, fuselage weight, as a proportion of the total, must be kept low. This is only possible with a sufficiently light construction.

The more or less easily understood aerodynamic properties of wing and fuselage, as individual bodies, result, after their assembly, in considerable complications. This is because they mutually influence each other (interference). These influences are due to the fact that the wing lies in the fuselage flow field and the fuselage lies in the wing flow field. The interference forces can be of the same order of magnitude as the individual aerodynamic forces generated by the fuselage or wing. Interference forces are largely design-dependent and therefore their magnitude can be influenced. A good design makes use of the interference effect to attain particular properties or to keep drag within limits. The critical dependence of the total aircraft drag on interference drag thus requires particular attention during design.

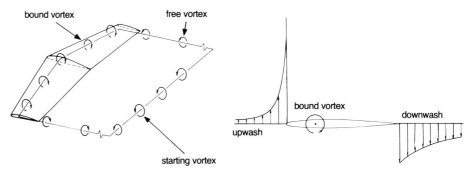

4-34 **Horse-shoe vortex from equivalent model of a wing.**

same flow-mechanical effects as the wing, and which generates lift when superimposed on the flow. According to the so-called Helmholtz vortex theorems, a vortex can neither begin nor end in the interior of a flow; it must, therefore, form a self-contained vortex filament converging into itself. Therefore, in the case of a wing (of finite span), the bound vortex in the downstream direction is continued in the form of the two tip vortices which come off the lateral wing-tips. In order to generate the self-contained vortex filament, the aerodynamic model starts from the assumption of the so-called **starting vortex,** which remains behind on the runway at take-off. However only the free vortex and the bound vortex are of practical importance; together they form the **horse-shoe vortex.**

The bound vortex (as a substitute model of the wing) induces an **upwash** in front of the wing which fades away towards the sides. In contrast a **downwash** lies behind the wing which is generated by the bound vortex and is reinforced by the two free vortices.

In total, a downward-directed flow always remains behind the wing. This tends to result in a smaller angle-of-attack for the tailplane, of a conventional aircraft, than that for the wing (see Section 4.7).

The fuselage lies in this flow field, which is characterised by an upward and then downward direction (Fig. 4-35). It can be seen that the upwash in front of the wing raises the local angle-of-attack. The fuselage is therefore in a curved flow created by the wing; this causes a nose-up pitching moment and has a destabilising effect.

INFLUENCE OF THE WING ON THE FUSELAGE

Even in the early days of aerodynamics, a simple model was developed for the theoretical calculation of wing flow which reflected practical experience relatively well and served to explain the flow at the wing and near it.

According to this concept, the wing is replaced by a **bound vortex,** having the

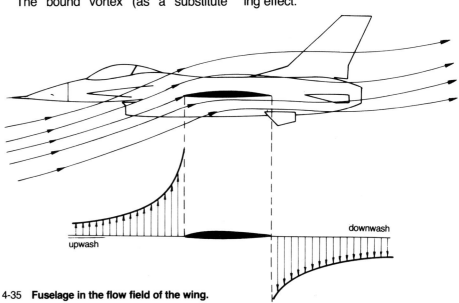

4-35 **Fuselage in the flow field of the wing.**

62

INFLUENCE OF THE FUSELAGE ON THE WING

The lift distribution generated by the wing alone, which is approximately elliptical, dips in the fuselage area, and this dip increases with increasing angle-of-attack (Fig. 4-36). The more conservative the aircraft design the greater the reduction in lift. In other words the more the fuselage and wing are considered as independent components, the greater the effect on the lift distribution. For this reason an effort is made in the design of modern combat aircraft to involve the fuselage more in the creation of lift so as to smooth out and increase the lift distribution. The result is flatter fuselage cross-sections and wing-body blending.

At the same time a greater fuselage volume is achieved without a corresponding increase in the surface affected by the flow (wetted area). This design feature is to be seen on the F-16 (Fig. 8-7).

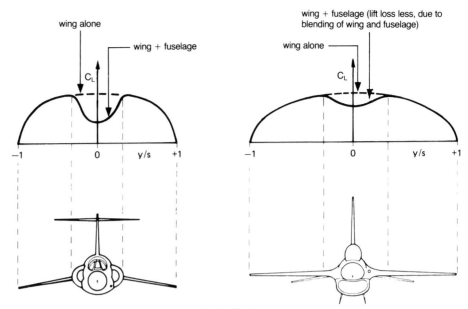

4-36 **Influence of the fuselage on the lift distribution.**

WING POSITION

The arrangement of the wing with respect to the fuselage is of considerable importance, particularly in conditions of unsymmetrical flow. The following are in common use: high-wing position, mid-wing position and low-wing position. From this it becomes clear that each position has its advantages and disadvantages (Fig. 4-37).

For operational and technical reasons, the high-wing position is desirable for a combat aircraft, because it offers ground personnel sufficient headroom and working space and facilitates the loading of the wing with external stores. However the high-wing position can turn out to be unfavourable from an aerodynamic point of view. This is because at high angles-of-attack the vortex coming off the wing leading edge or the strake does not receive sufficient guidance, due to the

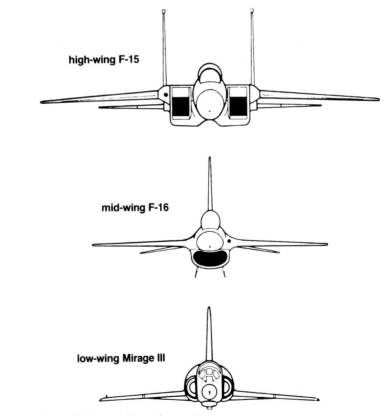

4-37 **High-wing, mid-wing and low-wing position.**

4-38 **Kfir with canard wings.**

lack of fuselage sidewall effect, and comes into contact with the vertical tail. In unsymmetrical flow (sideslip) this happens even at considerably lower angles-of-attack. Thus the directional stability of the aircraft is degraded and it no longer responds to the control. As a result of the high-wing position, it may be necessary to limit the angle-of-attack and sideslip angle, even though the performance potential of the wing is by no means exhausted.

The low-wing position does not produce these problems to the same de-

gree. This is because the fuselage sidewalls are more effective in guiding the flow and in turn the leading-edge vortex. The low-wing position also has the following disadvantage: the strong upward flow component favours a leading-edge separation in the wing root area at high angles-of-attack. This may impose an undesirable limitation on the angle-of-attack. As this also means a considerable restriction on the manoeuvring range, the Israelis chose, in addition, a rigid canard surface for their Kfir, a variant of the French Mirage III. This

canard foreplane aligns the flow better and damps the high upward flow component (Fig. 4-38) (the destabilising effect of the canard at high Mach numbers will be dealt with in Chapter 5).

4.7 Tail Surfaces

4.7.1 Functions of the Tail Surfaces

The essential aerodynamic properties of an aircraft are determined by the wing and the fuselage. For this reason, wind tunnel investigations are first carried out on the wing/fuselage combination, before further experiments follow. However, additional aerodynamic control surfaces are necessary for stability and control; the tail is known as the **empennage**.

The classical empennage shape of a fixed-wing aircraft consists of **one** vertical tail and **two** horizontal tails. In most cases the plan form corresponds to a sweptback wing of medium aspect ratio (Fig. 4-39, top left).

The large range of angle-of-attack and sideslip angles which modern combat aircraft must achieve can, nevertheless, lead to an empennage of above average size in the case of a single vertical tail or fin. This applies to the Tornado. The construction and aerodynamic problems en-countered with a large single vertical tail are circumvented by fitting twin vertical tails (Fig. 4-39, top right).

In the case of tailless aircraft types, such as the Mirage III, the flaps at the wing trailing edge assume the function of an elevator (elevon), so that only the vertical tail component of the empennage is seen (Fig. 4-39, bottom left).

The basic disadvantage of conventional controls, namely for producing a nose-down moment, is avoided by arranging the pitch control surfaces **in front of** the aircraft's centre of gravity. In this way we arrive at the **canard wing** (from the French), as on the Viggen (see Fig. 4-39, bottom right).

F-16

YF-17

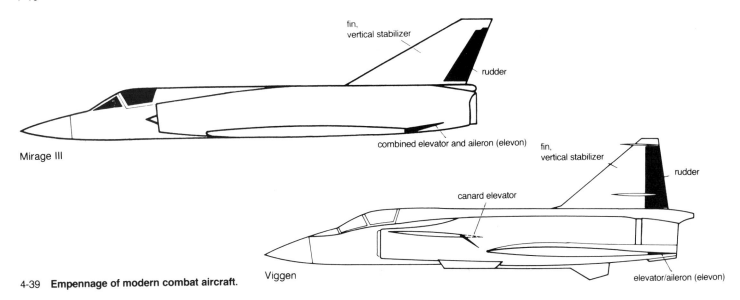

4-39   **Empennage of modern combat aircraft.**

65

ranging the pitch control surfaces **in front of** the aircraft's centre of gravity. In this way we arrive at the **canard wing** (from the French), as on the Viggen (see Fig. 4-39, bottom right).

The above examples emphasise the great range of variation in the design of tail surfaces. However they all have the common function of **stabilisation** and **control.**

Control means the ability to impose desired changes of direction on the aircraft. These take place as moments about the three axes of the aircraft. The control about the lateral axis is effected by means of the **horizontal tail,** and the control around the normal axis and the longitudinal axis by means of the **vertical tail** and the **ailerons** respectively.

Combat aircraft also need on occasions to generate motions around the longitudinal axis (roll) by means of differential tail control surfaces (tailerons). This option is particularly important when flying at high angles-of-attack, because the ailerons become largely ineffective following flow separation.

Of equal importance is the stabilisation of the aircraft. By this is meant the ability to offset unwanted alterations of motion unaided, i.e. without the involvement of the controls. This property is important, because turbulences which are always present in the atmosphere attempt to interfere with level flight. The stabilisation range covers all the design Mach numbers, lift coefficients and positions of centre-of-gravity, including the necessary safety margins.

Recently great efforts have been made to replace the natural stability of the aircraft with active controls, because of the resulting advantages in the performance. The problem of so-called 'artificial stability' will be dealt with in Chapter 13.

4.7.2 **Horizontal tail**

The general kinetic state of the aircraft is usually subdivided into longitudinal motion and lateral motion. The longitudinal motion takes place around the lateral axis and is characterised by **symmetrical** flow state; lateral motion takes place around the normal and longitudinal axis in conditions of **unsymmetrical flow** (sideslip).

As the aircraft is rotated about the lateral axis by the horizontal tail, this consequently serves to control and stabilise longitudinal motion. In the case of commercial aircraft, the horizontal tail is subdivided into the **stabiliser** (tailplane) and the **elevator.** With combat aircraft this sub-division is dispensed with in most cases, so that the control moment about the lateral axis is achieved by rotating the entire horizontal tail (all-moving tail, slab tailplane, flying tail).

GEOMETRY OF THE HORIZONTAL TAIL

As the horizontal tail is virtually a wing, its geometry can essentially be described by analogy to a wing; the concepts of span, plan-form, area and aspect ratio are equally applicable to the horizontal

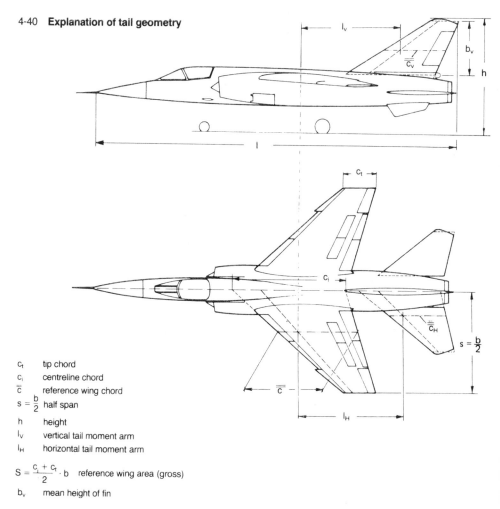

4-40 **Explanation of tail geometry**

c_t tip chord
c_i centreline chord
$\overline{\overline{c}}$ reference wing chord
$s = \dfrac{b}{2}$ half span
h height
l_v vertical tail moment arm
l_H horizontal tail moment arm

$S = \dfrac{c_i + c_t}{2} \cdot b$ reference wing area (gross)

b_v mean height of fin

tail. With a divided horizontal tail (stabiliser and elevator) moreover an **angle of incidence** and **elevator deflection** are defined, in the case of an undivided horizontal tail only the angle of deflection.

The position of the horizontal tail is dictated by the moment arm. In practice the distance between the geometrical neutral points of the wing and the horizontal tail defines the moment arm. The vertical position of the horizontal tail is also of importance. In the case of most combat aircraft the horizontal tail lies on the wing plane or somewhat below it; in contrast the T-tail, in which the horizontal tail is on top of the fin, is rare (Starfighter).

The following are important characteristic ratios of the aerodynamics of the horizontal tail:
– the area ratio S_H/S, and
– the relative tail distance $l_H/\bar{c}$.

These define the size and position of the horizontal tail in relation to the wing (S_H = horizontal tail area, S = wing area, $\bar{\bar{c}}_\mu$ = reference wing-chord). The product of both is the **tail volume**. Table 4.1 provides typical values for the characteristics of combat aircraft tails.

MODE OF OPERATION OF THE HORIZONTAL TAIL

The lift force acting at the horizontal tail contributes considerably to the pitching moment of the aircraft because of its large moment arm (Fig. 4-41). As combat aircraft are usually designed to be inherently stable, the resultant lift force of the wing always acts behind the aircraft's centre-of-gravity thus generating a nose-heavy (negative) moment.[11] To attain a level flight condition, such as steady level flight, it is necessary to counter this moment. To do this the horizontal tail must furnish a tail-heavy (hence rotation in the opposite direction) moment of the same amount. This requires the gener-

---

[11] The nose-up moment always has a positive sign

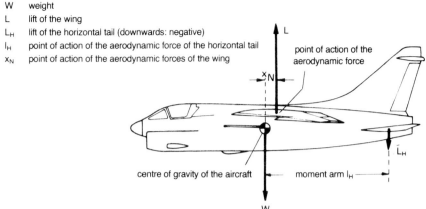

W	weight
L	lift of the wing
L_H	lift of the horizontal tail (downwards: negative)
l_H	point of action of the aerodynamic force of the horizontal tail
x_N	point of action of the aerodynamic forces of the wing

moment equilibrium (nose-up moment, positive):- $-L \times x_N + L_H \times l_H = 0$

4-41 **Forces on the horizontal tail for generating the moment equilibrium.**

ation of a downward force at the tail, i.e. negative lift. By means of this the total lift is reduced by the negative lift for trimming (see Fig. 4-41).

Induced drag is a function of the deflection of the horizontal tail and is analogous to the induced drag of a lift-producing wing. This induced drag influences the drag curve unfavourably.

A considerable complication of the flow at the horizontal tail results from its position at the aft end of the aircraft and in the downwash of the wing. The horizontal-tail flow is thus exposed to the intense interference influences of wing and fuselage. This results in loss of control effectiveness, particularly in strongly disturbed flow from the wing.

In the case of a wing with an elliptical plan-form (no longer used), the complete span of the horizontal tail lies in a constant downwash and is, therefore, uniformly subjected to a flow at an angle smaller than the angle-of-attack of the wing (Fig. 4-42).

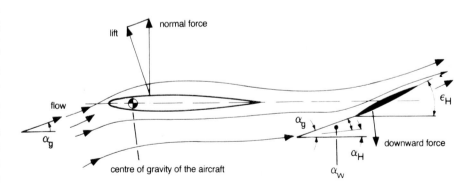

α_g	geometrical angle of attack
α_H	flow angle of the horizontal tail
α_w	downwash angle ($\alpha_g = \alpha_H + \alpha_w$)
ϵ_H	angle of incidence of the horizontal tail

4-42 **The horizontal tail in the downwash of the wing.**

Such conditions are also basically present in the case of modern combat aircraft wings, as long as the angle-of-attack is small; this is generally so only for cruising flight or for gentle manoeuvres. In these cases the trimming effect of the horizontal tail is sufficient to establish the moment equilibrium and to prevent the aircraft rotating about the lateral axis. Moreover the option must exist of generating **desired** rotations by means of sufficiently great elevator effectiveness. Take-off is especially critical in this respect, because the horizontal tail must be in a position to rotate the aircraft rolling along the ground, so that the requisite angle-of-attack to become airborne is attained.

The high-lift system of the wing causes considerable zero lift pitching moment (moments at zero lift, $C_L = 0$), as well as a powerful downwash as a result of increased camber. To establish the moment equilibrium, therefore, a negative tail deflection is first of all necessary, to offset the zero lift pitching moment of the wing; to rotate, a further deflection must then take place. Thus the flow at the horizontal tail can easily separate at ground speeds which are too low and therefore it becomes ineffective. A reduction of tail deflection, in order to restore normal flow, is only effective if a long enough runway is available.

The conditions at the horizontal tail are considerably more complicated when, during some flight manoeuvres, the leading-edge vortex or the strake vortex distorts the downwash of the wing so strongly that the horizontal tail lies in a completely disordered, strongly turbulent flow field. A horizontal tail of high aspect ratio is one solution so that, at least, some areas of the tail surfaces are in favourable flow conditions (for example in the F-18).

CANARD CONTROL SURFACES

The essential disadvantage of the conventional tail surface arrangement lies in the fact that a part of the total lift is

4-43 **Noticeable on the Viggen is the unusual aerodynamic design. The close coupling between the main wing and the canard foreplane gives the aircraft good short take-off and manoeuvring characteristics.**

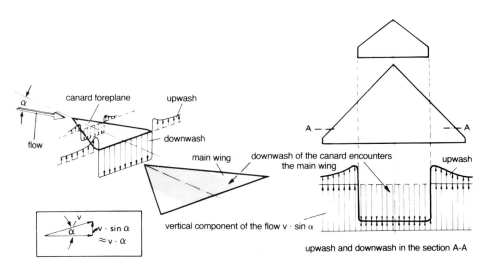

4-44 **Explanation of the close-coupled canard.**

68

subtracted from by the negative lift of the tailplane in order to establish equilibrium. In this way those phases of flight which require particularly high lift, such as take-off, landing and manoeuvring can become critical.

In principle the necessary counter-moment to compensate for the nose-down moment can be generated by putting the horizontal tail **in front of** the wing. This brings us to the **canard** or foreplane configuration, which is employed, for example, on the Viggen (Fig. 4-43). By means of the short coupling of the small foreplane, a combat aircraft design was achieved which has good short take-off properties as well as the required supersonic performance.

To understand the way in which the close-coupled canard acts, the idea of an isolated wing is used, which generates an upwash upstream and on both sides; however downstream it generates a downwash (Fig. 4-44). Of greater importance is the momentum of the downward accelerated air as a consequence of lift generation. It is in this field of disturbed flow that the main wing functions. As a result of its larger span it is affected by the downward flow off the foreplane only in the inboard regions. The outer areas lie in the upwash off the foreplane and generate additional lift.

The powerful lift variations over the span require a wing structure able to cope with this load. The delta wing fulfils the requirements for this, because its larger inner wing-chord (profile chord in the root area) provides sufficient overall height for strength in spite of a thin profile.

If one considers the canard configuration's lift balance, no advantage is noticeable at small angles-of-attack, i.e. in the linear range of C_L. The lift generated by the canard is largely negated by its downwash over the main wing. What remains is solely a nose-up moment at low angles-of-attack, which alone does not justify such an unusual configuration.

The potential of the canard or fore-plane can really only be fully exploited in non-linear flow. At high angles-of-attack

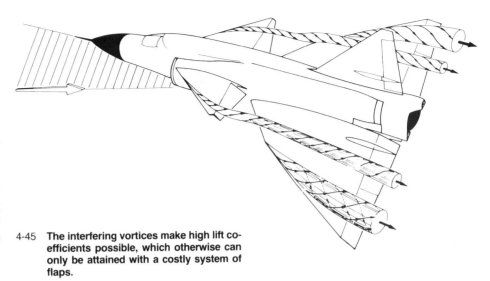

4-45 **The interfering vortices make high lift co-efficients possible, which otherwise can only be attained with a costly system of flaps.**

leading-edge vortices arise not only at the canard but also at the main wing; these interact with each other and make lift values possible which otherwise could only be attained with a complex system of flaps (Fig. 4-45). By favourably arranging both wings in relation to each other we can attain the mutual stabilisation of the vortex through interference effects. This happens when, as wind tunnel experiments show, the canard wing lies above the plane of the main wing and is close-coupled with it (Fig. 4-43).

The vortex off the leading edge of the canard continues over the main wing after leaving the canard, thereby inducing a downward flow over the inner area. However the flow is upward over the outer area (see Fig. 4-44). The down flow prevents the main wing from forming a leading-edge vortex near the fuselage, which is also supported by the reduced sweepback angle of the leading edge in this area. In the outer area of the main wing, on the other hand, the creation of a leading-edge vortex is encouraged by the upward component of the canard vortex as well as the greater sweepback. These two influences, the vertical flow off the canard and sweepback, only contribute to the leading-edge vortex at the

main wing which starts further out and with greater intensity.

Vortex development, as described above, is always to be aimed at with relatively thin combat aircraft wings, as this flow shape is very stable and remains effective up to high angles-of-attack. The fact should not be overlooked, however, that the generation of vortices requires a great deal of energy necessitating sufficient engine thrust.

What is of great importance in combat aircraft design is lateral motion, i.e. behaviour in unsymmetrical flow (sideslip). The close-coupled canard shows favourable properties here, because the vortex, lying far outside, does not penetrate the area of vertical-tail flow; even at larger sideslip angles. The fuselage has a supporting effect; it acts directionally for the flow, due to the low mounted main wing.

With combat aircraft the maximum effective angle-of-attack is usually less limited by the safety stall margin, but rather by inadequate directional stability. In this way much lift potential is lost. The close-coupled canard also differs favourably in this respect from other configurations.

4.7.3 **Vertical Tail**

The task of the vertical tail is to give the aircraft adequate directional stability. In unsymmetrical flow at a sideslip angle the vertical tail acts as a wing surface and produces **side-force** (Fig. 4-46). Because of its moment arm about the aircraft's centre-of-gravity, it generates a yawing moment which tries to reduce the sideslip angle and thus has a stabilising effect on aircraft yaw (weather-cock stability). As this side force acts above the aircraft's centre-of-gravity there is also a rolling moment.

Apart from the task of automatically generating a restoring moment, the vertical tail must, above all, be able to create yawing moments by deliberate rudder deflection so as to command a change of direction.

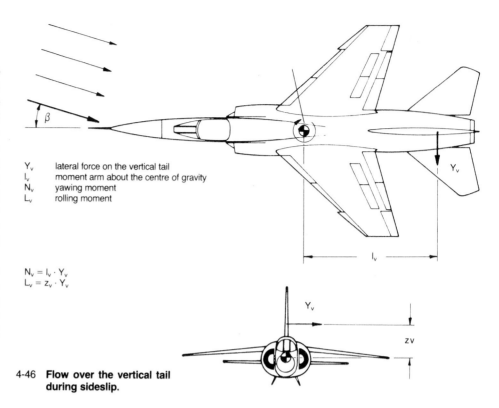

Y_v lateral force on the vertical tail
l_v moment arm about the centre of gravity
N_v yawing moment
L_v rolling moment

$$N_v = l_v \cdot Y_v$$
$$L_v = z_v \cdot Y_v$$

4-46 Flow over the vertical tail during sideslip.

GEOMETRY

The position of the vertical tail is indicated by the moment arm l_v, which is determined by the distance between the geometrical neutral points of the vertical lift and wing (see Fig. 4-40). The following characteristic quantities are important:-
– the area ratio S_v/S, and
– the relative tail distance l_v/S, referred to the wing half-span s.
(S_v = net tail area, S = wing area, s = wing half-span b/2. The product of these two is the tail volume V_v. Values of vertical tail characteristic quantities for a number of different types of combat aircraft are given in Table 4.1 on page 59.

DESIGN CHARACTERISTICS

What is important to decide in the design of the vertical tail is whether the various requirements for the corresponding flight conditions can be fulfilled.

Adequate vertical tail effectiveness is, for example, required for the following flight conditions:
– crosswind landing
– curved flight
– spin
– asymmetrical external stores
– transonic manoeuvring flight
– engine failure (in twin-jet aircraft).
Crosswind effects during landing can be compensated for by a wing down position in relation to the wind. In this case the longitudinal axis of the aircraft is aligned with the runway. However, most combat aircraft require large angles and considerable rudder forces for this. For this reason all NATO airforces prefer an approach to land angled into the crosswind with the wings level (crabbed approach). The alignment of the aircraft takes place immediately before touchdown with the aid of rudder and aileron.

The requirement of complete compensation of the sideslip angle would lead to tail surfaces which are very much too large for other phases of flight. For this reason criteria have been defined which specify compensation of sideslip up to a certain degree. These criteria form the basis for dimensioning the vertical tail.

Many combat aircraft, in particular those with large wing sweepback, tend to directional divergence at **high** angles-of-attack. This directional divergence can lead to a spin and eventually to loss of the aircraft and its crew.

As an obvious remedial measure the enlargement of the vertical tail surface can be considered. In fact an improvement is to be attained by this means in some cases. However numerous investigations have revealed that loss of directional stability is caused by the following:
a) the flow at the vertical tail no longer has sufficient dynamic pressure, or
b) the vertical tail lies in an area with a strong lateral flow.
Making the stabiliser fin larger would therefore only increase the destabilising effect.

4-47   **Combat aircraft with single tail surfaces (front to back: F-104, Tornado, F-4).**

In many cases the attachment of ventral fins is more effective than increasing the tail surface. However the small size of ventral fins makes them more or less ineffective at low angles-of-attack, particularly if they lie in the flow aft of external stores attached to the fuselage. The greatest effectiveness of ventral fins therefore lies in the higher angle-of-attack range.

Up to now the best method of avoiding directional divergence has turned out to be slats, such as on the F-4; at least in the case of wings with not too much leading-edge sweepback.

A further function which the vertical tail must fulfil is compensation of the yawing moment, which arises as a result of unsymmetrical external stores. But also in the case of symmetrical external stores, sudden yawing moments can arise when release does not take place simultaneously on both sides.

The decrease of rudder effectiveness at transonic speeds can also cause problems. Conventional rudder arrangements tend to produce a phenomenon called **rudder reversal** at flight Mach numbers around 1. For this reason the all-moving tail has been generally adopted. Acceptable behaviour at transonic speeds is attained by means of:
– a rudder of large area with large chord (in relation to the fin stabiliser)
– a sweptback trailing edge
– high torsional stiffness of the tail surface.

The fulfilment of these requirements is achieved in practice mainly with single-fin tails (Fig. 4-47). However relatively large tail surfaces can at times result ('barndoors'). For this reason a change is frequently made to twin-finned tails for highly manoeuvrable combat aircraft (see F-14, F-15 or F-18).

71

4.8 High-Speed Aerodynamics

The flows treated in this chapter up to now reflect conditions which are characteristic of relatively low speeds (up to about 370 knots). With increasing speeds however the air exhibits phenomena which can no longer be explained in terms of the behaviour so far.

In fact at higher speeds one property of air gains importance which is virtually non-existent in the low-speed area and is generally neglected: **compressibility.** The concept **high-speed aerodynamics** is intended to emphasise the fact that the flow shapes which occur are influenced decisively by compressibility.

Combat aircraft technology was first confronted with this phenomenon in World War II, as flight speeds, in particular after the introduction of jet propulsion, could be increased so far that suddenly conditions appeared for which hardly any explanation could be found, never mind a solution. Fighter aircraft, even those with propellers, which reached high speeds in a dive, were seized by violent buffeting and showed either no reaction at all, or the opposite reactions to control commands. Thus, for the time being, the further increase of flight speed seemed to have run into a natural limit. In this respect the speed of sound appeared to be a dream limit. Out of the inability at that time to reach or exceed this limit arose the concept of the **sound barrier.**

Research carried out during World War II in Germany in the field of high-speed aerodynamics was acknowledged by the Allies to be outstanding and was subsequently continued in both East and West with great intensity. In 1947 the speed of sound was exceeded for the first time in the USA with a manned research aircraft (Bell XS-1), and by 1953 supersonic combat aircraft were ready for service.

In the following sections the essential aspects of high-speed aerodynamics will be shown.

4.8.1 Speed of Sound and Mach Number

The **speed of sound** has a key role in the understanding of compressible flows. It refers to that speed which propagates small pressure changes (sound) in the air. The speed of sound (symbol: a) is principally dependent on the type and composition of the gas as well as on the (absolute) temperature t. The calculation is simple:

$$\text{speed of sound } a = kRt$$

where

k is the ratio of specific heats[12] of the gas (k = 1.4 for air)
R is the gas constant (R = 287 J/kg K for air),
t is the absolute temperature in K.

For the standard atmosphere[13] the speed of sound is derived as follows:

a) speed of sound at zero altitude: 15°C, corresponding to 273 + 15 = 288°K.

$$a = \sqrt{1.4 \times 287 \times 288}$$
$$= 340 \text{ m/s (670 knots)}$$

Conversion of the dimensions:

$$\sqrt{\frac{J \times K}{kg \times k}} \times \sqrt{\frac{Nm}{J}} \times \sqrt{\frac{mkg}{s^2 N}} = \sqrt{\frac{m^2}{s^2}} = \frac{m}{s}$$

b) Speed of sound at altitude of 11 km: temperature at 11 km altitude: −15.5°C, corresponding to 273-56.5 = 216.5° K
   a = 295 m/s (582 knots).

Thus the speed of sound decreases with increasing altitude because of the change in temperature.

---

[12] for further information see related textbooks

---

[13] see Appendix

With the aid of the equation for the state of ideal gases (see Appendix I), the product R × t in the equation for the speed of sound can be replaced by the quotient p/ρ.

The dependence on the air density and thus the influence of compressibility is hereby expressed more clearly.

This influence is of great importance for fast-flying aircraft, because the character of the flow is fundamentally changed. However as the speed of sound alters with flight altitude and the temperature of the air, as the above example shows, it is not possible to state a particular speed at which compressibility influences are significant. For this reason the Mach number is used, which is derived from the flight speed v and the speed of sound:

$$\text{Mach number } M = \frac{v}{a}$$

At subsonic speeds the Mach number is less than 1 (M < 1), at supersonic speeds greater than 1 (M > 1).

4.8.2 Subsonic and Supersonic

To explain the processes involved at supersonic flight speeds a concept will be explained which, although it is extremely simplified, nevertheless expresses the physical phenomena well.

When a body moves through the air, or if air flows past a fixed body, which is the same thing, such as in a wind tunnel, then the body attempts to divert the flow particles into a different path. When, for example, an aircraft flies through the air, then every single element of the aircraft surface displaces the adjacent air particles from their original position. Each of these local disturbances generates a pressure pulse, which is transferred to

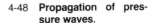

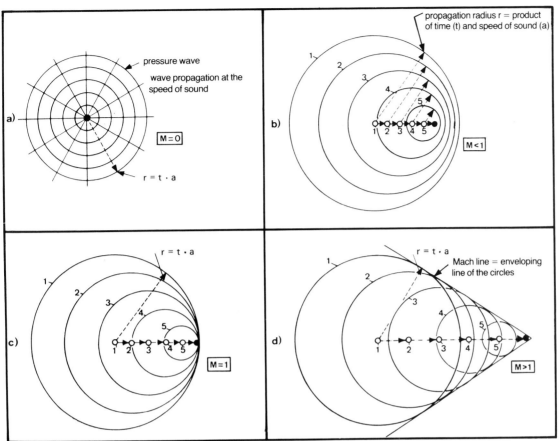

a) source is at rest, M = 0
b) motion at subsonic speed, M < 1
c) motion at the speed of sound, M = 1
d) motion at supersonic speed, M > 1

the surrounding air. After a certain time an observer on the ground will perceive a greater or lesser number of these elementary pressure disturbances as sound. The sound wave which the observer receives results from the overlap of a number of such simple sound generation processes.

Continuing these abstract trains of thought, we move away from an aircraft of finite dimension and find a source of disturbance in the form of a point without spatial extension. This transmits pressure waves at regular intervals, which diffuse spherically at the speed of sound in all directions. The pressure field which thus arises results as a temporal sequence through the overlapping of all pressure pulses.

As long as the source is at rest, the pressure impulse expands uniformly in all directions (Fig. 4-48a). An analogous picture of wave propagation is caused by a stone which falls into calm water and generates concentric surface waves.

If the source of disturbance moves through still air at subsonic speed (M < 1), the pressure disturbances are also radiated in all directions, but the pressure field is no longer concentric (Fig. 4-48b). The picture, as a snapshot of the kinetic sequences, shows that **in front of** the source the pressure pulses follow at shorter intervals than behind it, which is equivalent to different frequencies in front of and behind the source. For this there is also a simple analogy: the horn of an approaching car is perceived as a relatively high note due to the closer spacing of the sound waves; as the car passes, its frequency suddenly decreases. This phenomena is termed the Doppler

effect. It plays an important part in the explanation and interpretation of kinetic processes, such as in radar technology or in astronomy.

If the source of disturbance has exactly sonic speed (M = 1), i.e. flow speed and the speed of sound are identical, then the pressure pulses cannot move forward faster than the source itself (Fig. 4-48c). In this case a plane wave front is generated immediately in front of the body, and the source of disturbance is not audible to an observer located in front of it.

If the source of disturbance moves at supersonic speed (M > 1), then the volume of influence of the pressure waves is restricted to the inside of a cone, at the tip of which is located the source itself.

The aircraft is audible only when the observer is located inside the cone which contains the pressure waves. The angle of aperture of this so-called **Mach cone** is inversely proportional to the speed.

The numerical sequence of the pressure impulses spreading spherically is a measure of the intensity of the pressure disturbances at a random point in the flow field. In the case of the stationary source, disturbance pulses spread out on all sides and their distribution is symmetrical. Subsonic flows are also characterised by propagation in all directions, but the intensity of their development is unsymmetrical. In supersonic flows pressure disturbances can spread out only within the Mach cone. The disturbance source cannot send a signal into the area outside the cone. This zone is therefore called the 'silent zone'.

From this it becomes clear why an aircraft flying at the speed of sound remains inaudible as long as the wave front has not yet reached the observer. However if the concentrated wave reaches the observer then he perceives this as a **sonic boom.**

Wave information which corresponds in its outward form to supersonic speed in air is to be observed, for example, in the bow wave of a ship.

Supersonic flows can be made visible in the wind tunnel in various ways. The best known is the **Schlieren process,** which makes use of the density changes in the otherwise invisible wave fronts to make them visible (Fig. 4-49). It can be seen that Mach cones proceed from various parts, and in particular from contour jumps.

4.8.3 Vertical and Oblique Shock

It is well-known from numerous observations that a gas under particular conditions can undergo abrupt changes of its characteristic quantities (pressure, temperature, density).

As long as the pressure changes in

4-49 **Making the shock fronts visible by means of Schlieren optics (model of a Jaguar combat aircraft in the ONERA wind tunnel, France).**

particular are small they are termed **sound;** their speed of propagation is the **speed of sound.** If, however, sudden large changes of pressure appear, such as in explosions, then the pressure waves produced spread at supersonic speed. The waves cause a sudden rise of pressure at the points they pass, which we perceive as a sonic boom. This process is known as compression shock. The well-known sonic boom caused by fast-flying aircraft is one of these.

The typical characteristics of compression shock will be explained at a pitot inlet. If the flow takes place at supersonic speed, then a shock front builds up as a standing wave in front of the inlet (Fig. 4-50, see also Fig. 7-5). The moment the flow passes the shock front, an abrupt compression of the gas takes place, with static pressure and density increasing ($p_1 > p_O$, $\rho_1 > \rho_0$). The energy required for the compression process is taken from the kinetic energy of the flow, so that an abrupt deceleration takes

place in passing through the shock. The decrease in kinetic energy is indicated by heat, and the static temperature has become higher behind the shock ($t_2 > t_1$). However as no energy is taken from the total flow energy, the total temperature remains constant according to the Law of Conservation of Energy during the shock passage ($T_1 = T_2$).

However one of the characteristics of the compression shock is that the generated heat cannot be completely transformed back into kinetic energy; a certain proportion is not utilisable for the flow process and gets lost. Thus, in spite of the increase in static pressure, the total pressure[14] drops ($P_1 < P_0$, see Fig. 7-5).

In every case subsonic speed prevails behind the normal shock, however high the supersonic speed may have been before the shock. The higher the Mach

[14] The total pressure P is composed of the dynamic pressure q and static pressure p.

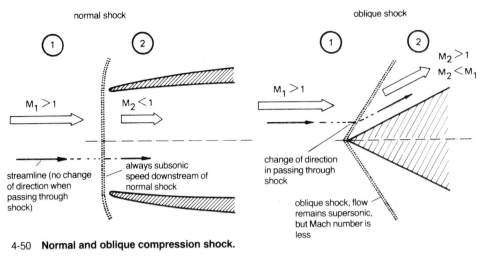

normal shock

① ②

$M_1 > 1$ $M_2 < 1$

streamline (no change
of direction when
passing through
shock)

always subsonic
speed downstream of
normal shock

oblique shock

① ②

$M_2 > 1$
$M_2 < M_1$

$M_1 > 1$

change of direction
in passing through
shock

oblique shock, flow
remains supersonic,
but Mach number is
less

4-50   **Normal and oblique compression shock.**

number leap the greater the total pressure loss.

Also characteristic of the vertical compression shock, apart from the changes of state mentioned, is the fact that the flow does not undergo a change of direction while passing through the shock.

However in many cases the supersonic flow is compelled to alter its direction, e.g. when encountering parts of the aircraft which, due to their displacement effect, themselves cause a flow deflection. If the deflection of supersonic flow takes place through only a small angle, a shock front is generated, sloping away from the flow direction (see Fig. 4-50). This shock is known as an **oblique shock,** and here the characteristic quantities of the flow also tend to behave similarly to the vertical compression shock. The rise in static pressure and the total pressure loss are considerably less, however. Behind an oblique shock, supersonic speed continues to exist, but it is smaller than in **front of** the shock ($M_2 > 1$, $M_2 < M_1$). This form of shock thus proves to be an excellent means of decelerating a supersonic flow step by step, and with relatively little loss.

4.8.4 Transonic Flows

A sharp division between subsonic and supersonic flows, such as in the case of the previously described point source, is not possible in practice. Rather, in the range around Mach 1, a mixed flow type prevails, which is characterised by the simultaneous appearance of subsonic and supersonic flows at the aircraft. This mixed type is called **transonic flow.**

The significance of transonic flows will be explained by considering a wing profile at various flow speeds (Fig. 4-51). If the flow Mach number is small (approx. $M = 0.2$) subsonic speed prevails everywhere at the profile (Fig. 4-51a). The flow starts to expand from the forward stagnation point and accelerates to a maximum value at the point of maximum thickness. The profile contour subsequently produces a deceleration, with the pressure rising again as far as the trailing edge.

If the subsonic Mach number of the flow is sufficiently large, the excess speed reaches the speed of sound at **one** point on the upper surface of the profile. In this case the flow has reached the **critical Mach number.**

If the flow speed now continues to rise, then a supersonic zone develops around

this point, which becomes larger with increasing speed. As long as a shock wave does not arise, the supersonic zone is limited by the so-called **sonic line.** At this line the flow has exactly the speed of sound; outside it subsonic speed prevails (Fig. 4-51b).

If the Mach number continues to rise, the flow at the end of the supersonic zone is no longer continuously decelerated to the subsonic range, but this process takes place abruptly by means of a compression shock.

The supersonic area is then limited upstream by the sonic line and downstream by a shock (Fig. 4-51c). Behind the shock the pressure rises abruptly, which is shown by the pressure distribution.

With rising flow speed the shock moves downstream. At the same time a supersonic zone also develops on the lower surface, which is sealed off by a compression shock (Fig. 4-51d). The shock intensity on the upper surface is enough to cause the boundary layer to separate.

At a Mach number which lies slightly below 1, both shock fronts have reached the trailing edge of the profile and have considerably increased in strength (Fig. 4-51e). The flow on the upper and lower surfaces of the profile lies, with the exception of the impact area at the nose, largely in the supersonic region. The generation of shock fronts involves high drag.

If the flow just exceeds the speed of sound, a bow wave forms in front of the profile which, together with the sonic lines, encloses a subsonic zone in the nose area (Fig. 4.51f). With increasing supersonic Mach number the local subsonic area decreases in extent (Fig. 4-51g), and the shock front attached itself increasingly as an oblique shock to the (sharp-edged) nose of the profile.

The local supersonic fields at flow speeds in the upper subsonic range can be made visible in the wind tunnel with optical aids. At times they can also be observed on fast-flying aircraft, if the humidity is high, and, as a consequence

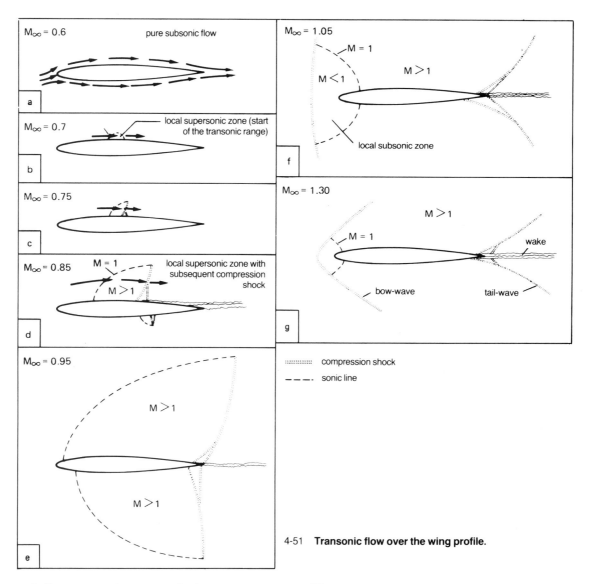

$M_\infty = 0.6$ pure subsonic flow

a

$M_\infty = 0.7$ local supersonic zone (start of the transonic range)

b

$M_\infty = 0.75$

c

$M_\infty = 0.85$ $M = 1$ local supersonic zone with subsequent compression shock

$M > 1$

d

$M_\infty = 0.95$

$M > 1$

$M > 1$

e

$M_\infty = 1.05$ $M = 1$

$M < 1$ $M > 1$

local subsonic zone

f

$M_\infty = 1.30$

$M > 1$

$M = 1$

wake

bow-wave tail-wave

g

┈┈┈┈┈ compression shock

── ── ── sonic line

4-51 **Transonic flow over the wing profile.**

of low pressures in the supersonic zones, the water content condenses out (Fig. 4-52).

These simple considerations at the wing make two essential problems of transonic flow clear, i.e.

1) the steep drag increase (drag divergence), which is involved in the generation of shock waves, and
2) the significant changes of pitching moment, which result from the different shock positions on the upper and lower surfaces of the profile.

The influence of the Mach number on the pressure distribution can be demonstrated with the aid of pressure distri-

bution measurements (Fig. 4-53). The steep rise of pressure on the suction surface characterises the corresponding shock position. A practically constant pressure behind the shock indicates shock-induced separations (cases IV and V).

One of the aspects of manoeuvrability of a combat aircraft in the transonic speed area is, among other things, changes of angle-of-attack while maintaining a high flight Mach number. The flow conditions for this case are also sketched (Fig. 4-54). With increasing angle-of-attack the intensity of the shock moving downstream consequently rises

(discernable from the greater pressure jumps, examples I-III). Behind the shock a separation bubble forms, whose length increases with shock intensity, as well as a thick boundary layer with high turbulence. As soon as the separation bubble has reached the trailing edge of the profile, the shock begins to move upstream (cases IV, V). An indication of this is the pressure drop at the trailing edge, whereby the greatest extension of the separation bubble relates to the lowest pressure (case IV). This phenomenon is used in wind tunnel testing to demonstrate separation zones.

Various steps are possible to mitigate

4-52 **Visible supersonic zone (F-4J, VX-4 Squadron, US Navy, Pt. Mugu, California.).**

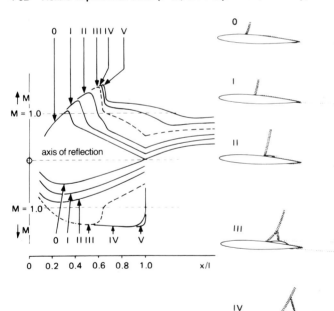

0
boundary layer thickens behind shock, no shock-induced separation

$M_I > M_0$
shock moves downstream, no shock-induced separation

$M_{II} > M_I$
small separation bubble behind shock, no effect on trailing edge, shock moves further downstream

$M_{III} > M_{II}$
separation bubble increasing, but does not reach trailing edge, significant increase in the boundary layer thickness, shock moves further downstream

$M_{IV} > M_{III}$
separation bubble extends beyond trailing edge, boundary layer continues to thicken, shock moves downstream

$M_V > M_{IV}$
separation bubble continues to increase, shock continues to move downstream

4-53 **Transonic flow separations at increasing Mach number, but constant angle-of-attack.**

the difficulties involved in transonic flows, for example:
– reduction of the profile thickness,
– special profiles,
– alteration of the wing plan-form.

As profiles with minimum thickness generate the lowest drag, thin profiles are always used for combat aircraft.

Various attempts are made to attain the reduction of drag with novel types of profile adapted to the special conditions of transonic flow (supercritical profiles). However, sensitivity to the flow and inadequate performance outside their design Mach number makes these profiles unsuitable for supersonic combat aircraft.

One means of reducing transonic drag, which has been known for a long time, is the sweepback of the wing leading edge, because of the importance of the Mach number perpendicular to the leading edge. The realisation that:

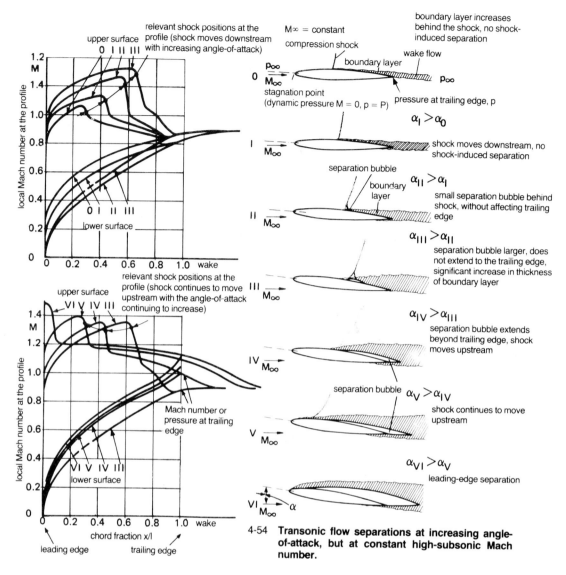

4-54 Transonic flow separations at increasing angle-of-attack, but at constant high-subsonic Mach number.

a) a sweptback wing is advantageous for transonic and supersonic flight, and

b) for the low speed range (take-off, landing, holding pattern or loitering) a straight only slightly sweptback wing is more suitable,

led to the development of the swing-wing, which ideally can be adapted to the particular speed range (Fig. 4-55).

Transonic flows over wings of low aspect ratio are extremely complicated. Several flow effects can act at the same time, such as shock waves, vortex systems, and separating and re-attaching boundary layers, which are all interrelated with one another and show strong temporal and local variations. It is almost impossible to describe these processes theoretically, yet reliable wind tunnel measurements also turn out to be very difficult.

Optimum wing position for transonic flight Mach numbers and manoeuvring flight.

Wing position for supersonic flight and high-speed, low-level flight.

Wing position for low-speed flight as well as for take-off and landing.

4-55 **The swing wing can be effectively adjusted to a particular Mach number (General Dynamics F-111).**

4.8.5 Transonic Problems in Aerial Combat

It is known from analyses of tactical aerial combat that engagements usually begin at transonic flight Mach numbers and at altitudes of 15,000 to 18,000 ft. During a fight the altitude and speed potential is fully exploited. The participating aircraft become increasingly slower and increasingly lose altitude, until there is a winner or the action is broken off.

Decisive phases of the aerial combat thus take place in Mach number ranges in which the performance capability of the aircraft is severely restricted from the aerodynamic point of view; this is caused by a process called **buffeting**. Buffeting is caused by irregular boundary layer separations in areas with pressure rise.

The cause of the rise in pressure in transonic flows is primarily the shock wave on the upper wing surface.

Vibration phenomena cause changing strains and stresses in the structure which represent considerable danger in terms of flight mechanics and strength.

In addition other factors are critical for a 'combat aircraft system'. For example the tactics used in aerial combat, the weapons system, psychological influences on the pilot, electronic countermeasures, and not least the characteristics, performance and tactics of the opponent.

The following will outline the effects of **transonic flows** on aerial combat capability.

4.8.5.1 Analysis of Aerial Combat

AERIAL COMBAT ARENA

Aerial combat takes place in the airspace in which the aircraft performs its manoeuvres. Elements of these manoeuvres are: turning flight, roll, acceleration and deceleration.

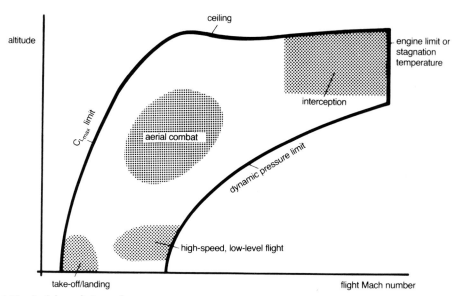

4-56 **Aerial combat envelope.**

A combat pilot will always state as the most important criterion the capacity of an aircraft to engage in manoeuvring air combat. The limitations of the aircraft become more apparent here than in all other manoeuvres, because during combat turns the aircraft and its pilot are taken to the limits of their endurance.

A combat aircraft must also be safe in the pilot's hands and obey the controls under extreme conditions. In the transonic range these conditions can often no longer be fulfilled. The aircraft must be capable of being manoeuvred as a gun platform in such a way that exact tracking is possible. Here too problems of flow dynamics in the transonic range diminish the combat capability of the system and lead to a limitation of operational effectiveness.

From the aerodynamic point of view the combat arena is represented by the values of altitude and speed. Altitude defines the properties of the atmosphere, and with speed the interaction of aircraft and airflow is covered. Performance is usually represented by an altitude-Mach number diagram which outlines the performance limits of the aircraft (Fig. 4-56).

According to this, for example, maximum Mach numbers are attainable only at high altitude, while the large load factors and small turning radii which occur in combat turns only allow the aircraft to be flown in the medium altitude and Mach number range.

PHASES OF AERIAL COMBAT

In order to recognise in which parts of aerial combat manoeuvres transonic influences are significant, a classification is made according to the individual phases. We distinguish between the following phases in the sequence in which they occur:
– detection
– identification
– target acquisition
– tracking
– weapon release.

80

1. Detection

The detection of a potential opponent is made visually by the pilot or by means of electronic systems which are either on board or on the ground. Examples: direct visual contact, location by radar or by infra-red systems.

2. Identification

The sequence of actions will depend on the preceding events and actions. If it is determined that the target is an opponent with hostile intentions, then the pilot will take an offensive flight path and adjust his guided missile system to the target, even before positive identification takes place. However in most cases positive identification is made **visually.**

This can be expressed as a degree of uncertainty, because until recently identification friend or foe (IFF) by electronic means with absolute certainty has not been available.

3. Target acquisition

This means that:
a) the weapons system is aimed at the hostile aircraft, and
b) the peripheral conditions for successful weapon release are fulfilled.

4. Tracking

The use of guns makes the execution of precise manoeuvres necessary because the aiming is done with the aircraft. If missiles are used then the requirements regarding aiming accuracy are less strict, particularly in the case of the latest models with large acquisition angles.

5. Weapon Release

The effectiveness of the weapons system is generally impaired by the motion of the aircraft, with transonic buffeting phenomena in particular leading to restrictions. For the pilot there is the physical strain of an aircraft which is lively and difficult to fly, in addition to the psychological stress of combat.

4.8.5.2 Transonic Phenomena at High Angles-of-Attack

BUFFETING

The appearance of compression shocks at transonic speeds leads to a phenomenon called buffeting. Buffeting is not only restricted to the transonic range, but can also appear at any speed. It is caused by irregular boundary layer separations in areas with pressure rise. In transonic flows, shock is the principal cause of the pressure rise.

Vibration phenomena cause changing strains and stresses in the structure which endanger flight mechanics and strength.

From the combat pilot's point of view buffeting is a vibration phenomenon whose severity impairs concentration and causes serious difficulties in tracking a target. However, this need not always be the case. As the intensity of the buffeting increases with the angle-of-attack, a lower angle-of-attack can be found where buffet onset is just taking place. For a pilot who knows his aircraft, buffet onset represents a valuable piece of information, such as when, in moments of intense concentration during aerial combat, he cannot pay attention to his instruments.

The buffeting intensity is a yardstick for the restriction of manoeuvrability. We can distinguish between four different intensity levels. These are determined according to subjective impressions and are stated as acceleration values perpendicular to the flight path (n_Z) Table 4.2).

Buffet **onset** usually has no adverse influence on the manoeuvrability.

The combat pilot with average training still does not perceive this intensity as a handicap, but rather as information. He is familiar with it and is adapted to flying often in this range. **Light** buffet, the next level of intensity, is clearly felt but still permits target tracking. **Moderate buffet** is generally considered the highest level of intensity at which aiming with the gun or with missiles is still possible.

The **most severe** degree of buffet can be endured physically by the pilot only for a short period, but still permits control over the aircraft. Therefore pilots fly through the **heavy-buffet** limit only in aerial combat manoeuvres, when this is the only way in which a better combat position can be reached. In defensive manoeuvres, given the nature of the situation, the highest degree of buffet has to be risked by **increasing** the angle-of-attack, if necessary up to complete stall. Aerodynamically this touches on the problem of the separated flow at the wings, with the type of separation depending mainly on the wing geometry.

WING ROCK AND YAW

At angles-of-attack above buffet onset, oscillations set in which are perceived by the pilot as wing rock. They are accepted

Table 4.2 Buffeting intensities.

Intensity	Acceleration n_Z	Effect
buffet onset	± 0.035 to ± 0.1	barely or just noticeable, information for the pilot
light buffet	± 0.1 to ± 0.2	distinctly perceptible, target tracking still possible
moderate buffet	± 0.2 to ± 0.6	perceived as unpleasant, target tracking impossible, manoeuvrability severely restricted
severe buffet	± 0.6 to ± 1.0	only to be endured for a few seconds, corrective measures necessary

as a necessary evil, if by this means an improved combat position can be established.

A roll rate of ± 10°/s (degrees per second) is the limit which still permits target tracking. As long as the roll amplitudes are sufficiently small they are still not perceived as unpleasant.

When aiming with a gyro-stabilized gunsight, yaw can arise, which is coupled with the wing rock and makes further tracking impossible. Such rock-yaw oscillations are known as 'Dutch roll' and appear with all transonic aircraft.

Pure wing rock (without a noticeable yaw component) occurs at almost all transonic speeds. It is feared because of its unpredictability. Before the pilot has taken action to reduce the angle-of-attack the flight path, which began as a left bank, for example, can change abruptly and end up as a right bank. Obviously this makes tracking impossible.

A form of oscillation can also occur when the roll amplitude increases even if the roll rate of about 10°-20°/s is relatively low (wing drop). This motion, which builds up, requires immediate action on the part of the pilot, otherwise the aircraft can get out of control.

An equally undesirable motion is when the aircraft turns away from the chosen direction (nose slice), which indicates an impending loss of control. In this case too, it is not possible to continue aiming. If the pilot does not recognise the danger of this motion in time, then corrective actions usually come too late and the transition into a spin can no longer be checked. This situation can arise, for example, when the pilot tries to extract the utmost performance from his aircraft in a turn.

There is another form of yaw which is not only restricted to the transonic range but can appear at all flight Mach numbers. This is usually initiated unknowingly by the pilot when the marker of the weapon-aiming sight is already close to the target with only slight corrections in azimuth[15] needed. This form of oscil-

---
[15] Angle of horizontal deviation (yaw)

lation, known as 'nose wander' or 'snaking', considerably impedes target tracking.

All forms of wing rock and yaw specified up to now involve more or less severe restriction of control. It requires skill and practice to fly the aircraft, using its remaining control potential, back into a safe flight condition. In the angle-of-attack range just before stall, the control completely disappears (departure). This is always to be expected if the pilot reacts too late or incorrectly to one of the previously described oscillations. Return to a controlled flight condition is only possible, if at all, after a certain period of time has elapsed and by means of carefully practised manual control inputs.

THE A-7 AND F-4 AT HIGH ANGLES-OF-ATTACK

To illustrate the problems which arise at high angles-of-attack in the manoeuvring range, let us consider the trimmed lift curves of two operational combat aircraft, the A-7 and the F-4.

The A-7 is a carrier-based, fighter-bomber which has been in service since 1966 with the US Navy. The USAF also has a land-based version of this type, known as the Corsair II (Fig. 4-57, top).

The F-4, also originally conceived as a naval fighter, has in the meantime become a main component of numerous airforces and is given many mission tasks to fulfil (Fig. 4-57, bottom). Both aircraft types have been largely overtaken by technological progress. However, this has the advantage that details are published which were previously military secrets. This also includes the behaviour of both aircraft at high angles-of-attack in the manoeuvre range.

The A-7 has a lift curve with a clearly defined maximum (Fig. 4-58, top). Buffet onset is at 10° to 12° angle-of-attack (α).

After reaching $\alpha = 17°$ a warning signal is triggered by violent shaking of the rudder pedals, which is intended as a

stall warning for approach and landing (rudder pedal shaker). This simultaneously indicates the onset of severe buffeting, between $\alpha = 17°$ and $\alpha = 19°$. The intensity of the aerodynamically-induced buffeting is so severe that the artificially generated shaking of the rudder pedals cannot be distinguished from the buffeting of the aircraft, and is thus scarcely perceived as a warning signal.

At an angle-of-attack of 18.5° the roll augmentation system is automatically switched off, so that aileron deflections which might induce a spin at high angles-of-attack do not take place. The roll is then controlled only by the rudder.

Stall occurs at $\alpha = 20°$ and is characterised by violent buffeting. As a consequence of too little lateral stability the aircraft tends to turn its nose away from the intended flight path (nose wander).

At angles-of-attack between 20° and 24° the aircraft goes out of control (departure). The A-7 suddenly rotates about its normal axis (nose slice) and starts to roll (snap roll) in the same direction (i.e. if it departs to the left, a left roll). As a rule the pilot becomes disorientated at this point, because in addition the pitch motions of small amplitude overlap the violent wing rock and yaw. The following corrective actions are recommended:

a) immediately reduce back-pressure on the control-stick, and

b) wait until the spiral instability stops by itself.

The aircraft thus goes into a vertical dive and, if the altitude is sufficient, can be brought back into straight and level flight, provided that the controls can be operated correctly.

In contrast to the A-7, the F-4's lift curve shows its first maximum at $\alpha = 18°$, followed by a second maximum at $\alpha = 26°$ (Fig. 4-58, bottom). Light buffeting begins at angles-of-attack between 9° and 12°. In order to prevent a tendency to spin as a result of operating the ailerons, they must not be used above an angle-of-attack of 11°: only the rudder must be used, otherwise an uncontrollable flight condition can arise.

The artificial stall warning, intended for

4-57 **A-7 and F-4 combat aircraft.**

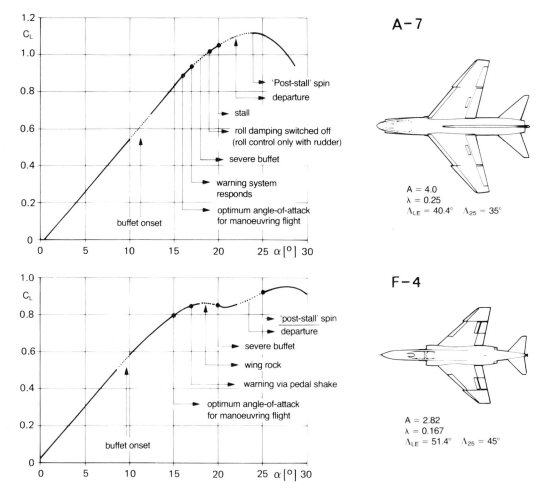

A-7 and F-4 at high angles-of-attack.

A-7

A = 4.0
λ = 0.25
$\Lambda_{LE} = 40.4°$ $\Lambda_{25} = 35°$

F-4

A = 2.82
λ = 0.167
$\Lambda_{LE} = 51.4°$ $\Lambda_{25} = 45°$

the approach and landing, responds at $\alpha = 17°$ and sends signals to the rudder pedals. Between 18° and 20° angle-of-attack wing rock starts. At $\alpha = 20°$ severe buffet occurs, which is accompanied by an increase in the roll amplitudes. Stall sets in at $\alpha = 20°$ to 24° and is marked by the simultaneous occurrence of violent buffeting, wing rock and a tendency to pitch-up. From $\alpha = 25°$, the F-4 is uncontrollable, roll and yaw suddenly occurring in the same direction.

The pilot's corrective action is to push the control-stick forward so as to reduce the angle-of-attack, and, at the same time, move the ailerons to their neutral position. Using the brake parachute is a

last-resort possibility. If the F-4 is not immediately returned to a controllable flight condition, it goes into steep spin, or, more rarely, into a fast flat spin, which always leads to a crash.

It is noticeable that the F-4 can be flown beyond the first maximum of the lift curve. Although the thrust is not enough to maintain the speed, angles-of-attack above the first maximum can be used briefly. In fact, this range is frequently flown in aerial combat manoeuvres.

To give the reader an idea of how brief the periods in which problems of the kind described above appear, a deliberately initiated stall manoeuvre of the A-7 will be considered (Fig. 4-59). At the beginning

of this manoeuvre the aircraft was positioned in a horizontal left turn with decreasing radius (left tightening turn), recognisable from the yaw rate of −4°/s (negative sign = rotation to the left). The sideslip angle is about +1°.

After three seconds, and at an angle of attack of 20°, the aircraft begins to depart from its path (departure): Within another two seconds the yaw rate rises to +20°/s (i.e. yaw to the right), while the sideslip angle falls to −10° (flow from the left). This aperiodic departure cannot be stopped by increasing opposite rudder ($\delta_r > 0$) either; on the contrary, a roll begins at high and uncontrollable rate.

This situation was a sign to the pilot to

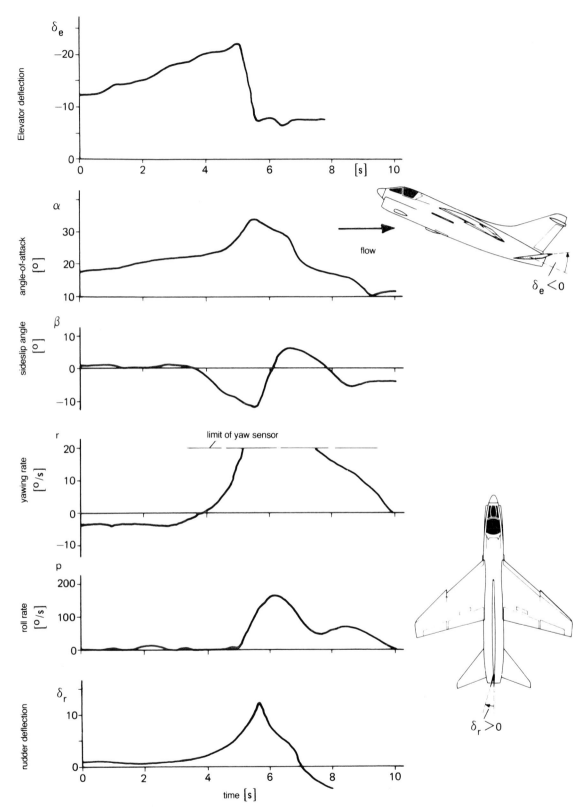

4-59 **Stall behaviour of the A-7.**

85

initiate corrective actions, in this case releasing all controls, after which the aircraft returned to the normal condition.

The maximum yaw rate could not be determined by the measuring apparatus on board; according to calculations it was around 65°/s. During the entire manoeuvre the ailerons remained in the zero position, to avoid further encouraging the tendency to spin.

4.8.6 Problems of High-Speed Flight

4.8.6.1 DRAG

Drag represents one of the greatest problems in flight technology. The buffeting, particularly at transonic speeds, together with the enormous drag increase just before reaching the speed of sound, constitutes the real factor concealed behind the concept of the sound barrier.

To show the significant quantities which determine drag, we shall refer again to the drag equation introduced in chapter 4.3.1.

According to this, aircraft drag depends on the drag coefficient C_D, on the dynamic pressure q, and on the wing area S:

$$D = C_D \, qS$$

The dynamic pressure is a quantity specific to flow, which depends only on the flight altitude and the flight Mach number (Fig. 4-60). In contrast the drag coefficient C_D expresses the aerodynamic properties of the aircraft.

DRAG POLAR

Drag is usually represented in graphic form as the so-called drag polar, which indicates the development of the drag coefficient in relation to the lift coefficient (Fig. 4-61). What is significant is the

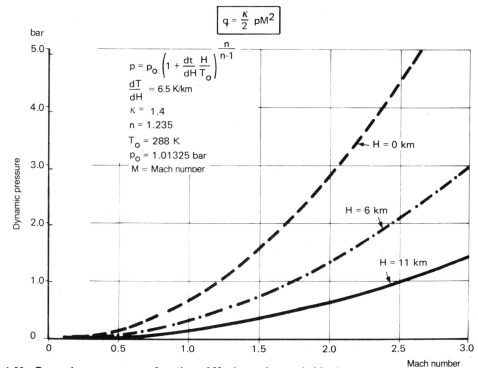

$$q = \frac{\kappa}{2}\, pM^2$$

$$p = p_o \left(1 + \frac{dt}{dH}\frac{H}{T_o}\right)^{\frac{n}{n-1}}$$

$\frac{dT}{dH} = 6.5\ \text{K/km}$

$\kappa = 1.4$

$n = 1.235$

$T_o = 288\ \text{K}$

$p_o = 1.01325\ \text{bar}$

$M = \text{Mach number}$

4-60 **Dynamic pressure as a function of Mach number and altitude.**

practically **quadratic** increase of drag with lift which is observed at all Mach numbers.

The drag curve derives from the sum of several drag contributions which arise in various ways. In particular we can distinguish between drag which is independent of lift, and drag which arises only with lift. The sum of all the **lift-independent** drags, i.e. those already acting at $C_L = 0$, is called **zero-lift drag**.

Taking all these contributing drag values into account, the total drag can be expressed in simplified form as follows:

$$C_D = C_{D_{Pmin}} + \Delta C_{D_p} + C_{D_i} + C_{D_{trim}} + C_{D_D}$$

$C_{D_{Pmin}}$ is the minimum profile drag.
It is independent of angle-of-attack and comprises
– friction drag,
– pressure drag,

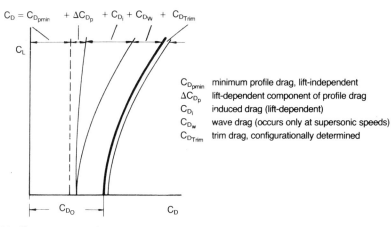

$$C_D = C_{D_{pmin}} + \Delta C_{D_p} + C_{D_i} + C_{D_w} + C_{D_{Trim}}$$

$C_{D_{pmin}}$ minimum profile drag, lift-independent
ΔC_{D_p} lift-dependent component of profile drag
C_{D_i} induced drag (lift-dependent)
C_{D_w} wave drag (occurs only at supersonic speeds)
$C_{D_{Trim}}$ trim drag, configurationally determined

4-61 **Drag components.**

- interference drag,
- roughness drag,
- drag from excrescences.

The friction drag results from the (tangentially acting) shear stresses, which are generated by the entire surface of the aircraft as a result of air viscosity. This process is connected with the formation of a boundary layer. An altered pressure distribution results as a consequence, which explains the pressure drag. Normally both components cannot be measured independently of each other and are therefore measured together. However, friction drag significantly exceeds pressure drag.

The numerous **excrescences** form a particularly difficult problem in determining drag; they alter the original contour of the aircraft and disturb the flow. Among these are: aerials; intakes; coverings for flap drives, mountings for weapons and other external stores, gun housings and similar items. Determining the **parasitic** drags resulting from these excrescences is possible as a rule only by estimation or by large-scale wind tunnel experiments.

ΔC_{Dp} represents the **lift-dependent** part of friction and pressure drag, arising from changed flow conditions as a result of the angle-of-attack. In addition to this, influences are included in the classical drag calculations for non-elliptical lift distribution and camber effects.

Induced drag is a purely lift-dependent quantity. Its origin has already been described in detail in section 4.3.2. This component expresses, in the usual method of drag determination, the elliptical lift distribution caused by potential flow (frictionless flow). However there is another drag component which must be taken into account. This arises from the non-linear additional lift which comes from vortex flows, which play an extremely important part in combat aircraft aerodynamics.

The **trim drag** $C_{D_{trim}}$ arises with elevator deflection used to generate the moment equilibrium. This component is a function of aircraft configuration.

Shock waves appear in compressible flow, i.e. at transonic and supersonic

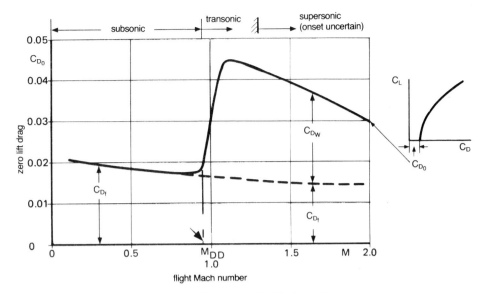

4-62 **Typical development of zero lift drag above the Mach number.**

speeds, causing an additional pressure drag which would even be present in frictionless flow. This drag component is termed **wave drag.**

In every aerodynamics study the first principle is the reduction of drag. Of particular importance here is lift-independent zero lift drag, which is determined by the configuration, and can be influenced during the design process. The path of zero lift drag above Mach number shows the drag increase in the range around Mach 1 (Fig. 4-62). Characteristic correlations of Mach number and zero lift drag for combat aircraft result as follows:

Mach number	0.2	0.95	1.05	2.0
Zero lift drag	0.020	0.015	0.045	0.030

Good designs, particularly the latest combat aircraft, lie below the outlined curve at all Mach numbers.

In the subsonic region, zero lift drag is caused primarily by friction. Near the speed of sound there are subsonic as well as supersonic zones around the aircraft. After exceeding the critical Mach number, at which the speed of sound is reached on the upper wing surface for the first time, there is a considerable rise

in zero lift drag (drag rise, drag divergence). At Mach numbers between 1.1 and 1.2 the zero lift drag reaches its highest value. It is composed of friction drag, wave drag, as well as a component resulting from shock-induced separation. The transition from near the speed of sound to the supersonic area cannot be exactly defined. A typical characteristic of supersonic flow is that the disturbances emanating from the aircraft can spread out only within the Mach cone (open at the rear). In the supersonic range zero lift drag is composed of about one-third friction drag and two-thirds wave drag.

In order to reach high subsonic Mach numbers with least possible engine power, we try to displace the critical Mach number upwards. There are several ways of doing this. Those measures having the greatest influence which aim to reduce flow acceleration overspeeds at the wing, include:
- reduction of profile thickness,
- absorbing the thickness maximum by using a longer chord,
- increasing the sweepback angle of the wing leading edge,
- reducing the aspect ratio.

A further effective step is a suitable

4-63 The principle of transonic area rule was applied successfully to the Buccaneer. Its noticeable characteristic is the bulging of the fuselage to give additional cross-section to compensate for the corresponding cross-section of the wing. In this way a uniform distribution of cross-section is created in the longitudinal direction without steps. (Buccaneer Mk 2, aircraft carrier, HMS Eagle).

shaping of the fuselage by means of narrowing and widening the cross section at particular points. The theory on which this measure is based states that the transonic drag of an aircraft is dependent mainly on its axial cross-sectional distribution. This is the famous transonic area rule, which was successfully applied on the Buccaneer (Fig. 4-63). The advantages of such a 'custom designed' aircraft are limited to a relatively small Mach-number range. With increasing supersonic Mach number, the favourable drag behaviour gets lost, and even additional drag occurs.

The application of the area rule is therefore meaningful only in the case of those aircraft whose maximum speed is in the region of Mach 1.

DETERMINATION OF DRAG

The breakdown of drag into its individual components provides a solid working basis for carrying out calculations. The methods applied (mathematical and experimental) depend on how far advanced the project is. First assessments in initial design are made using relatively simple procedures which describe the influences of the individual components with sufficient accuracy. If the aircraft

configuration is already available in its final form, the amount of calculation and wind tunnel testing, naturally, is greater. This leads to a considerable extension to the simple list of drag components.

To determine drag all available means must be used:

- statistical data
- empirical procedures
- theoretical procedures
- wind tunnel experiments.

The way the various sources for predicting drag are used is dependent largely on the experience of the design team, which has already dealt with the same or similar aircraft configurations. The numerous shortcomings of each procedure make continual improvements necessary and these are incorporated into the existing methods. For example, it is not possible at present to make reliable predictions about the vortex flows over an aircraft. However, this is only one of the many unsolved problems in determining drag. This is why there is no generally valid rule from which to determine drag with any reliability. However, there are some extensive standard works used in the industry, and these contain basic information on the drag values to be expected from individual components (such as USAF Datcom, RAeS Data Sheets, Hoerner). The results obtained, whether good or unsatisfactory, are, of course, company secrets and represent an essential part of a manufacturer's 'know-how'.

The attainable accuracy of the calculated polar diagrams depends largely on the type of drag and the flight Mach number. For example: profile drag can be far more reliably predicted than, say, the onset of drag rise; the path of zero drag between $M = 0.95$ and $M = 1.05$ is subject to considerable uncertainty. The lift system is also a considerable source of error. If not enough care is taken, it can become the greatest uncertainty factor in the drag balance.

Determining drag by purely theoretical procedures is possible only to a limited degree. These **procedures,** for which large computers are necessary in every case, generally relate the influences of potential flow (frictionless flow) with separate boundary layer calculations. The major disadvantage is that they are limited to small angles-of-attack and to purely subsonic or purely supersonic flows. The transonic area, precisely the area which is important for combat aircraft, is practically inaccessible mathematically.

An exclusively theoretical drag determination at high angles-of-attack, taking separations into consideration, is equally impossible. Take-off and landing, for example, belong to this category.

Further problems, for which a theoretical solution can scarcely be expected in the foreseeable future, are

- calculation of the vortex flow over slender aircraft shapes
- determining drag from external stores
- reliably predicting wave drag on realistic shapes and
- drag from excrescences.

The reason for this lies mainly in an insufficient understanding of the physics of such complicated flows. In this situation a wind tunnel turns out to be the only way of reliably determining the aerodynamic properties, and thus of establishing a realistic flight polar diagram. The measurement of aerodynamic forces on a model is necessary for this; the model is subjected to flow at various angles-of-attack and sideslip, and at various Mach numbers. The information to be attained in the wind tunnel consists mainly of such **force measurements.** Pressure distribution measurements are carried out in parallel, the pressure being measured over a multitude of tiny holes on the surface of the model. This pressure is that generated in the area of each individual hole. This permits the determination of load distributions, whose integration yields the total forces. Pressure distribution measurements involve a great deal of measuring and are carried out only on particularly critical components of an aircraft, such as on the wing, for example.

With the aid of woollen tufts or oil film patterns, it is possible to make the flow visible in the area near the tunnel wall (see Figs. 4-22 and 4-23). At supersonic Mach numbers there is the additional possibility of obtaining primarily qualitative impressions of flow by optical methods (such as Schlieren; see Fig. 4-49).

The results of wind tunnel experiments can be transferred to the full-scale aircraft in many cases. In this respect, however, corrections of the measurement data are necessary, which result, for example, from the restriction of the test section by the fixed walls of the wind tunnel and by the elastic deformation of the model's sting support.

EXTENDED DRAG BALANCE

Determining the drag caused by the propulsion system involves a relatively large degree of uncertainty. Painstaking investigations in the wind tunnel are necessary to determine the effects of different engine power settings at the air intake and the nozzle, and to determine the quantity **thrust minus drag** with adequate precision. A clearly defined book-keeping system is necessary for this, to convert the performances claimed by engine manufacturers and the 'no-propulsion' wind tunnel data into useful flight predictions. Above all, it must be categorically laid down which force components are to be assigned to the propulsion system and which to the airframe (thrust-drag book-keeping).

If the forces caused by the propulsion system are included in the balance, then the following list of all forces acting in the longitudinal direction results as an extension of the drag equation:

$$K_{total} = \underbrace{F_{net} + \Delta F_{intake} + \Delta F_{jet} + \Delta F_{trim}}_{\text{thrust}} \text{ minus } \underbrace{D_{model} - \Delta D_{intake} - \Delta D_{jet} - \Delta D_{trim}}_{\text{drag}}$$

K_{total} = resultant force in the horizontal flight direction at a given flight attitude, altitude and Mach number.

F_{net} = installed thrust (net thrust), allowing for the influences of pressure recovery, distortion, nozzle efficiency, bleed air, and power loss (generators, fuel and hydraulic pumps).

ΔF_{intake} = increment of the external forces exerted by the intake, dependent on the power setting of the engine.
The reference value is usually the full thrust $\Delta F_{intake} = D_{intake}$ (full load) $- D_{intake}$ (part load); H, M, α, β = constant.

ΔF_{jet} = increment of the external forces exerted by the jet efflux, dependent on the power setting of the engine, reference value = full thrust.

ΔF_{trim} = increment of the trim drag, dependent on the power setting of the engine, reference value = trim condition at full thrust.
($\Delta F_{trim} = D_{trim}$ at full load minus D_{trim} at partial load).

D_{model} = drag of the wind tunnel model in the reference condition, i.e. at full load.

ΔD_{intake} = increment of the external forces exerted by the intake which are **not** dependent on the power setting of the engine but on the flight condition (angle-of-attack, sideslip angle), Mach number and altitude.

ΔD_{jet} = increment of the external forces caused by the exhaust system, dependent on the flight condition, Mach number, altitude, but not on the throttle control setting, however.

ΔD_{trim} = increment of the trim drag, which arises by adjusting the elevator to generate moment equilibrium; dependent on flight attitude, Mach number, altitude. Reference value: trim condition at full load.

DETERMINATION OF F-15 DRAG

For the preparation of a drag balance, three types of wind-tunnel model are basically necessary, namely:

a) the Aero Force and Moment Model, with which the aerodynamic forces and their effects are measured, such as lift, drag, moment, lift/drag ratio;

b) the Inlet Model, which includes the influences in the interaction of aircraft and inlet, such as pressure recovery, distortion, turbulence, spillage drag (see Chapter 7);

c) the Jet Effects Model, which takes into account the influences of the jet, such as nozzle setting, nozzle pressure ratio, tailplane position, nozzle spacing, afterbody contour (see Chapter 8).

The fundamental scheme, from which the drag behaviour of the F-15 can be determined, is shown by Fig. 4-64. The determination of the lift and drag behaviour was made on a 1:13 scale model which incorporated an operating inlet and inlet ramp bleeds. The model was equipped with adjustable tail surfaces and flaps. The intake flow could be regulated by simple convergent nozzles of different cross-sections. The model had a conventional afterbody sting suspension, which inevitably led to an unrealistic afterbody contour. By means of this model all necessary data for the basic drag polar were determined, different engine throttle settings being taken into consideration. Drag values arising from internal flow in the model had to be accounted for; as is usual in such cases.

The altered afterbody contour caused by the wind-tunnel support for the model was an inevitable source of errors and had to be taken into account in the calculations. For this purpose a 1:21 scale model was built, mounted on a strut and having a realistic afterbody (see Fig. 4-64, 1).[17]

A further 1:21 scale model with a sting support was used, particularly for the higher angle-of-attack range (Fig. 4-65, see Fig. 4-64, 3).

This model was also used to investigate the influence of external stores (4) on the drag polar.

The last element of those drag components belonging to the airframe concerned the mathematical estimation of roughness drag, including that of smaller excrescences, such as measuring probes and antennas. The 'no-propulsion' component of drag was defined in this way.

Determination of the drag influences caused by the propulsion system needed two further wind tunnel models, i.e. a 1:6 scale inlet model and a 1:21 scale jet effects model. The inlet model permitted determination of the flow quality at the compressor air inlet. Allowing for the nozzle effectiveness (7), and the loss of

---

[17] The numbers stated correspond to the numbers in the drawing.

mechanical power, as well as bleed air from the compressor (9), the **net thrust** resulted from the engine characteristic data. The drag components had to be deduced from this; these arise, for example, due to momentum losses during the boundary layer suction and cockpit ventilation. With the aid of the jet effects model (see Fig. 4-64, 10), the influence of realistic nozzle pressure ratios in comparison to simple flow was determined.

Finally, the net propulsive force resulted from all the drag components which is decisive for flight performance.

4.8.6.2 Lift

Two quantities determine the lift characteristic, i.e. the lift curve slope C_{L_α} and the maximum lift $C_{L_{max}}$ (see Fig. 4-10). The lift curve slope, i.e. the angle formed by the linear part of the lift curve with the α-axis, is one of the most important components of the wing, and at a given Mach number is dependent primarily on the wing plan-form. Fig. 4-66 shows the development of lift curve slope over the Mach number for a typical combat aircraft configuration as measured in the wind tunnel.

The limits of the linear part of the lift curve are given by:

$$C_{L_\alpha} = \frac{\Pi}{2}A = 1.57 \times A$$

(valid for very small aspect ratios, $A < 1$)

and

$$C_{L_\alpha} = 2\Pi = 6.28$$

(valid for very large aspect ratios, in the extreme case $A \to \infty$).

In general the lift curve slope becomes smaller with increasing sweepback angle

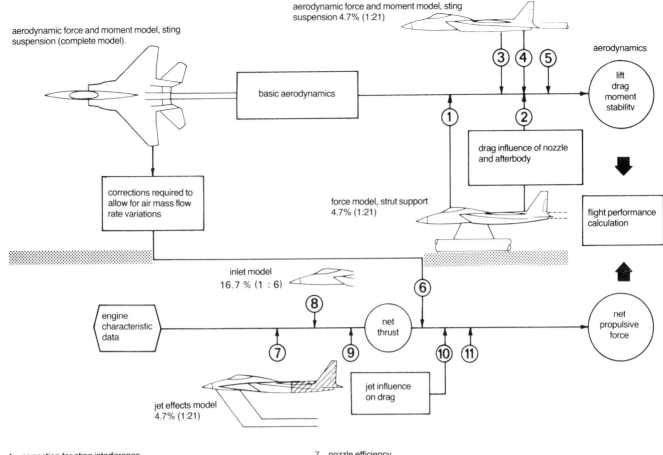

aerodynamic force and moment model, sting suspension 4.7% (1:21)

aerodynamic force and moment model, sting suspension (complete model).

basic aerodynamics

aerodynamics

lift
drag
moment
stability

corrections required to allow for air mass flow rate variations

drag influence of nozzle and afterbody

force model, strut support 4.7% (1:21)

flight performance calculation

inlet model
16.7 % (1 : 6)

engine characteristic data

net thrust

net propulsive force

jet effects model
4.7% (1:21)

jet influence on drag

1 correction for sting interference.
2 influence of the nozzle geometry (cruise, afterburner).
3 behaviour at high angles-of-attack
4 drag of external stores
5 roughness and Reynolds number correction
6 correction for inlet drag, influence of the mass flow ratio

7 nozzle efficiency
8 inlet flow, distortion, pressure recovery
9 power extraction, bleed air
10 drag correction from flow through to operating jet pressure ratios
11 boundary layer suction in the inlet, bypass, cabin ventilation, leakages,
     ECS (environmental control system).

4-64 **Determination of thrust and drag for the F-15.**

of the wing leading edge. This effect is counter-balanced to a large extent by the Mach-number influence at subsonic speeds, since the lift curve slope becomes greater with increasing Mach number in the range M < 1. The drop immediately beyond Mach 1 and in the supersonic range is connected with the occurrence of compression shocks.

4-65 **Model of the F-15 in a wind tunnel.**

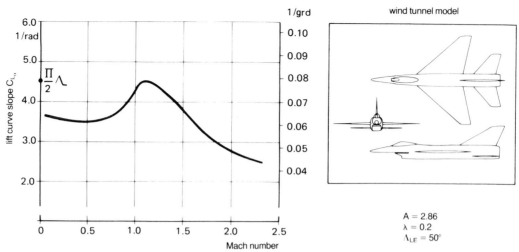

4-66   **Typical development of the lift curve slope as a function of the Mach number.**

In contrast to the lift curve slope, which characterises the normal operating range of the wing or the aircraft, the maximum lift constitutes the upper limit of manoeuvrability. At subsonic and transonic speeds, the buffeting behaviour of the aircraft influences the effective maximum lift (through correlations of lift coefficients and flight Mach numbers), with various buffeting intensities occurring (Fig. 4-67).

The upper limit of the manoeuvre range is formed by the line of maximum lift, which discounts buffeting behaviour and can be determined from wind tunnel measurements or by estimation procedures. Another important curve is the development of buffet onset. With decreasing Mach number the line of buffet onset approaches the maximum lift curve. Determination of buffet onset as well as of various buffet intensities takes place in the wind tunnel, or during the flight test by means of built-in accelerometers.

Combat aircraft, in contrast to commercial aircraft, are able, due to their structural strength, to penetrate ranges beyond buffet onset. This occurs frequently when manoeuvring at high angles-of-attack (manoeuvring air combat).

Knowledge of the behaviour of the aircraft is important in this range, as the use of the weapons system can be made difficult or impossible by buffet phenomena. Moderate buffet is generally taken to be the limit at which guns and missiles can still just be used. At heavy buffet, although the aircraft can be flown, it cannot be used a gun platform.

In the supersonic range, the maximum

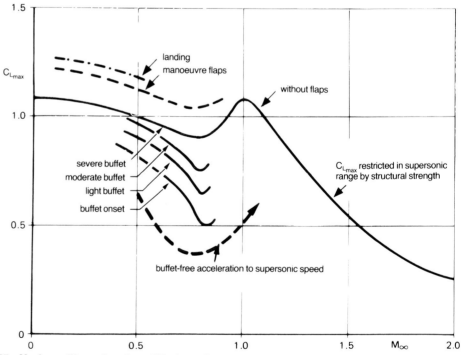

4-67   **Maximum lift as a function of Mach number.**

effective lift is limited only by the strength, and no longer by the aerodynamics. Using the maximum load factor, the maximum lift results from the simple lift equation as a function of wing loading and dynamic pressure as follows:

$$C_{L_{max}} = \frac{n_{max} \cdot W/S}{q}$$

Example:

n_{max}	= 9
W/S	= 3924 N/m²
	(82 lb/ft²)
M	= 2.0
H	= 11 km (36000 ft)
q	= 0.63 bar (9 lb/in²)
	(from Fig. 4-60)
$C_{L_{max}}$	= 0.56

where n (9g) is the limiting manoeuvring load factor.

This value is considerably lower than the aerodynamic maximum lift. At an altitude of 6 km (q = 1.32 bar) (20000 ft), the maximum effective lift for M = 2 is still only half as much, namely 0.27.

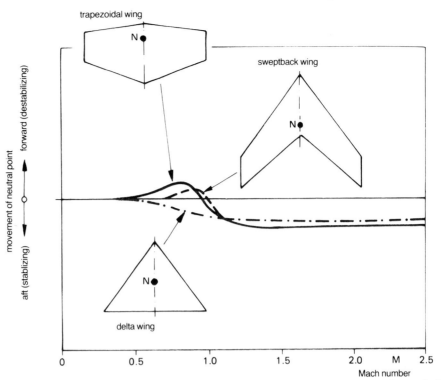

4-68 **Movement of neutral point (aerodynamic centre) as a function of Mach number and wing plan-form.**

4.8.6.3 Stability

However valuable a high maximum lift is, without knowledge of the relevant stability no statement about its actual usefulness is possible. This is especially true at speeds close to the speed of sound. Stability and control changes occur which have significant effects, depending on the wing shape. The considerable movements of the aerodynamic forces on the wing and tail surfaces cause a rapid change to the aircraft's load distribution. This behaviour can be represented graphically by the position of the wing aerodynamic centre at different Mach numbers (Fig. 4-68).

The forward movement of the aerodynamic centre in the case of straight and sweptback wings near the speed of sound means that the pitching moment becomes more positive and the wing loses in stability. Therefore the centre-of-gravity of the aircraft must always be so positioned that adequate stability is still guaranteed when the aerodynamic centre is at its maximum forward position (centre-of-gravity in front of the aerodynamic centre, see Chapter 5).

In contrast to the straight wing and the sweptback wing, the stability behaviour of the delta wing shows a comparatively well-balanced development from the subsonic to the supersonic area: the movement of the aerodynamic centre takes place only in the direction of greater stability. The control of an aircraft with a delta wing thus turns out to be less difficult when flying through the speed of sound range.

The considerable increase of stability in the supersonic range, which is to be observed on all wings, has the disadvantage that the elevator deflections required to control the large (nose-down) pitching moment increase the trim drag.

Here we have the significant advantage of the canard wing, which helps instead of hinders lift, and whose position in front of the aerodynamic centre avoids overstability (Viggen, Kfir). Strake wings are also able to counteract an increased stability.

A further factor in stability behaviour is the horizontal tail. The conventional horizontal tail is usually designed in such a way that its aspect ratio is lower than that of the wing, so that the lift curve slope dependent on the Mach number rises less strongly. In this way the detrimental influence of the downwash on the horizontal tail is reduced.

With increasing Mach number, the stability contribution of the horizontal tail decreases at subsonic speeds, so that at speeds just below Mach 1 a stability hole (trim hole) arises. The greater the tailplane area, the more noticeable the trim hole becomes.

Wing-mounted stores located upstream of the horizontal tail also have a considerable destabilising effect.

In addition to the longitudinal stability, the reduction of lateral stability can also restrict the maximum effective angle-of-attack.

With increasing supersonic Mach number, the vertical tail loses its stabilising effect, because the lift curve slope decreases, just as in the case of the wing (see Chapter 5).

4.8.6.4 Sonic Boom

The increase of flight speed beyond the speed of sound has led to a phenomenon which is popularly known as the **sonic boom.**

The pressure disturbances emanating from an aircraft spread out in all directions at the speed of sound (see Fig. 4-48). If the aircraft itself is travelling at supersonic velocity, then it is faster than the pressure disturbances it generates. The disturbances spread out inside the Mach cone, which trails after the aircraft and contains all disturbances emanating from it (Fig. 4-69). The Mach cone's contact with the ground generates a line (conic section), on which the pressure disturbances are perceived as a sonic boom.

In the microstructure of this effect a sudden pressure rise is perceptible first of all, whose cause is the oblique com-

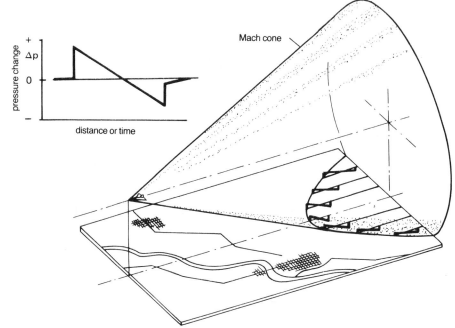

4-69 **Explanation of the sonic boom.**

pression shock emanating from many parts of the aircraft. Then a linear drop takes place below the ambient pressure, followed by a further compression shock, back to restoration of the ambient pressure (see pressure development in Fig. 4-69). These are the two shocks which an observer on the ground perceives. The loudness depends on the size of the pressure difference Δp. Along the aircraft's track it is at its greatest, and it decreases towards the sides. The zone in which the boom is audible may be up to 100 km wide (50 nm), depending on flight altitude and Mach number.

With a sufficient interval of time between the two pressure peaks, two booms are heard in quick succession. If the intervening time is very short, however, only one single boom can be heard. The actual interval depends on the aircraft linear dimensions, the path inclination and the properties of the atmosphere.

4.9 Vertical Take-off

The vulnerability of conventional airbases is an important argument for the development of aircraft which can take off and land vertically. In spite of effective camouflage techniques, conventional runways are relatively easy to locate, while smaller operational airfields can only be detected with difficulty. In addition, large airbases represent desirable targets whose temporary elimination may be decisive for the outcome of the conflict. The possibility of distributing a tactical airforce among many small airfields, to be chosen at will, gains in significance by using combat aircraft with vertical take-off properties.

The only operational combat aircraft with vertical take-off capability in the early 80s is the British Harrier (Fig. 4-70). A promising position in VTOL technology possessed by the Federal Republic of Germany with the VAK-191B from VFW, Do 31 from Dornier and VJ-101 from MBB, was unfortunately not made use of. The Soviet Union's Yak-38 obviously does not have the performance capability of the Harrier.

4-70　**Harrier in hovering flight: the swiveling nozzles are directed downwards (Harrier GR.3, 3 Squadron, RAF Wildenrath).**

4.9.1 **Aerodynamic Effects of Vertical Take-off**

The different aerodynamic interference phenomena of a jet-supported VTOL[18] combat aircraft make this type of aircraft more difficult to fly than conventional jet aircraft. The essential reason for this is that the engine thrust must provide the aircraft lift in the low-speed regime in place of wing lift. The jets issuing from the swivelling nozzles give rise to secondary forces and moments at the wing through the effect of induction; these forces and moments may be of the same order of magnitude as the aero-dynamic forces. In addition, the mass flow rates at

the intake generate forces which react on the flight properties.

Typical flight phases for vertical take-off are **hovering flight** and **transition.**

Hovering flight is characterised by the lack of forward speed; the entire lift force is generated by reaction forces of the jets. The emerging jets entrain air from around the aircraft (Fig. 4-71). In doing so, a secondary downflow is set in motion which flows around the hovering aircraft and acts as **suckdown.** This suction effect is particularly pronounced when the jet spreads out as a wall or ground jet immediately after emerging from the nozzle. In the case of small ground clearances (take-off, touchdown), particularly large suckdown effects occur.

In the transition phase, which is the transition to airborne flight, the suction effect with vertical or obliquely pointed

nozzles is also considerable, in spite of forward speed. The sucked-in surrounding air, even at low downward speed, gives rise to noticeable angle-of-attack and dynamic pressure changes on the wing and on the tail surfaces which generate jet-induced suckdown and pitching moments.

4.9.2 **Thermal Effects**

The thermal effects of vertical take-off are of especial importance in the hovering flight phase. The essential problems in this connection include the heating-up of the airframe and the reingestion of hot gases via the engine intakes.

---

[18] VTOL = Vertical Take-off and Landing

95

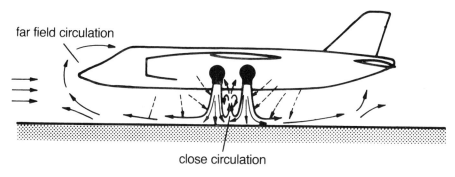

far field circulation

close circulation

4-71 The emerging jets entrain air from around the aircraft by a process of turbulent mixing.

The heating-up of the airframe can be kept within limits by means of suitable construction and the selection of special materials. However, the weight and cost increases caused by these steps must remain within justifiable limits.

What is considerably more problematical is the reingestion of hot gases through recirculation (see Fig. 4-71). It is generally true that a temperature increase of the sucked-in air by 10° causes a power loss of 2%. The outer areas of the exhaust gases flowing away on the ground can separate from the ground and return to the aircraft due to unfavourable wind conditions in the far field.

Recirculation problems are extremely complex and scarcely understandable theoretically. Therefore all that remains is experimental investigation on suitable models. For this purpose a scale model rig is equipped with hot gas supply pipes, intake and exhaust (Fig. 4-72). While the hot gas emerges from the nozzles, air is taken in via the intakes and its temperature profile measured at the front compressor. By vertically adjusting the ground plane, the influence of the hovering altitude on the flow quality can be determined. A fan set up nearby simulates the wind flow.

4-72 Recirculation model of a VTOL aircraft and research model in the experimental gas-dynamic rig at VFW Bremen (now MBB).

5 Stability and Control

When it is at rest or in uniform motion, every body is in equilibrium. The equilibrium of an aircraft refers to uniform motions.

A stable aircraft returns automatically to its original flight attitude after a disturbance, which can, for example, be a gust (Fig. 5-1). This form of stability is also termed **static stability.** However, it also depends on **how** the stability state is attained after a disturbance. If at first there is a deviation to one side and then to the other side with increasing amplitude, then this is dynamic instability. Should the aircraft oscillate with constant amplitude about its equilibrium state then it is dynamically neutral. If, in contrast, after a disturbance the oscillation takes place with decreasing amplitude, without the pilot having to intervene, then the aircraft is dynamically stable.

High stability means low manoeuvrability. As modern aircraft usually have an autopilot, the designer aims for relatively low stability or even neutral behaviour. The combat aircraft of the next generation are designed to be unstable, because in this way drag can be reduced. In this context much depends on the reliability of the automatic pilot, because the aircraft can no longer be flown 'by hand' if the autopilot breaks down.

When considering stability, a distinction

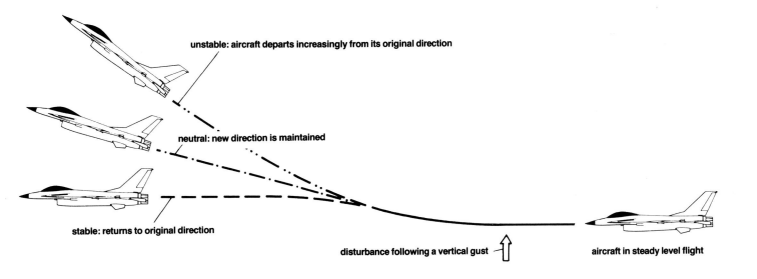

unstable: aircraft departs increasingly from its original direction

neutral: new direction is maintained

stable: returns to original direction

disturbance following a vertical gust

aircraft in steady level flight

5-1 **Explanation of static longitudinal stability.**

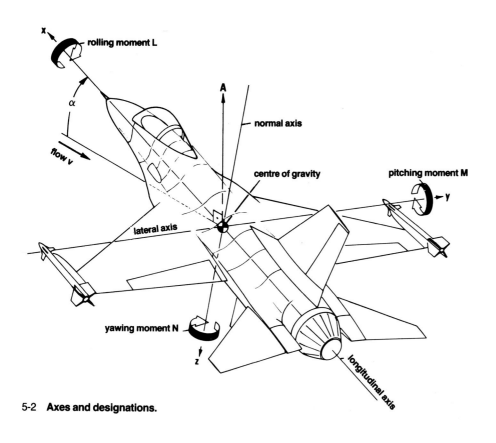

rolling moment L

normal axis

centre of gravity

pitching moment M

lateral axis

yawing moment N

longitudinal axis

5-2 **Axes and designations.**

is made between longitudinal and lateral motion. Longitudinal motion is characterized by **symmetrical** flow; there is thus no sideslip angle ($\beta = 0$), the flow comes 'directly from the front'. In the description of this form of motion, the angle-of-attack and **pitching moment** is understood to be a rotation about the lateral axis (Fig. 5-2). The wing is always horizontally aligned, while the centre of gravity executes a motion in the vertical plane.

On the other hand, lateral motion is characterized by unsymmetrical flow; a sideslip angle appears ($\beta \neq 0$), the flow comes 'obliquely from the front', and therefore includes a lateral component. The lateral motion is understood as a rotation about the normal and longitudinal axes. Among these are included **sideslip, roll** and **yaw** motions, while the angle-of-attack remains unchanged. Longitudinal and lateral motion are generally treated separately.

5.1 **Static longitudinal stability**

The steady flight condition in symmetrical flow is described by the static longitudinal stability behaviour. An aircraft can maintain its steady unaccelerated flight, only if the sum of the resultants of the external forces and moments about the centre of gravity is zero. In particular, the **pitching moment** about the lateral axis, which runs through the aircraft's centre of gravity, must become zero. Otherwise the aircraft would experience a rotational acceleration in the direction of the unbalanced moment.

In order to be able to make a state-

ment about the magnitude of the stability, the forces and moments acting at the aircraft must be considered. From this, permissible centre of gravity positions as well as design criteria for the horizontal tail surfaces can be derived.

Using simplified assumptions (thrust acts in the longitudinal axis and angle-of-attack is small), the following summation of moments[19] can be made up with

---
[19] The moment is formed as the product of aerodynamic force (lift, drag) and lever arm about the centre of gravity.

clockwise rotating (nose-up) moments being counted positively (Fig. 5-3):

$$M = \underbrace{L \cdot \Delta x_N + D \cdot \Delta z_N - M_0}_{\text{wing}} \underbrace{+ M_F}_{\text{fuselage}} \underbrace{- L_H l_H}_{\substack{\text{horizontal} \\ \text{tail}}}$$

M	resultant pitching moment
L	lift of the wing (positive upwards)
L_H	lift of the horizontal tail
D	drag of the wing
Δx_N, Δz_N	longitudinal distance or vertical distance between wing aerodynamic centre and aircraft centre of gravity
l_H	distance between aerodynamic centre of the horizontal tail and aircraft centre of gravity
M_0	zero lift pitching moment of the wing (nose-down, therefore negative)
M_F	fuselage moment (as a rule nose-up, therefore positive; fuselage has a destabilizing effect)

Divided by the reference moment $q S \bar{\bar{c}}$ (q = dynamic pressure, S = wing area, $\bar{\bar{c}}$ = reference wing chord), the moment equation results as follows in a dimensionless form[20]:

$$C_m = -C_L \frac{\Delta x_N}{\bar{\bar{c}}} + C_D \frac{\Delta x_N}{\bar{\bar{c}}} - C_{m0}$$

$$+ C_{mF} - C_{L_H} \frac{S_H l_H}{S \bar{\bar{c}}}$$

C_m	pitching moment coefficient
C_L	lift coefficient
C_D	drag coefficient
C_{m0}	zero lift moment coefficient
Index F:	fuselage
Index H:	horizontal tail

To generate equilibrium C_m has to become zero. This happens by adjusting the horizontal tail, its lift coefficient C_{L_H} being changed. Together with the lever arm l_H a moment results which, as a rule, is **nose-up** (positive), in order to balance the **nose-down** moment of the wing (first term in the moment equation). The conventional (i.e. statically stable) design, which still predominates in present aircraft designs, consequently produces **negative lift** to provide the moment equilibrium at the horizontal tail. This so-called **trim lift** must be additionally generated by the wing and appears in the lift balance as a loss. Therefore in the latest designs an effort is made to plan an **unstable** design, by means of which lift become possible while trimming at the horizontal tail (see Chapter 13).

The pitching moment coefficient C_m is above all dependent on the lift coefficient C_L and thus on the angle-of-attack. The slope of the curve $C_m = f(C_L)$ can be seen as a direct measure of the static longitudinal stability (Fig. 5-4). To make this clearer, it will be assumed that the aircraft is in a state of equilibrium at a given elevator angle (point A). Because of a vertical gust, the angle-of-attack and,

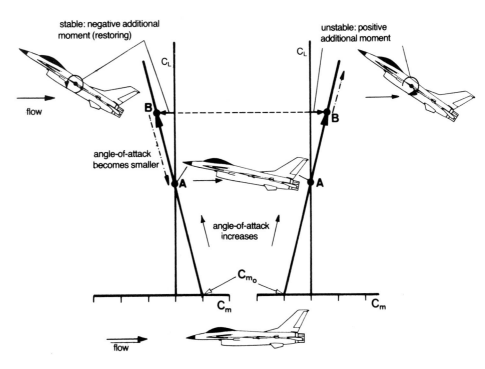

α	angle-of-attack
$\bigcirc$	centre of gravity of the aircraft
M	moment, clockwise rotating positive
Δx_N	distance neutral point of wing/centre of gravity of aircraft
l_H	distance neutral point of horizontal tail/centre of gravity of aircraft
D	drag
L	lift
Δz_N	vertical distance of the wing neutral point from aircraft centre of gravity
M_F	fuselage moment
Index	H horizontal tail
	N neutral point

5-3 **Forces and moments in steady flight.**

5-4 **Stable and unstable behaviour are indicated by the slope of the moment curve.**

[20] The moment coefficient is generally defined as follows: $M = C_m S \bar{c}$; corresponding indices characterize the specific moment coefficients, e.g. C_{mF} = fuselage moment coefficient.

99

as the flight speed does not change in the short time, also the lift coefficient are increased (point B). If the aircraft is stable, a negative (nose-down) additional moment arises, which returns to the original equilibrium state in A. In contrast with an unstable aircraft, a positive (nose-up) moment is generated which tries to rotate the aircraft further away from its equilibrium state.

Hence it follows as a condition for static stability that the curve $C_m = f(C_L)$ must have a negative slope[21]. In mathematical terms, this is expressed by the so-called **stability derivative** dC_m/dC_L, which is the result of differentiating the moment equation with respect to the lift coefficient. The stability behaviour can accordingly be expressed in a simple manner:

$$\frac{dC_m}{dC_L} \begin{cases} < 0 \text{ stable} \\ = 0 \text{ neutral} \\ > 0 \text{ unstable} \end{cases}$$

5.1.1 Influences on Stability

The previously mentioned moment equation states that the resultant longitudinal moment is composed of moment contributions from the wing, fuselage and horizontal tail. If one assumes that there is no vertical distance between the centre of gravity of the aircraft and the aerodynamic centre (neutral point) of the wing ($\Delta z_N = 0$), then the moment contribution of the wing depends only on the lift force and its point of application, as well as on the zero lift pitching moment. The zero lift pitching moment, which is the sole effective moment in the zero-lift state (at $C_L = 0$), is generated by the camber of the profile and the twist of the wing. It is independent of lift. An untwisted wing with symmetrical profile has no zero lift pitching moment. The stability contribution of the wing is then dependent only on the relative distance of the wing neutral point to the centre of gravity:

$$\frac{dC_m}{dC_L} = -\frac{\Delta x_N}{\overline{\overline{c}}}$$

The important conclusion can be drawn from this that the wing always provides a contribution to stability whenever the point of application of the aerodynamic force lies **behind** the centre of gravity. If the centre of gravity and the aerodynamic point of application are related to an arbitrary origin (e.g. the wing tip), then according to definition (see Fig. 5-3):

$$\Delta x_N = x_N - x_{C.G.}$$

x_N = distance between the aerodynamic point of application and the reference point.
$x_{C.G.}$ = distance between the centre of gravity and the reference point

As long as the aerodynamic point of contact lies behind the centre of gravity, then it is always true that $\Delta x_N > 0$ ($x_N > x_{C.G.}$) and the pitching moment slope is thus negative, so that the contribution of the wing increases stability. Should the aerodynamic point of contact lie in front of the centre of gravity, then $x_N < 0$ and $dC_m/dC_L > 0$; the contribution of the wing has a destabilizing effect.

The stability ratio is stated in percentages of the mean aerodynamic chord $\overline{\overline{c}}$. With combat aircraft a stability of 3% to 5% is usual:

$$-\frac{dC_m}{dC_L} = \frac{\Delta x_N}{\overline{\overline{c}}} = 0.03/0.05$$

Excessive stability demands large horizontal tail surfaces and large deflections.

INFLUENCE OF THE HORIZONTAL TAIL

The task of the horizontal tail is to generate a balancing moment to maintain the steady flight condition or, by producing an additional moment, to make possible desired changes of flight path. This is expressed by the lift coefficient C_{L_H} of the horizontal tail (see moment equation).

The position of the tail surfaces in the downwash of the wing restricts their effectiveness to a greater or lesser extent. With a tail arrangement below the wing plane, as is typical for most combat aircraft, the wake of the wing strikes the horizontal tail at small lift coefficients; the stability contribution of the horizontal tail decreases in this case. With increasing angle-of-attack (aerial combat manoeuvre), however, the tail unit moves out of the disturbance area and gains increasing lift: the stabilizing effect becomes greater as a result.

If, in contrast, the aircraft has a T-tail (Starfighter), then at **small** angles-of-attack the tail surfaces lie far above the wake area. In order to attain stability a relatively small area is already sufficient. The problems begin, however, at high angles-of-attack, which are characteristic of combat aircraft. The T-tail then gets into the downwash and wake field, which have become considerably stronger, so that is is now completely disturbed. For safety reasons, therefore, a restriction (undesirable) of the maximum permissible angle-of-attack is necessary. In the Starfighter a so-called 'stickpusher', an automatic control mechanism, was used for a time; after exceeding a critical angle-of-attack this rotates the horizontal tail in such a way that a nose-down moment is generated. If the aircraft is at low altitude (low level flight, landing approach), this behaviour, which cannot be overridden by the pilot, may have a disastrous effect. In fact, there were Starfighter accidents due to this, until it was decided to remove the system.

---

[21] Negative slope = sloped to the left

INFLUENCES OF THE FUSELAGE

The fuselage always has a destabilizing effect on the moment balance. Complicated fuselage shapes make a theoretical understanding difficult, so that experimental determination takes place in the wind tunnel. What usually happens is that fuselage and wing as a **wing/body** combination are tested as one unit. Their stability contribution results from the measured values, by putting the tangent on the curve $C_m = f(C_L)$ and its slope is determined at $C_L = 0$. It is enough if the wing/body combination shows neutral or even slightly unstable behaviour (Fig. 5-5). By adding the horizontal tail, the aircraft become stable. The flow, encountering the tail at a positive angle-of-attack in spite of the downwash from the wing, generates a lift force which results in a nose-down moment. If the horizontal tail is so adjusted that negative lift arises, the moment curve shifts parallel to the right, i.e. to positive C_m values, as a positive additional moment is generated. The opposite tail deflection generates a nose-down moment, so that the stability curve shifts to negative C_m values. The gradient (slope) is, however, not influenced by this.

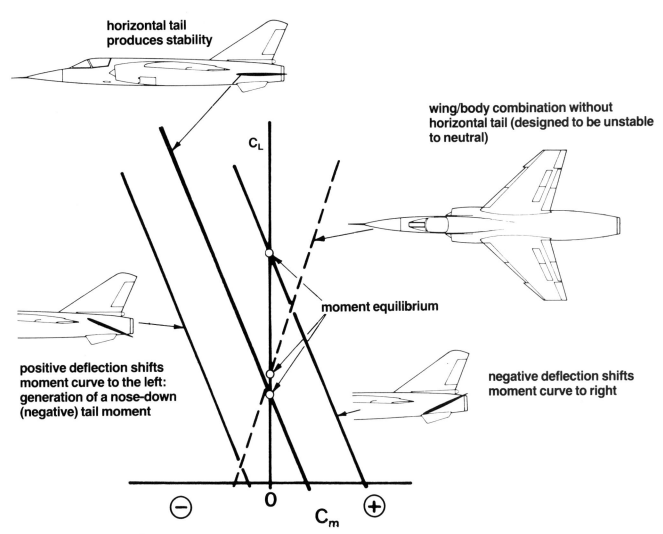

horizontal tail produces stability

wing/body combination without horizontal tail (designed to be unstable to neutral)

C_L

moment equilibrium

positive deflection shifts moment curve to the left: generation of a nose-down (negative) tail moment

negative deflection shifts moment curve to right

$\ominus$ 0 $\oplus$

C_m

5-5 **Influence of the horizontal tail on the moment curve.**

INFLUENCE OF MACH NUMBER

An important criterion in the design of the horizontal tail is neutral point development as a function of Mach number (Fig. 5-6). As with increasing flight Mach number, when the resultant aerodynamic force on the wing moves back, the distance to the centre of gravity increases; the aircraft becomes increasingly stable. On the other hand, the downwash increases in intensity, so that the stabilizing contribution of the horizontal tail becomes less when approaching the speed of sound.

The generation of sufficient stability in the speed of sound range could now be attained by means of a tail which is very large and oversized for the remaining flight Mach numbers. To avoid this unfavourable solution, the wing/body combination alone is so designed that, with increasing Mach number, it becomes stable enough. In the case of combat aircraft, this possibility is essentially available if a sufficiently slender wing (low aspect ratio) is used. Frequently there is even a tendency for slender wings to exhibit overstability, which is equally undesirable. Strake wings (F-16, F-18) turn out to be advantageous here, as the aerodynamic forces acting on the strakes lie **forward of** the aircraft's centre of gravity, thereby giving a destabilizing effect. For the same reason, the Israeli Kfir combat aircraft has additional canard foreplanes whose lift forces act **in front of** the centre of gravity to reduce the overstability of the delta wing.

AFT POSITION OF CENTRE OF GRAVITY

If the neutral point is fixed, the position of the aircraft's centre of gravity can no longer be chosen at random. As in conventional designs a certain degree of

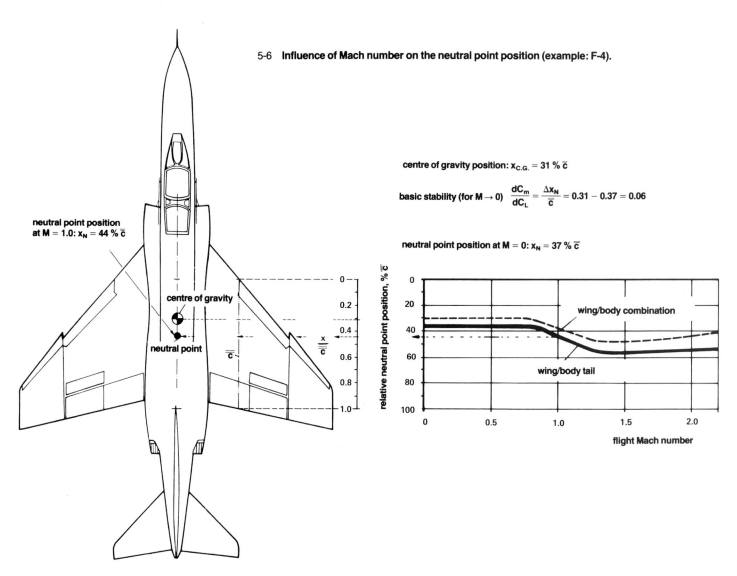

5-6   **Influence of Mach number on the neutral point position (example: F-4).**

neutral point position at M = 1.0: x_N = 44 % $\overline{\overline{c}}$

centre of gravity

neutral point

centre of gravity position: $x_{C.G.}$ = 31 % $\overline{c}$

basic stability (for M → 0) $\dfrac{dC_m}{dC_L} = \dfrac{\Delta x_N}{\overline{c}} = 0.31 - 0.37 = 0.06$

neutral point position at M = 0: x_N = 37 % $\overline{\overline{c}}$

wing/body combination

wing/body tail

relative neutral point position, % $\overline{c}$

flight Mach number

static longitudinal stability must be guaranteed; under no circumstances may a load condition be possible, in which the centre of gravity lies behind the neutral point.

The aircraft's centre of gravity is not invariable. Its position moves with fuel consumption, firing of weapons, as well as the weight of various weapon loads. Early in the design stage the probable range of movement of the centre of gravity must be assessed and combined with the calculated neutral point positions in such a way that, in all conceivable load cases, the centre of gravity always lies in front of the neutral point.

5.1.2 Longitudinal Control

In the previous section it was shown that the degree of static stability is given by the gradient dC_m/dC_L of the curve $C_m = f(C_L)$. The equilibrium condition exists when the moment contributions of the individual aircraft components (wing, fuselage, tail, lift) add up to zero ($C_m = 0$). It will now be shown which options the pilot can use to achieve the equilibrium state for every permissible lift coefficient. This ability to control the aircraft and bring about the desired changes of the flight condition is termed **control**. To make this clear, the development of lift against the pitching moment is considered (Fig. 5-7). Assume the aircraft is flying at a lift coefficient $C_L = 0.5$, is in equilibrium ($C_m = 0$), and has a stability of 10 per cent ($dC_m/dC_L = -0.10$, point A in the illustration). This lift coefficient relates to a given wing loading W/S, a certain flight altitude (which is determined by the density ρ) and an airspeed which can be derived from the lift equation as follows:

$$v = \sqrt{\frac{2W/S}{\rho\, C_L}}$$

If a reduction of speed is necessary, e.g. during the landing approach, this can

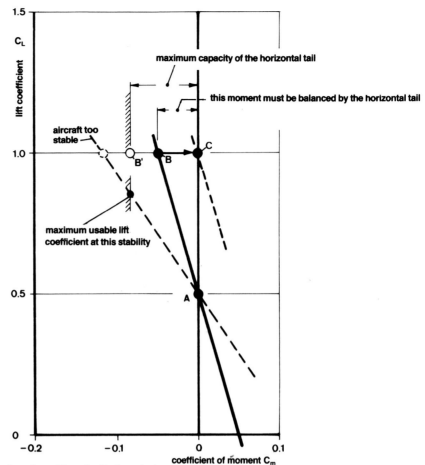

5-7 **Explanation of longitudinal control.**

be effected only by increasing the lift coefficient. A control potential must be available to balance the nose-down moment ($C_m = -0.05$, line B-C in Fig. 5-7). The more stable the aircraft is, i.e. the stronger the curve $C_m = f(C_L)$ is inclined to the left, the greater the elevation forces needed to create equilibrium[23]. The capacity of the horizontal tail therefore represents a limit to the permissible stability of the aircraft.

The moment equation gives information about the possibilities of influencing the moment by means of control measures. If the vertical distance between the wing neutral point and the aircraft's centre of gravity is neglected ($\Delta z_N = 0$), only three influence factors still remain, namely

– the zero lift pitching moment C_{m0}
– the relative neutral point distance $\Delta x_N/\bar{c}$
– the angle-of-attack of the horizontal tail α_H.

The zero lift pitching moment is determined by the camber of the profile and the twist of the wing. It can be influenced by flap deflections at the wing, which cause a local change of the camber. In the case of tailless aircraft, which of course have no horizontal tail, such as the French Mirage III or Mirage 2000 combat aircraft, the equilibrium is brought about mainly[24] by such flap adjustments.

---

[23] The line B-C becomes larger with increasing stability.

[24] Further ways of influencing the moment are by means of spoilers, airbrakes and leading-edge flaps.

The generation of moment equilibrium by influencing the position of the centre of gravity involves a lot of effort and is impractical, but sometimes unavoidable. Thus, for example, in the case of the Concorde, also a tailless aircraft, fuel is pumped for the transonic and supersonic flight phase into the tail tanks, some of which are in the vertical stabilizer. By this means a part of the usable aircraft volume is lost to this ballast fuel.

The stability problem, as a consequence of substantial neutral point or centre of gravity shifts, is one with which the MiG-21 pilots are also confronted. Like every delta wing the MiG-21 wing also suffers from overstability, which increases with rising Mach number.

The reason for this is the movement of the neutral point in a rearward direction, with the result that the lever arm to the centre of gravity becomes longer. At flight numbers which are typical of aerial combat, a considerable part of the horizontal tail capacity must therefore be expended in maintaining the moment equilibrium. As long as the rear tank is filled and acts as ballast, the centre of gravity lies sufficiently far back and the horizontal tail is fully active for aerial combat. However, if this tank has been flown dry, the capacity of the horizontal tail is not enough, at a high Mach number, to eliminate the resulting nose-down moment. High speed flight is no longer feasible under these conditions. A slow and scarcely manoeuvrable aircraft is, however, an easy prey for an opponent. The MiG-21 pilot therefore has to break off an aerial combat before the stabilizing effect of the ballast tank wears off. Indeed the pilots of the F-4, inferior in manoeuvrability but superior in range, took advantage of this during the Vietnam war by often staying at a safe distance until the MiG fighters were compelled to break away.

However, the MiG-21 can scarcely be landed with an empty rear tank either, because, due to deflection of the landing flaps on the wing, a nose-down moment arises which, as a consequence of the strong downwash, cannot be balanced by the tail.

The method mainly used to balance **undesirable** or to generate **desirable** pitching moments is the adjustment of horizontal tail surfaces. This gives rise to a lift force dependent on the angle of attack α_H of the horizontal tail, just as on the wing. This lift force, with the relatively long lever arm, yields the desired moment. The greatest effect can be attained if the entire horizontal tail as **all-moving tail** can be rotated (Fig. 5-8). By means of differential deflection roll can also be controlled by it.

The effectiveness of the conventional horizontal tail is impaired by its position in the downwash of the wing. Also vortex flows, which arise at low angles-of-attack, generate unfavourable flow conditions. However in all cases it must be ensured that the flow first separates on the wing and only then on the horizontal tail. As this property can be influenced by the sweepback of the leading edge, the leading edges of horizontal tails are at least as strongly sweptback as, but usually more strongly sweptback, than that of wing[25].

5.1.3 Design Criteria for Horizontal Tails on Combat Aircraft

The tail size on a conventionally designed aircraft is determined by the following three tasks to be fulfilled by the horizontal tail:

1. Stabilization of the aircraft in the case of a rear centre of gravity position;
2. Trimming in the case of a forward centre of gravity position with extended flaps;
3. Rotating the aircraft during the take-off procedure, centre of gravity in front.

In all cases **undesired** moments must be capable of being trimmed or **desired**

moments generated. Moreover, further criteria must however be considered, such as:-
– stick force per g
– transient response to control
– configurational influences
– power control discrimination
– inertial effects.

These individual points will be discussed below.

In determining the permissible centre of gravity range it is not only the longitudinal moment behaviour of the aircraft which is important, but also the influence of longitudinal stability in **roll** must be investigated. In a fast roll, yaw occurs in addition to roll, which – like the precession of a gyro – creates a pitching moment, leading to changes in the angle-of-attack and in the load factor. This phenomenon is all the more marked, the less the stability ratio dC_m/dC_L is. Here there is a danger of the airframe being overloaded or of flow separation over the wing. Maintaining the intended flight path becomes impossible, and flight comfort for the crew is considerably reduced. At the present time there are still no official design requirements which consider the longitudinal moment behaviour of a combat aircraft in fast roll.

The size of the horizontal tail with forward centre of gravity is above all dictated by the need to rotate the aircraft at take-off or to flare out on landing. The necessary control forces for supersonic manoeuvring flight may be an additional assessment criterion, but take-off and landing performance usually carry greater weight.

To summarize, the following parameters are important for the design of the horizontal tail:

A very important criterion of manoeuvring flight is the stick force input by the pilot on the control stick. This criterion is of importance in pull-out and in turning flight. It is usually expressed as the stick force needed to increase normal acceleration by 1 g.

During pull-out a load factor n arises, which on the one hand is connected with the lift coefficient C_L, and on the other

---

[25] This can be easily seen from the plan-forms, Table 4.1.

5-8 **With an all-moving tail the entire tail surface is adjusted (F-15).**

hand with the angular speed ω (see chapter 9). This load factor may not exceed a certain maximum value for reasons of strength. Therefore an aircraft must not only have good control characteristics in all flight conditions but the pilot must be able to 'feel' the manoeuvring loads imposed on the aircraft.

On the other hand, the stick forces must not be so large that they tire the pilot or cannot be applied. The design criteria provide for minimum stick forces (with an aft centre of gravity position) of between 10 and 15 Newton per g (2-3 lb per g) and for maximum stick forces with a forward centre of gravity position of 35-40 Newton per g (7-8 lb per g).

With small distances between the neutral point and the centre of gravity the stability ratio is so small that even small tail deflections are enough to attain large load factors. This causes dynamic problems which have to be taken into account.

The extension of manoeuvring flaps or airbrakes and the release of external loads (bombs, tanks) are configurational influences which alter the trimmed condition of the aircraft and make it impossible to keep to the intended flight path if uncorrected. For example, one of these is a minimum required dC_m/dC_L for high-speed flight with external stores. The design requirements often provide that

the load factors occurring during weapon release must not exceed $+1$ g nor be under -0.5 g.

The corrective deflections of the horizontal tail needed to maintain the flight path must not cause any greater load factors than ± 0.1 g for combat aircraft. This means that, at the surface power unit, which moves the control surface, every arbitrary position must be adjustable with great accuracy. From this corresponding requirements are derived for power control discrimination. Therefore it is necessary, for example, to attain every power unit output position with an accuracy of 1/1000 of the complete range of movement.

In determining the permissible centre-of-gravity range, not only the longitudinal behaviour of the aircraft must be considered, but also the repercussions which rolling motions have on the longitudinal characteristics. At high roll rates, due to gyroscopic effects, the aircraft also is yawing, which in turn creates pitching moments with changes in angle-of-attack and load factor. This is especially the case for small values of the stability derivative dC_m/dC_L, which can lead to overstressing the airframe and/or wing flow break-down.

In summing up, the following parameters must be observed in sizing the horizontal tailplane:

1. **Centre of gravity forward position**
   - zero lift pitching moment C_{m0} in the take-off and landing configuration (i.e. flaps, landing gear, airbrake extended)
   - neutral point of the wing/body combination for the take-off and landing configuration (this must always lie **behind** the centre of gravity, to fulfil the condition $dC_m/dC_L < 0$)

5.2 **Lateral Stability**

The static longitudinal stability is determined by the behaviour of the aircraft in **symmetrical** flow. In this case the lateral axis remains in a horizontal position, and the centre of gravity of the aircraft moves in a vertical plane. The **longitudinal motion** thereby appears as a rotation about the lateral axis; it can be described both qualitatively as well as quantitatively with the aid of the angle-of-attack and the lift coefficient.

In contrast, the lateral motion is characterized by **unsymmetrical** flow. It includes roll, yaw and sideslip, i.e. rotations about the longitudinal and normal axes; angle-of-attack, airspeed and trajectory angle remain unchanged.

5.2.1 **Directional Stability**

The unsymmetrical flow state is characterized by the fact that the relative

- maximum lift $C_{L_{Hmax}}$ of the horizontal tail (by this means the greatest moment to be generated is determined).

2. **Centre of gravity aft position**
   - neutral point of the wing/body combination
   - lift curve slope $dC_L/d\alpha_H$ of the horizontal tail
   - downwash gradient
   - influence of Mach number on the neutral point, lift curve slope of the horizontal tail and downwash
   - aeroelastic influences on the neutral point and lift curve slope of wing and horizontal tail
   - rigidity of the fuselage
   - influences of the inlet flow and the exhaust jet on longitudinal stability.

Determining the forward position of the centre of gravity is relatively uncomplicated. On the other hand, determining the centre of gravity aft position can be difficult, because numerous influencing parameters have to be considered.

airflow forms an angle with the longitudinal axis of the aircraft which is called **sideslip angle** (Fig. 5-9). As a consequence of the unsymmetrical flow additional aerodynamic forces, in addition to the characteristic magnitudes of longitudinal motion (lift, drag, pitching moment), arise at the vertical and sloping surfaces of the airframe. These **side forces** are applied mainly on the vertical tail and the fuselage causing moments to develop about the centre of gravity.

Directional stability describes the behaviour of the aircraft during a disturbance of the static equilibrium state with reference to the normal axis. If the aircraft is in sideslip due to such a disturbance (as in a lateral gust), then directional stability generates a yawing moment which tries to turn the longitudinal axis of the aircraft back in the direction of flow (see Fig. 5-9). The directional stability can be determined, like longitudinal stability, by adding up the

stability contributions of the aircraft components. Fuselage, vertical tail and wing generate yawing moments in sideslip which are dependent on sideslip angle.

The cause of the yawing moment N is a side force Y, which acts at a certain distance from the centre of gravity. As is usual in aerodynamics, it is not the dimensioned yawing moment but the dimensionless **yawing moment coefficient** C_n which is used. This results from the division of yawing moment N, obtained by measurement (or calculation), by a reference moment. For this purpose the product of dynamic pressure q, wing area S and half-span s is chosen. Thus the yawing moment coefficient takes the following form:

$$C_n = \frac{N}{qSs}$$

The magnitude of the directional stability can be determined by plotting the yawing moment coefficient C_N, determined in the wind tunnel, against sideslip angle (Fig. 5-10). In the wind tunnel experiment the procedure is carried out in such a way that, at a set angle-of-attack (about $\alpha = 10°$), the intended sideslip angle range is gone through point-by-point or continuously. The side force Y, occurring at every sideslip angle, is measured. From this the yawing moment coefficient C_n can be formed. The sideslip angle range may lie, for example, between $\beta = -15°$ and $\beta = 15°$. As a result the development of the yawing moment coefficient C_n as a function of the sideslip angle β is obtained for **one** particular angle-of-attack and **one** particular flow speed (see Fig. 5-10).

The magnitude of the directional stability results from the tangent at the point $\beta = 0$ on the resulting curve. Should the curve $C_n = f(\beta)$ already demonstrate non-linear behaviour in the low sideslip angle range, the tangents can in addition be determined at another sideslip angle, e.g. $\beta = 5°$. The stability parameter obtained in this way is called the **yawing moment due to sideslip** $C_{n\beta}$[26], or also

---
[26] pronounced C-N-Beta

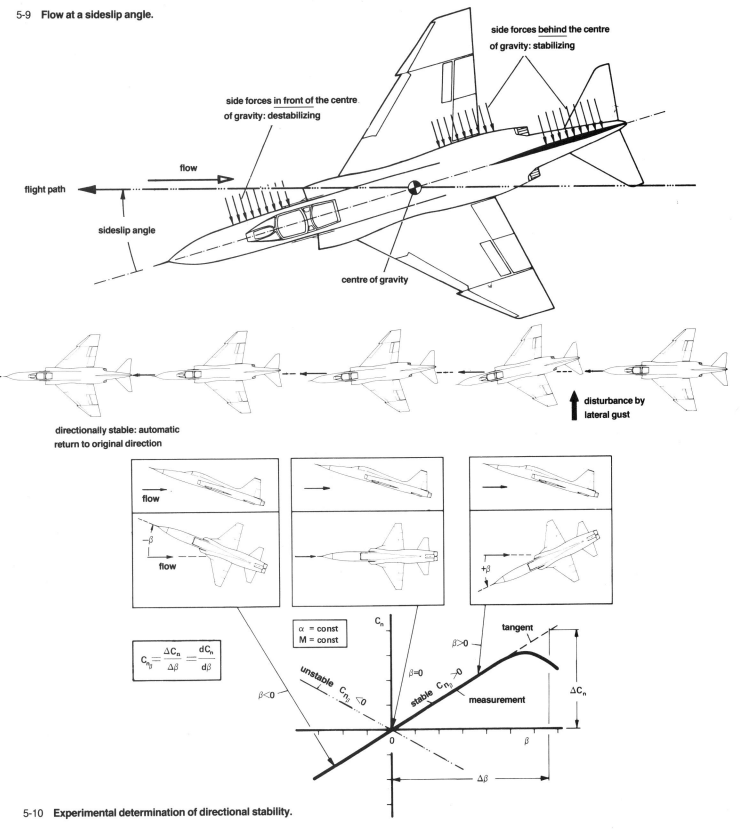

5-9 Flow at a sideslip angle.

side forces behind the centre
of gravity: stabilizing

side forces in front of the centre
of gravity: destabilizing

flow

flight path

sideslip angle

centre of gravity

disturbance by
lateral gust

directionally stable: automatic
return to original direction

flow

−β

flow

+β

$$C_{n_\beta} = \frac{\Delta C_n}{\Delta \beta} = \frac{dC_n}{d\beta}$$

α = const
M = const

C_n

tangent

$\beta > 0$

$\beta = 0$

unstable $C_{n_\beta} < 0$

$\beta < 0$

stable $C_{n_\beta} > 0$

measurement

ΔC_n

0

β

$\Delta \beta$

5-10 Experimental determination of directional stability.

the static directional stability. According to aeronautical practice, the sideslip angle is positive when the airflow, seen in the flight direction, comes from the right and the clockwise yawing moment also counts positively, stability means that $C_{n\beta} > 0$ must be true. This condition can be fulfilled at low angles-of-attack and sideslip angles by any aircraft. It is also called weathercock stability. The directional problem becomes difficult only at the high angles-of-attack in typical combat manoeuvres. This will be dealt with further in detail below.

5.2.1.1 INFLUENCES OF STABILITY

INFLUENCE OF THE VERTICAL TAIL

The **vertical tail** provides, for every aircraft, the largest contribution to directional stability. That is as long as the angle-of-attack is not too large. If the aircraft slips, the sideslip angle acts as an angle-of-attack at the vertical stabilizer. This causes lift and is called a side force. The neutral point of the vertical stabilizer is assumed as the point of application of the side force. Between the point of application of the side force and the aircraft's centre of gravity lies the lever arm l_v (Fig. 5-11, left). Side force Y and lever arm l_v form the yawing moment of the vertical tail $N_s = Y \cdot l_v$, from which the moment results:

$$C_n = \frac{Y \cdot l_v}{qS_v}$$

The side force Y, analogous to the lift force (see Chapter 4), can be expressed by means of side force coefficient, dynamic pressure and tail surface (index V for vertical tail):

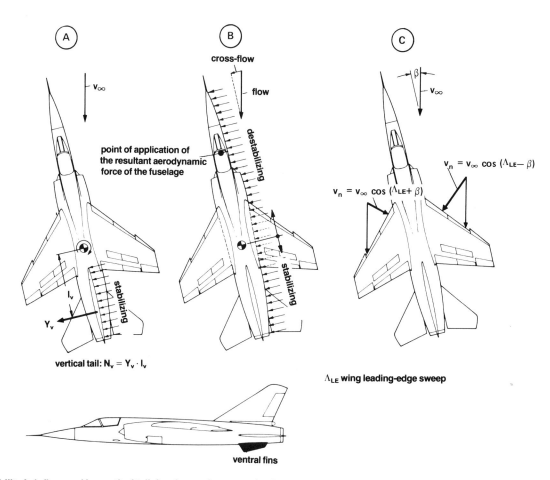

5-11 **Directional stability is influenced by vertical tail, fuselage, wing sweepback and ventral fins.**

5-12 **Single and twin vertical tails (Tornado, F-14).**

side force $Y = C_y \cdot qS_v$

lift $L = C_L qS$ (for purposes of comparison)

In the linear range the side force co-efficient can be expressed in terms of lift curve slope and flow angle, again analogous to the conditions at the wing:

$$C_Y = \frac{dC_Y}{d\beta} \cdot \beta = C_{Y\beta} \cdot \beta$$

Thus the yawing moment coefficient appears in a form which allows us to make statements about the tail design:

$$C_n = C_{Y\beta} \cdot \beta \cdot \frac{S_v l_v}{S \cdot s} = C_{Y\beta} \cdot \beta \cdot V_V$$

V_V = volume of the vertical tail (see chapter 4).

According to this it is possible to influence the yawing moment behaviour by altering the tail volume, e.g. by increasing the tail area S_v and/or the lever arm l_v. The lift slope $C_{Y\beta}$ can be influenced by altering the plan-form (it was shown in Chapter 4 that aspect ratio and sweepback are the essential parameters of to influence the lift curve slope).

The fulfilment of sufficient directional stability characteristics by increasing the tail volume cannot be carried out indefinitely in the case of single tails, as very large surfaces easily result. These cause structural difficulties and then the oscillation behaviour is problematic. The Tornado, for example, has a very large vertical stabilizer (Fig. 5-12). For combat aircraft recourse is sometimes made to twin tails which permit smaller individual surfaces and are more effective in unsymmetrical flow and at high angles-of-attack (see Fig. 5-12).

INFLUENCE OF THE FUSELAGE

At subsonic speeds the point of application of the resultant aerodynamic forces lies at about 25% of the fuselage length. As the centre of gravity of the aircraft lies much further back, the fuselage has a destabilizing effect, i.e. a positive sideslip angle generates a negative yawing moment (see Fig. 5-11, middle). As a consequence of flow separations at the fuselage nose, the destabil-izing effect becomes less at large sideslip angles.

The $C_{n\beta}$ of the fuselage is practically beyond mathematical calculation and must be determined experimentally in the wind tunnel. The lateral motion of the fuselage without tail and wing also has to be investigated.

INFLUENCE OF THE WING

The contribution of the wing to directional stability is slight. Straight wings, such as the A-10 wing, have a slight de-stabilizing effect, because the leeward wing-half, shielded by the fuselage, has a lower drag than the 'upwind' wing-half. This causes a clockwise-rotating (positive) moment at positive sideslip angles.

With wings having a sweptback leading edge, which are found almost exclusively with combat aircraft, the positive contribution may be larger, but also relatively small. The component of the flow vertical to the leading edge, which is critical for the wing lift (normal component V_n) is, because of its cosine effect at the windward wing, larger than at the leeward wing (see Fig. 5-11, right). Vari-

5-13 **In many cases ventral fins provide better directional stability over the high angle-of-attack range than an enlargement of the vertical tail surface (General Dynamics F-16).**

ations of the normal components generate different lift forces on the right and left wing and therefore also different induced-drag values. The greater drag of the leading wing therefore generates a restoring (stabilizing) moment.

5.2.1.2 VENTRAL AND DORSAL FINS

Inadequate directional stability, particularly at high angles-of-attack, can be improved considerably by attaching ventral and dorsal fins. **Ventral fins,** in particular, are frequently used with combat aircraft (Fig. 5-13). This is, in many cases, more effective than enlarging the vertical tail surface.

The advantages of ventral fins result from their favourable interference behaviour with the fuselage flow at high angles-of-attack. In this case the directional property of the fuselage causes a favourable flow and a noticeable stability gain. As a result of their small span, ventral fins are relatively rigid and can therefore be of minimum thickness.

In the lower angle-of-attack range the effectiveness of ventral fins is limited, because they lie in the wake of externally carried loads under the fuselage and are in the relatively thick fuselage boundary layer. **Dorsal fins** turn out to be more effective here. A dorsal fin arranged in front of the vertical tail acts as a strake under the influence of the sideslip angle and moves the maximum lift point of the vertical tail to a higher sideslip angle. In the higher angle-of-attack range, however, dorsal fins lie in the separated fuselage flow and are therefore less effective.

5.2.1.3 STABILITY BEHAVIOUR AT HIGH ANGLES-OF-ATTACK

With increasing angle-of-attack, the flow is no longer able to follow the fuselage contour. Vortices separate from the fuselage and the cockpit canopy and these get into the area of the tail flow.

Moreover, at the wing the powerful leading-edge vortices move with increasing angle-of-attack in the direction of the fuselage and begin to separate from the wing itself. They thus get dangerously near to the vertical tail, whose effectiveness is severely restricted or is completely lost. This state can occur without a cross-flow. Conditions are even more unfavourable when the flow has a lateral component, because then the vertical tail is involved and is influenced by the separating vortex flow. The vortex of the windward wing is responsible for this process: it is squeezed by the lateral flow in the direction of the tail, while the leeward vortex can develop relatively freely (Fig. 5-14).

The different vortex lift on the two wing halves causes a rolling moment which the pilot can no longer control by conventional means (aileron, differential elevator). The aircraft rolls over and goes into a spin (see 5.2.2).

In order to determine the stability behaviour at high angles-of-attack, a series of sideslip angles is run through in the wind tunnel, the angle-of-attack being changed from series to series, but is kept constant within a series. The coefficients of the measured yawing moments are plotted against the sideslip angle (Fig. 5-15). This shows that the slope of the curves $C_n = f(\beta)$ decreases with increasing angle-of-attack and even becomes negative. The zero transition of the $C_{n\beta}$ development marks the limit at which directional stability collapses and controllable flight is no longer possible. The aim of the designer must be to shift this limit, if at all possible, in such a way that it does not occur at an angle-of-attack smaller than that for maximum lift, so that the angle-of-attack potential of the wing can be fully exploited.

5-14　Photographic study, using paint, of flow development at high angle-of-attack and in cross-flow on a combat aircraft configuration. The windward vortex (left) is compressed in the direction of the vertical tail by the cross-flow, while the leeward vortex (right) can develop freely (delta-strake concept by VFW (now MBB) in the wind tunnel at Bremen).

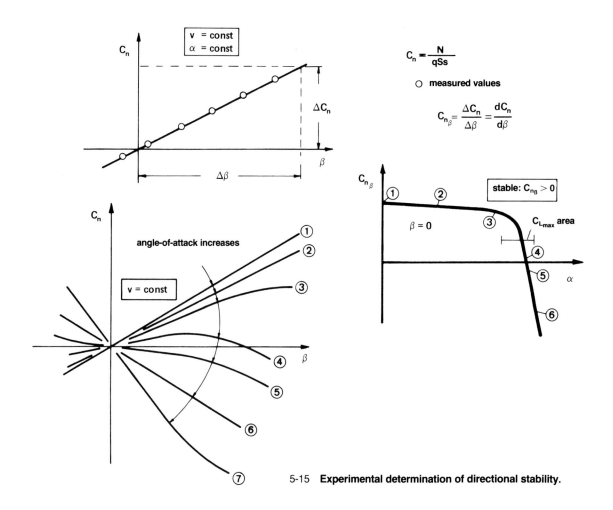

$$C_n = \frac{N}{qSs}$$

o **measured values**

$$C_{n_\beta} = \frac{\Delta C_n}{\Delta \beta} = \frac{dC_n}{d\beta}$$

5-15 **Experimental determination of directional stability.**

5.2.2 Roll

Rotations about the longitudinal axis are called **roll.** This form of motion is of great importance for combat aircraft in combat manoeuvres, for target acquisition as well as in evasive manoeuvres. Inadequate roll performance restricts combat effectiveness; because of inertia coupling, oversensitive response to roll control commands causes undesirable rotations about the normal and lateral axes. It is the task of the aircraft designer to provide a roll performance between these two extremes which matches the aircraft's role. The maximum attainable roll angle per second is given as a measure of this. According to the aircraft type the following standard values are aimed for:

fighter bomber	140°/s
(strike against ground targets)	
interceptor	60°/s
(equipped with missiles)	
air superiority fighter	90°/s

Attaining these roll performances is no problem at high speeds. In contrast, meeting roll requirements at low speeds is difficult, because the dynamic pressure may be too low or the control surface too small. If the roll control surfaces (aileron, differential elevator) lie in separated flow, which occurs at high angles-of-attack, then roll cannot be controlled.

5.2.2.1 THE WING IN ROLL

During rotation about the longitudinal axis, a vertical velocity component varying with span occurs at the wing. This, together with the speed of flow, results in an unsymmetrical angle-of-attack distribution (Fig. 5-16). On the downward-moving half, this rotation appears as an increase in the angle-of-attack, where it appears as a reduction at the upward-moving wing half. By this means the downward-moving wing receives a greater lift, from which arises a moment about the longitudinal axis. This tries to impede the rotation and is called the **roll damping** moment.

As lift, according to definition, acts

112

perpendicular to and drag **parallel** to the undisturbed flow, a smaller resultant aerodynamic force arises at the upward-moving wing half, whereas a larger one arises on the downward-moving wing half (see Fig. 5-16). The differences in their direction of action generate a yawing moment. This tries to rotate the downward-moving wing half forwards and is called the **yawing moment due to roll.**

The wing influences the yawing behaviour of the aircraft only to a small degree. On the other hand, it has a large influence on the roll moment.

INFLUENCE OF DIHEDRAL AND ANHEDRAL

Wing design affords various ways of influencing roll behaviour by means of constructive steps. Among these are dihedral (and anhedral), sweepback, aspect ratio and taper. The wing position relative to the fuselage is also of importance.

Dihedral is the term for the angle of each wing half in relation to the x-y plane. It is particularly important under the influence of lateral airflow (sideslip).

The lateral airflow component v_y can be resolved on each wing half into a component perpendicular to the wing surface (normal component v_n), and into a component parallel to the wing surface (tangential component v_t, Fig. 5-17). With dihedral (F-4), the normal component causes on the windward, i.e. leading

wing half, an angle-of-attack increase, whereas it causes an angle-of-attack reduction on the leeward side. Connected with this is a corresponding lift increase ($+\Delta L$) or lift loss ($-\Delta L$) respectively. This asymmetry in lift generates a rolling moment which is called **rolling moment due to sideslip** (dihedral effect). At a positive sideslip angle (airflow coming from the right), dihedral leads to an anti-clockwise (negative) rolling moment due to sideslip (example: F-4, see Fig. 5-17, left), while, at a negative dihedral (anhedral) under the same conditions, a clockwise (positive) rolling moment due to sideslip occurs (example: F-104, see Fig. 5-17, right). From the rotation of the wing a decreasing speed ($-v_n$) results on the downwards-moving wing half and on the upward-moving wing an increasing speed ($+v_n$).

The effective flow, which determines

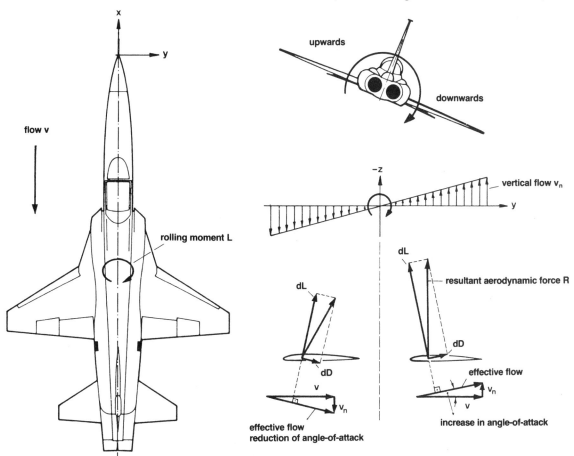

5-16   **The wing in roll.**

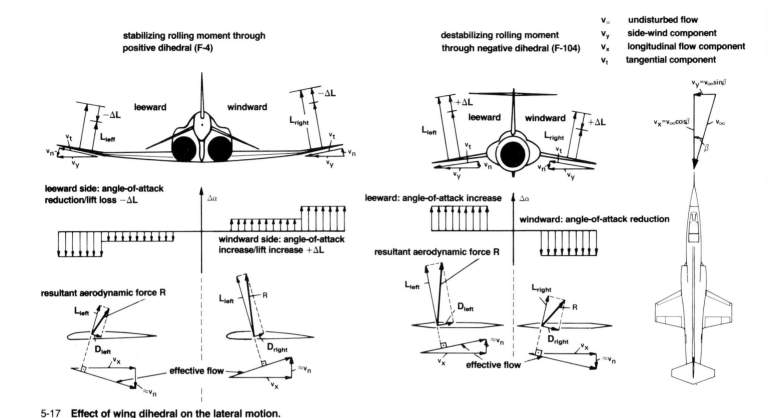

stabilizing rolling moment through positive dihedral (F-4)

destabilizing rolling moment through negative dihedral (F-104)

v_∞ undisturbed flow
v_y side-wind component
v_x longitudinal flow component
v_t tangential component

5-17   **Effect of wing dihedral on the lateral motion.**

the aerodynamic effect arises from the influence of the component v_x (see velocity triangle, upper right, Fig. 5-17).

The different effective angles-of-attack on the right and left wing halves produce corresponding different values for the resultant aerodynamic force, both according to magnitude and to direction. This is the reason for the formation of a yawing moment in addition to the rolling moment. Both moments have the same sense of rotation in the linear angle-of-attack range, i.e. in the case of an anti-clockwise rolling moment the yawing moment also rotates anti-clockwise and vice versa.

The wing is now termed **stable in roll** (stable dihedral effect), if at a positive sideslip angle (flow from the right) a negative (anti-clockwise moment) is caused. Hence a wing with positive dihedral is always stable in roll (F-4), and a wing with negative dihedral is **unstable in roll** (F-104).

The concept 'stability in roll' is not as readily understood as the concepts directional stability and longitudinal stability. However, it can be imagined as follows: in the case of a stable in roll aircraft the pilot, to control a sideslip angle, must make control actions having the same direction for yaw and roll, which corresponds to one's natural senses.

The choice of wing dihedral takes place exclusively in the light of the most favourable rolling moment due to sideslip coefficient for the complete aircraft in relation to the mechanics of flight. In this respect both positive and negative dihedrals may be applied. The F-104 has a negative dihedral, while the F-4 exhibits positive dihedral.

In many cases, particularly with the modern lightweight fighters, dihedral is completely dispensed with. Adequate roll stability can also be attained by other means, for example, by sweepback.

INFLUENCE OF SWEEPBACK

Aerodynamic theory shows that the lift of a sweptback wing is determined by the component of flow velocity **perpendicular** to the wing leading edge (normal component). In the case of a sweptback sideslipping wing, the normal component on the windward wing half is greater than that on the leeward wing-half (see Fig. 5-11, right). This causes different lift forces and a rolling moment which, at a positive sideslip angle (side flow from the right) is anti-clockwise. The leading-edge sweepback thus has the same aerodynamic effect as the dihedral. This explains why, with many combat aircraft dihedral can be dispensed with.

5.2.2.2 INFLUENCES OF CONFIGURATION ON THE ROLLING MOMENT DUE TO SIDESLIP (DIHEDRAL EFFECT)

The most important design-determined influences on the rolling moment due to sideslip come from the vertical tail and wing position.

INFLUENCE OF THE VERTICAL TAIL

In the case of a sideslipping aircraft the lateral flow component acts on the vertical tail like an angle-of-attack. As a result a laterally directed lift force arises, which is called **side force.** The side force, which is distributed on the surface, can be imagined as a concentrated individual force which acts at the neutral point of the tail surface. The neutral point normally lies above the aircraft's centre of gravity, so that the side force generates a negative (anti-clockwise) rolling moment (Fig. 5-18). Thus the vertical tail also supplies a stabilizing contribution to the rolling moment due to sideslip.

If the neutral point of the vertical tail is at a great distance from the roll axis, this contribution may be considerable. In the case of the relatively slightly sweptback wing leading edges of the F-104 and F-5 combat aircraft, the rolling moment generated by the vertical tail even provides the principal share of the aircraft's rolling moment due to sideslip. This is particularly marked in the case of the Starfighter (F-104), where the stabilizing rolling moment is considerably increased by the end-plate effect[27] of the T-tail. In fact, the contribution of the vertical tail is so large that the roll stability must be reduced by the negative dihedral (anhedral) of the wing (see Fig. 5-17 and 5-8). This step by itself is not enough, however, so that a ventral fin was additionally attached. Its side force acts below the aircraft's centre of gravity and thus also generates a de-stabilizing rolling moment.

INFLUENCE OF A HIGH WING POSITION

The interferences[28] between wing and fuselage have a decisive influence on the rolling moment due to sideslip in un-symmetrical flow. In sideslip the lateral flow component causes a flow about the fuselage which is more or less vertically directed upwards or downwards in the area of the wing root (Fig. 5-19). Through superposition with the main flow the angle-of-attack of the wing is thereby locally increased or reduced.

If the wing is in the high position (e.g. F-15), the angle-of-attack is increased on the windward side, whereas on the leeward side it is reduced (see Fig. 5-19, left). This results in a negative rolling moment at a positive sideslip angle, and consequently makes a stabilizing contribution to the rolling moment arising from a sideslip.

---

[27] An end plate prevents the pressure equalization between the pressure side and suction side at the tip of a wing or other surface, due to which the lift curve slope develops more steeply.

[28] Interference = reciprocal influence between different aircraft components.

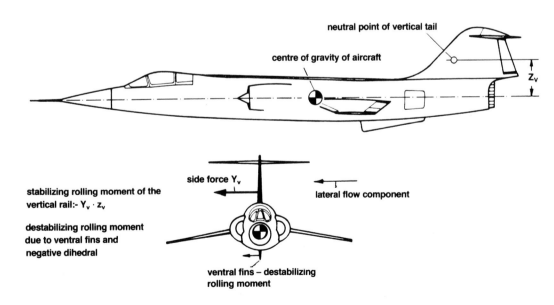

neutral point of vertical tail

centre of gravity of aircraft

z_v

side force Y_v

lateral flow component

stabilizing rolling moment of the vertical rail:- $Y_v \cdot z_v$

destabilizing rolling moment due to ventral fins and negative dihedral

ventral fins – destabilizing rolling moment

5-18 **In non-symmetric flow the aerodynamic force generates a rolling moment at the vertical tail around the centre of gravity.**

115

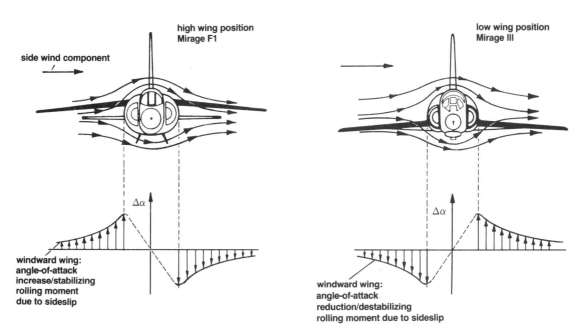

high wing position
Mirage F1

side wind component

low wing position
Mirage III

$\Delta\alpha$

$\Delta\alpha$

windward wing:
angle-of-attack
increase/stabilizing
rolling moment
due to sideslip

windward wing:
angle-of-attack
reduction/destabilizing
rolling moment due to sideslip

5-19 **Influence of wing position on rolling moment due to sideslip.**

The conditions are opposite for a low wing position. These provide a destabilizing contribution to the rolling moment due to sideslip. This explains why low wings often have a positive dihedral, while this is unnecessary for high wing positions. With large transport aircraft, such as the C-5 and C-141, the stabilizing influence of the high wing position may be so great that it has to be reduced by means of a negative dihedral (anhedral) of the wing. In this respect the large masses of the engines, which are suspended far away from the centre of gravity, play a part.

When determining the influences of a high wing position roll behaviour is not the only criterion. In particular at high angles-of-attack, during which control is essential for combat aircraft, the directional effect of the fuselage side walls has a positive influence on the vortex flow over the wing. This is one of the reasons why the mid-wing position was chosen for the F-16 and F-18 lightweight fighters. The strakes, alongside the fuselage, and the vortex flows they cause, practically exclude a high wing position.

5.2.2.3 DETERMINATION OF THE ROLLING MOMENT DUE TO SIDESLIP

The rolling moment due to sideslip of a configuration is usually determined in the wind tunnel. The procedure is similar to that for the determination of yawing moment behaviour (see chapter 5.2).

The rolling moment L measured on the wind tunnel balance is, analogous to the yawing moment, made dimensionless with dynamic pressure q, wing area S and half-span s. In this way the rolling moment coefficient C_l is obtained:

$$C_l = \frac{L}{qSs}$$

At a constant angle-of-attack, a sequence of points results, which in the low angle-of-attack range can be connected together to form a linear curve (Fig. 5-20). The slope of the curve, i.e. the angle of its tangent with the β-axis, provides information on the variation of the rolling moment as a function of sideslip angle. This magnitude is called the **rolling moment due to sideslip or dihedral effect** $C_{l\beta}$[29], which has a negative sign in a **stable** configuration.

With increasing angle-of-attack the curve reaches larger negative slopes, until finally an angle-of-attack is reached at which the advancing wing has exceeded its maximum lift. As the leeward wing is still subject to a flow with an angle lying below the angle-of-attack for maximum lift, its lift is greater. As a result a clockwise (positive) rolling moment arises (Fig. 5-20, left, point 6). The tangent has a positive slope, and the rolling moment due to sideslip has a destabilizing effect.

The dihedral effect $C_{l\beta}$ determined for every curve $C_l = f(\beta)$ produces a $C_{l\beta}$-curve form against the angle-of-attack (see Fig. 5-20 right). The point of intersection of this curve with the α-axis limits the maximum usable angle-of-attack. Configurational influences, such as flaps and external stores, displace this point to smaller angles-of-attack and thus restrict the usable angle-of-attack range.

---

[29] pronounced: C-L-Beta

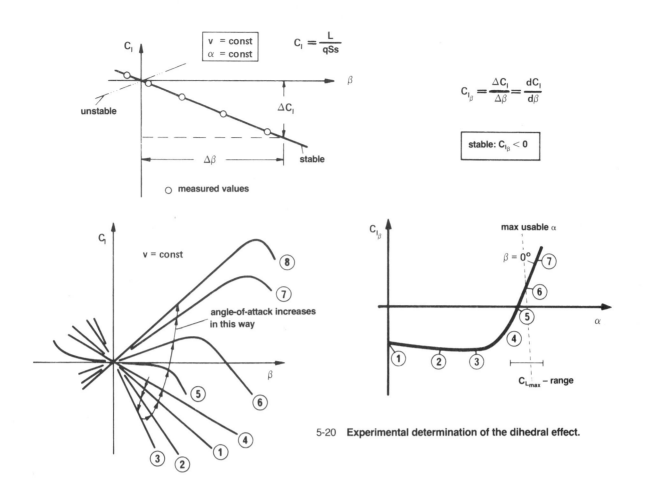

$$C_l = \frac{L}{qSs}$$

$$C_{l_\beta} = \frac{\Delta C_l}{\Delta \beta} = \frac{dC_l}{d\beta}$$

stable: $C_{l_\beta} < 0$

○ measured values

5-20 **Experimental determination of the dihedral effect.**

3.5 **Roll Control**

5.3.1 **Controlling the Roll**

The bank angle (angle of rotation about the longitudinal axis) of an aircraft is traditionally controlled with the aid of the **ailerons.** Aileron deflection causes a local lift change, which acts on one wing half as lift increase, on the other wing half as lift reduction, from which a rolling moment results. At the same time a destabilizing yawing moment arises.

At high angles-of-attack the ailerons lie in an increasingly tangential flow, or are located in fully separated flow. This is induced by the separating leading-edge vortex. In every case they are more or less inefficient. Many modern combat aircraft are therefore equipped with a differential tail (taileron) which controls the roll at high angles-of-attack (see Fig. 5-8).

5.3.2 **Criteria for the Assessment of Roll Control**

ROLL RATES IN AERIAL COMBAT MANOEUVRES

Insufficient roll performance has an adverse effect on the combat capability of an aircraft. The approximate values of rates of roll initiated by the control surfaces were indicated in Chapter 5.2.2.

NON-SYMMETRICALLY ARRANGED EXTERNAL STORES

The non-symmetrical release of external stores or one-sided deceleration effects during symmetrical release cause additional rolling and yawing moments. With **underwing stores** the influence of the rolling moment predominates, while with **fuselage-mounted** external stores (such as missiles) the increase of yawing moment predominates. These additional moments not only have to be trimmable, but moreover there must be a margin of manoeuvrability for evasive manoeuvres, e.g. when escaping from hostile anti-aircraft defences.

LANDING REQUIREMENTS

The certification requirements specify that, with a cross-wind up to a particular strength, a safe landing must be possible. The fulfilment of these requirements is less critical during the approach than during the landing itself. As a consequence of the high lift coefficient during landing, a powerful rolling moment due to sideslip arises on strongly sweptback wings which must be controllable. Often an approach procedure is chosen, in which the longitudinal axis is at an angle to the centre line of the runway. On touchdown this angle must be reduced to zero by aligning the aircraft. To make matters more complicated, the dynamic pressure is small because of the low airspeed. These problems give rise to the requirement for adequate low speed control.

Landing with a side wind can be carried out according to two procedures:

1. **Landing with bank angle**

The aircraft flies at a roll angle, but with the longitudinal axis aligned with the runway.

2. **Landing with sideslip angle**

The wings are level, but the longitudinal axis is at an angle to the centre line of the runway. This procedure requires the greater roll control power.

The USAF's design requirements for this are laid down in MIL-F-8785B standard. According to this it must be possible to keep the wings horizontal at a particular cross-wind strength; a maximum of 80 per cent of the available roll control potential may be allocated to this.

In the design requirements a touchdown speed datum is established which lies about 15% above the stalling speed v_s ($v_{land} = 1.15 \, v_s$). As touchdown takes place at a high angle-of-attack, roll control effectiveness must not decline too strongly with increasing angles-of-attack. As a rule of thumb one can say that it must be possible, with a reduction of landing speed by 10 per cent (from 1.15 v_s to 1.05 v_s), to keep the wings horizontal with 100 per cent of the roll control potential (as opposed to 80 per cent at 1.15 v_s).

SPIN BEHAVIOUR

The roll control surfaces are also employed to terminate a spin. If the generation of a particular combination of rate of roll and positive pitch angle rate with the aid of the roll control surfaces during spin is successful, a yawing moment arises due to the coupled motions which counteracts and stops the spin.

5.4 Directional Control

5.4.1 Design Criteria for the Fin

It is the task of the fin
- to remove the destabilizing influence of the fuselage nose,
- to eliminate the sideslip angle arising as a result of a disturbance within a particular time, and
- to remove yawing moments occurring as a result of aileron deflection, weapon release or inertial coupling.

The design of the vertical tail is influenced
- by Dutch roll behaviour,
- by behaviour at high roll rates, and
- by behaviour during phugoid oscillations.

DUTCH ROLL BEHAVIOUR

The lift difference at the wing halves of a sweptback wing causes the formation of a type of oscillation in which roll and yaw occur simultaneously. This phenomenon, known as **Dutch roll,** is by nature unstable and develops with increasing amplitude, if measures are not planned to damp it. If the aircraft is brought into a sideslipping motion by a lateral gust or excessive aileron operation, then a roll arises from this, due to the aerodynamic effect of the sweepback, which is coupled with yaw. The stabilizing influence of the fin in particular tries to damp this motion, after which roll and yaw start in the opposite direction. If the damping properties are insufficient, then the oscillations build up, with high acceleration forces arising. The consequence is a considerable deterioration of flight properties. A critical flight condition may even arise.

The requirements for adequate oscillation damping in relation to the Dutch roll frequency are also included in the USAF specification MIL-F-8785B (this standard is largely observed by the aircraft industry). According to this, stronger damping is required for manoeuvring flight than for slow flight. The fin can be designed in such a way that the Dutch roll requirements are fulfilled. However, the situation may easily arise where the aircraft's response to control inputs leads to undesirable flight properties. From this it becomes clear that the fulfilment of **one** requirement must not lead to a situation where **other** requirements cannot be fulfilled.

BEHAVIOUR AT HIGH ROLL SPEEDS

Even when the roll oscillations develop in a slightly damped manner, if directional stability is insufficient considerable yaw amplitudes may occur which are manifested in the following forms of motion:

1. Persistence of roll

In MIL-F-8785B the limits are set forth in which the roll oscillation behaviour can be described as good or acceptable. This criterion agrees well with subjective descriptions given by pilots.

2. High lateral accelerations

Their effect may be greater in the cockpit than at the aircraft's centre of gravity. The cause of this is the side forces which arise as a result of operation of the roll control surfaces (aileron, differential elevator, spoiler) in symmetrical flow.

3. Autorotation

By this is meant the tendency of an initiated roll to be preserved, even if the roll control surfaces are not deflected. This behaviour is dependent on the size of the yawing moment due to sideslip $C_{n\beta}$, which must not drop below a particular limit.

Under normal combat conditions the occurrence of autorotation is inadmissible. The only exceptions are extreme manoeuvres executed at low speed at high altitude. However, a way must exist of stopping this condition by control inputs.

The roll behaviour is investigated over the complete operational range of the aircraft (altitude/Mach number), in order to determine possible limits of restricted roll control; as a result alterations to the fin may be necessary.

PHUGOIDS

With some aircraft, particularly those with low-aspect/ratio wings and large leading-edge sweepback, an oscillation occurs, if directional stability is inadequate, in which a fading roll and a rotary oscillation overlap to form a slightly damped oscillation with a long period (lateral phugoid). In this case the determining parameter is the yawing moment due to sideslip $C_{n\beta}$. However, a critical $C_{n\beta}$ value is attained in combat aircraft because of deterioration of roll behaviour rather than because of phugoids.

5.4.2 Possibilities of Assessing Directional Stability

An exact assessment of the yawing moment due to sideslip $C_{n\beta}$, in particular its dependence on Mach number, angle-of-attack and dynamic pressure, is difficult or impossible for the following reasons:

1. The destabilizing contribution of the fuselage nose may at best be estimated with an accuracy of ±10%. This is because the aerodynamic processes of the complicated fuselage shape, particularly at high angles-of-attack and sideslip angles, are difficult or impossible to calculate.
2. The influence of fuselage-mounted external stores is considerable during a sideslip. Since theoretical procedures are also insufficient here, the effect of this influence is carried out by means of wind tunnel experiments or during flight testing.
3. Vortices which come from the fuselage and from the wing leading edge and strike the vertical tail have yet to be reliably determined. This applies both to single and twin-tail configurations.
4. Aeroelastic influences may be considerable. Due to the twisting of the fin under load, 25% of its effectiveness may be lost. These influences can rarely be determined at the project stage.

5.3.3 Geometry of the Fin

After the degree of directional stability necessary for different flight conditions has been defined and the destabilizing influences of fuselage nose and external stores estimated, the size of the fin can be established, taking into account the stability requirements.

The following aspects are of relevance here:
1. Sufficient directional stability in the high angle-of-attack range requires a large fin. Due to aeroelastic considerations, however, the fin cannot be designed as large as one likes.
2. In many cases a ventral fin is more effective than enlarging the main fin. The reasons for this have to do with the favourable interference behaviour between ventral fins and fuselage; as well as their greater rigidity and the destabilizing influence in roll.

Establishing the fin geometry is, in the end, a compromise between conflicting requirements. How little these influences can be determined beforehand can be seen from the fact that alterations to the fin are necessary in the case of almost every combat aircraft during flight testing.

5.4.4 Design Criteria for the Rudder

The rudder must, under normal flight conditions, be able to eliminate a sideslip angle. What is crucial, however, for the design is that a particular sideslip angle can be generated. Determining factors for this are:-
- cross-wind landing
- spin recovery
- asymmetric stores
- turn co-ordination
- transonic characteristics, and
- maximum rudder deflection angle.

5.4.5 Directional Control on the Ground

Adequate control of an aircraft on the ground is particularly important when a relatively high speed is present after touchdown with a cross-wind. Therefore the following points must also be taken into account.

1. The control of the aircraft (in particular of the nosewheel) must take place in such a way that the aircraft does not react oversensitively at high speed.

2. Response behaviour and resolving power of the servo-control of the nose-wheel must not cause the aircraft to lurch following pilot control inputs (pilot-induced steering oscillations).

3. The controllable yawing moments must be determined for various cross-winds in taxiing experiments in relation to ground speed.

Therefore, the following must be taken into account:

- runway state: dry, wet, pools
- brake parachute or thrust reversal; with and without
- wheel brakes: full braking, normal braking
- nosewheel steering: functioning, inoperative
- longitudinal control: pushing, pulling, neutral.

6 Engines

The performance achieved by modern combat aircraft would be unattainable without corresponding advances in engine technology. Particularly worthy of mention is the significant increase in thrust/weight ratio, as well as the lower fuel consumption. Whereas with civil engines, economy and environmental compatibility are paramount, the requirements for military engines by comparison are very different. This becomes clear when the typical flight phases of a combat operation are considered:

1. **Short take-off,** frequently with high weapon load; requires brief maximum thrust with afterburner switched on.
2. **High climbing speed** as well as **longitudinal acceleration** require maximum thrust with the aid of the afterburner over various periods of time.
3. High **supersonic speed** at high altitude requiring brief use of maximum thrust with afterburning.
4. **Manoeuvrability** at supersonic and transonic speeds requires brief and frequent use of maximum thrust with afterburning at all altitudes. Moreover,

high maximum thrust without afterburning is also necessary.
5. For **high-speed low-altitude flight** over long distances, high sustained thrust without afterburning is necessary. An additional peripheral condition is low fuel consumption.

These requirements lead to the typical features of military engines, all of which are gas turbines, as indicated by their configuration. Before dealing with this in greater detail, the combat aircraft engine needs to be allocated a particular place in the spectrum of aircraft engines in general.

6.1 **Classification of Engines**

DISTINCTIVE FEATURES

In practical applications, numerous types have developed, both civil and military. These are distinguished by the following features:
– number of rotating shafts
– division of airflow into primary and secondary
– compression principle
– utilization of the hot gas

What is distinctive within the range of applications is the utilization of the hot gas and the division of the airflow inside the engine. According to these criteria there are four typical configurations (Fig. 6-1):
1. turbojet engines
2. turbofan engines
3. turboprop engines
4. turboshaft engines

With turbojet and turbofan engines the energy of the hot gas is converted into jet thrust. The engines of combat aircraft fall into this category.

With turbofan engines the airflow is divided within the engine, with **one** part flowing through the basic engine, while the remainder, after travelling through the fan or low-pressure section, is conducted around the engine in the form of a bypass.[32] Turbofan engines are classified according to the size of the **bypass**

_____
[32] Hence the occasional use of the term "bypass engine".

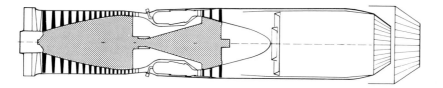

Turbojet engine
with/without afterburning

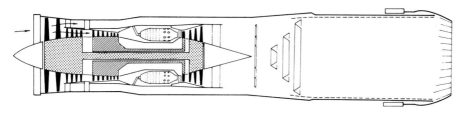

Turbofan engine
with/without afterburning

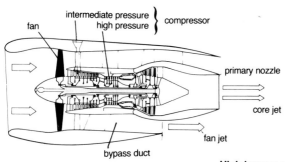

fan

intermediate pressure
high pressure } compressor

primary nozzle

core jet

fan jet

bypass duct

High bypass-ratio engine
without afterburning

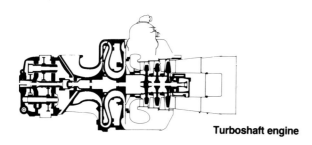

Turboshaft engine

6-1 **Engine types.**

ratio (BPR). Particular emphasis is placed on engines having high bypass ratios. The only high bypass engine relevant to combat aircraft is the General Electric TF34. Apart from that, this type of engine is to be found only in military transport aircraft and commercial aircraft.

In the turboprop engine, most of the gas energy (about 90%) is converted into mechanical shaft power, while the remainder is expanded in the nozzle and provides additional thrust.

Combat aircraft equipped with turboprop propulsion are extremely rare. They are only used for very special tasks, such as North American Rockwell's OV-10 Bronco counter-insurgency aircraft.

With turboshaft engines, in distinction to turboprop engines, the entire energy of the hot gas is delivered to a free turbine, so that no jet thrust at all occurs. Turboshaft engines are used for helicopters. However, they are also found in numerous combat aircraft and practically all commercial aircraft as auxiliary power units (APUs) to generate on-board energy.

CLASSIFICATION OF COMBAT AIRCRAFT ENGINES

Combat aircraft engines may be classified according to their configuration as follows (Fig. 6-2):
- **single-shaft turbojet,** with and without afterburning – examples: J79, J85, Atar 8K50, Atar 9K50
- **single-shaft augmented turbofan** with afterburning, low bypass ratio – example: M53
- **two-shaft turbofan** with and without afterburning, low bypass ratio – example: F404, YJ101, F100, TF30, RM8, Adour

- **two-shaft high-bypass turbofan** without afterburning – example: TF34
- **two-shaft turbofan** without afterburning for VTOL. This special form of the **two-shaft turbofan** has four swivelling nozzles and, as a VTOL propulsion unit, is equally suited for hovering and for cruising flight – example: Pegasus
- **three-shaft augmented turbofan** with afterburning, low bypass ratio – example: RB199

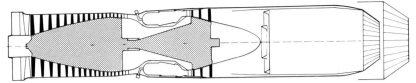

Single-shaft turbojet
with afterburning
(J79, J85, Atar 9K50)

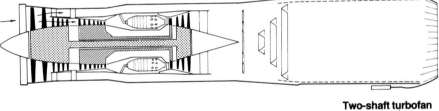

Single-shaft augmented turbofan
with afterburning
(M53)

6.2 **Fundamentals**

6.2.1 **Gas Characteristics**

Large energies are exchanged between adjacent parts of a gas turbine engine. The carrier for these energies is atmospheric air, which, in view of its composition, constitutes a special gas.

It is one of the features of gas molecules that they absorb energy in a simple way and can release it again relatively easily. The particular energy state of the gas is described by means of **thermodynamic** state variables, such as temperature, enthalpy, entropy, internal energy,[34] and by **aerodynamic** variables, such as velocity, pressure, density, and mass.

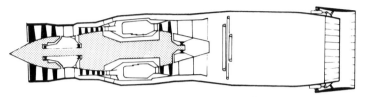

Two-shaft turbofan
with afterburning
(RM8, F404, YJ101, F100, TF30, Adour)

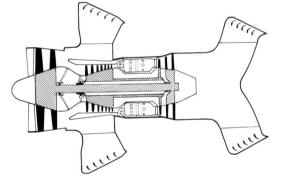

Two-shaft high-bypass turbofan
for VTOL four vectored nozzles (Pegasus)

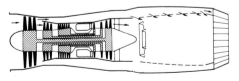

Three-shaft augmented turbofan
with afterburning
(RB.199)

---

[34] Definitions can be found in the relevant physics textbooks.

6-2 **Combat aircraft engine designs.**

6.2.2 Mode of Operation of Engine

The gas turbine is a heat engine that uses air as its working medium and, as well as mechanical shaft horsepower, also generates thrust. For this it is necessary for the exhaust speed of the gas jet to be greater than the airspeed. This is attained by supplying energy to the working medium in the compressor using mechanical energy to raise the pressure and in the combustion chamber as heat energy to raise the temperature. After partial expansion in the turbine and further acceleration in the exhaust nozzle, the gas passes into the free atmosphere and finally reaches its initial state again. Such a sequence of changes of state, which begins with the working medium being taken from the free atmosphere and ends with it being conducted back there, is termed a cycle. The calculation of the cycle is a combination of thermodynamic and aerodynamic subprocesses which makes it possible to determine thrust and other performance variables, such as specific fuel consumption.

$$F = m(c_j - v_0) + m_f c_j + (p_j - p_0)A_j$$

F = thrust (N, daN, kN)
m = mass flow (kg/s)
m_f = fuel consumption (kg/h)
c_j = exhaust speed of the jet (m/s)
v_0 = air speed (m/s)
p_j = static pressure at the outlet
p_0 = atmospheric pressure (N/m^2)
A_j = outlet cross-section (m^2)

If the gas cannot fully expand in the exhaust nozzle up to the ambient pressure of the atmosphere, there is a subsequent expansion in the free atmosphere. This occurs, for example, when a supercritical state prevails in a convergent nozzle: although the velocity of sound exists, therefore, at the outlet (which corresponds to the highest velocity in a convergent nozzle), the static pressure of the jet (p_j) is above the pressure of the atmosphere (p_0). Thus an additional pressure force $(p_j - p_0)A_j$ acts on the surface A_j. Nevertheless, the theoretically possible maximum thrust decreases, because the additional pressure force does not compensate for the insufficiently utilized energy potential of the gas.

Example of a thrust calculation:

m = 103 kg/s (230 lb/s)
c_j = 600 m/s (2000 ft/s)
v_0 = 0 (stationary case)
m_f = is neglected
p_j = p_0 (complete expansion)
F = $m \times c_j$ = 103 x 600 $\dfrac{\text{mkg}}{\text{s}^2}$
= 61,800 N = 61.8 kN (about 14,0000 lb)

The development of thrust above the relevant Mach number shows, in the case of a turbojet engine, first of all a slight drop, as the incoming air momentum mv_0, which reduces thrust, rises strongly and the dynamic pressure in front of the engine is small (Fig. 6-3). However with increasing airspeed dynamic pressure increases. This leads to an increase in density of the air absorbed by the engine and thus to a rise of the mass flow rate. Because of this, the thrust rises again. At very high flight Mach numbers the temperature rises so much, due to the compression process, that, since the turbine entry temperature T_4 must be kept constant, the tempera-

6.2.3 Characteristic Variables

An engine is rated according to characteristic variables, of which the most important are thrust, specific thrust and specific fuel consumption.

6.2.3.1 THRUST

Thrust is that characteristic variable, according to which jet engines are usually rated. The thrust equation derives from the theorem of conservation of momentum as follows:

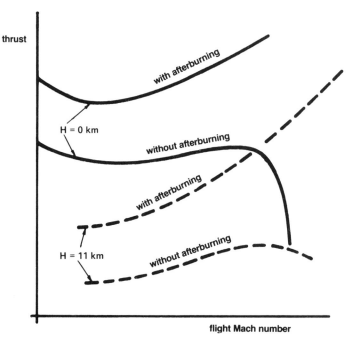

6-3 **Typical variation of thrust with Mach number in the case of a turbojet.**

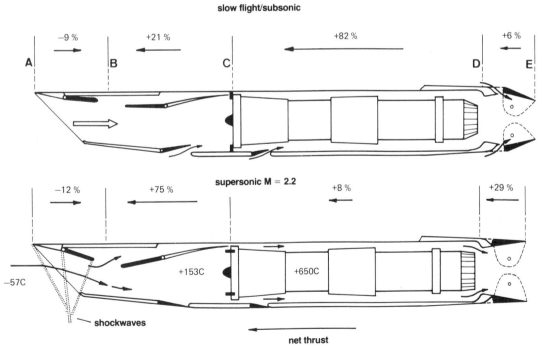

slow flight/subsonic

−9 %   +21 %   +82 %   +6 %

A   B   C   D   E

supersonic M = 2.2

−12 %   +75 %   +8 %   +29 %

−57C

+153C   +650C

shockwaves

net thrust

6-4 **Characteristic distribution of thrust on the components of the propulsion system of the Concorde.**

ture increase $T_4 - T_3$ decreases in the combustion chamber. This causes a reduction of the heat energy per mass unit which can be supplied, so that the thrust decreases again.

When using the afterburner, the restrictions regarding maximum heat supply do not apply, so that in the case of almost constant mass flow but considerably increased exhaust velocity, the thrust curve continues to increase with the Mach number.

Because of decreasing air density, the thrust curves shift to smaller values with increasing altitude (see Fig. 6-3). Thus the density at 11 km (36000 ft) altitude has only about 30% of its sea level value, which also leads to a thrust drop to 30% of the sea level value.

The thrust division within the propulsion system is not constant, however, but varies with Mach number. This will be shown on two examples (Concorde and SR-71).

First of all the Concorde (Fig. 6-4): the propulsion system basically contains the same elements as the propulsion system of a supersonic fighter: wedge-shaped shock diffuser with adjustable ramps, engine with afterburning, adjustable convergent-divergent exhaust nozzle.

If one puts the net thrust available to propel the aircraft at 100%, then in slow flight 82% of the thrust is produced by the actual engine. This force acts on the engine mountings and must be transferred to the structure. On the contrary, only 6% of the thrust acts on the exhaust nozzle section (ejector nozzle, D-E). This is exclusively due to the air flowing in from outside (the convergent nozzle itself does not generate any thrust). A large thrust proportion, namely 21%, is provided by the divergent part of the inlet diffuser (B-C). Here the shape of the duct, widening in the direction of flow, enforces a pressure rise with a component directed forwards which acts as thrust. On the other hand, a drag of 9% net thrust is generated at the ramps of the inlet (A-B).

The conditions in the supersonic range (M = 2.2, H = 11 km) (36000 ft) are completely different. The actual engine and the nozzle up to the narrowest cross-section provide only 8% of the total thrust. By far the largest part, namely 75%, arises in the **subsonic section** of the diffuser (B-C), because considerable pressure rise is involved in the deceleration process. On the contrary, the deceleration is manifested in the **supersonic section,** i.e. at the ramp system (A-B), as drag, caused by high pressure at the convergent duct walls (the mode of operation of such inlets is described in Chapter 7). A considerable propulsion force is also provided by the divergent part of the nozzle (D-E). The increasing cross-section in the direction of flow also permits pressure forces to act which have a component in the direction of thrust, just as in the subsonic section of the inlet diffuser.

This example shows that at high flight Mach numbers the inlet and the divergent part of the thrust nozzle are critical components of the propulsion system.

Practically the entire net thrust is produced by them, so that here a particularly high efficiency has to be aimed for.

The second example deals with the thrust division of the SR-71 (Fig. 6-5). Here, too, the actual engine (2-3) only provides about 17% of the propulsive thrust at high Mach numbers. The remainder results from the integrated pressure distribution at the walls of the inlet system and the ejector nozzle. The contribution of the inlet system consists of 14% drag, which acts on the front part of the cone (0-1) and 70% thrust, which is generated in the subsonic diffuser (1-2). The component of the ejector nozzle (3-4) amounts to 27% thrust.

At maximum Mach numbers, the task of the engine is to maintain the flow necessary to generate thrust inside the propulsion system, while its contribution to the thrust balance is minimal. At low speeds, on the other hand, the largest part of the thrust is generated in the **engine.**

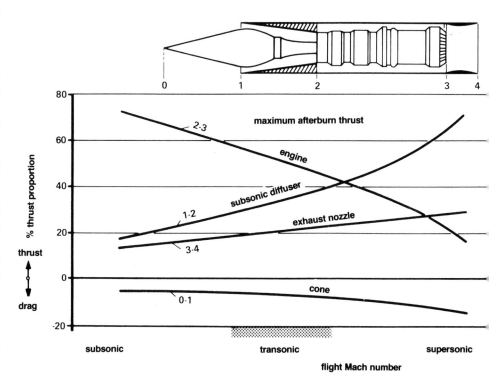

6-5 **Thrust and drag of the propulsion system in the case of the SR-71 high-altitude reconnaissance aircraft (influence of flight Mach number).**

126

		General Electric J79-17	General Electric YJ101-GE-100	General Electric F404-GE-400	Pratt & Whitney F100-PW-100	Pratt & Whitney TF30-P-412A	Volvo RM8B	Turbo Union RB.199	Rolls-Royce/ Snecma Adour Mk.804/ RT.172-26	Snecma M53-5
1	Maximum static thrust at sea level, with afterburning, daN	7970	6590	7100	10 700	9200	12 500	6500	3580	8800
2	Maximum static thrust at sea level, without afterburning, daN	5255	4210	4550	6 400	5800	7 200	3800	2370	5440
3	Specific fuel consumption, with afterburning, kg/daN × h	2,0	1,88	–	2,55	2,78	2,57	2,25	–	2,14
4	Specific fuel consumption, without afterburning, kg/daN × h	0,86	0,78	< 0,78	0,68	0,66	0,65	0,62	–	0,89
5	Maximum mass flow rate kg/s	77	57,6	63,5	103	110	150	72	45	84
6	Bypass ratio	0	0,2	0,34	0,71	0,91	0,97	0,95	0,8	0,4
7	Engine mass, kg	1760	913	953	1377	1760	2350	850	767	1450
8	Specific mass, kg/daN with (without) afterburning	0,221 (0,335)	0,139 (0,217)	0,134 (0,209)	0,129 (0,215)	0,191 (0,303)	0,188 (0,326)	0,131 (0,224)	0,214 (0,324)	0,165 (0,267)
9	Specific thrust, daN/kg/s with (without) afterburning	104 (68)	114 (73)	112 (72)	104 (62)	84 (53)	83 (48)	90 (53)	80 (53)	105 (65)
10	Thrust/weight ratio with (without) afterburning	4,6 (3,0):1	7,4 (4,7)	7,6 (4,9):1	7,9 (4,7):1	5,3 (3,4):1	5,4 (3,1):1	7,8 (4,6):1	4,8 (3,2):1	6,2 (3,8):1
11	Maximum pressure ratio	13,5	25	25 +	23	19,8	16,5	24	11	8,5
12	Number of compressor stages	17	3 + 7	3 + 7	3 + 10	3 + 6 + 7	3 + 3 + 7	3 + 3 + 6	2 + 5	3 + 5
13	Combustion chamber type	Can-annular combustor with 10 ducts	Annular	Annular	Annular	Can-annular combustor with eight ducts	Can-annular combustor with nine ducts	Annular	Annular	Annular
14	Turbine entry temperature, K	1261	1573	1589	1590	1433	1453	1553	1450	1503
15	Number of turbine stages	3	1 + 1	1 + 1	2 + 2	1 + 3	1 + 3	1 + 1 + 2	1 + 1	2
16	Length, m	5,3	3,68	4,03	4,85	5,99	6,23	3,20	2,97	4,85
17	Maximum diameter, m	0,99	0,83	0,88	1,18	1,29	–	0,87	0,56	1,05
18	Beginning of development	1952	1969	–	1967	1967	1964	1969	–	–
19	First test run-up	–	Sept. 1972	Jan. 1977	1969	1969	1971	1971	1967	1970
20	Quantity production	–	–	1980	1975	1972	–	1976	1971	–
21	First flight	1956 (F-104) 1958 (F-4)	1974	–	1972 (F-15) 1974 (YF-16)	1970	1974	1974	–	1974
22	Application	F-104 F-4 RA-5C Kfir B-58	YF-17	F-18	F-15 F-16	F-14 F-111 (TF30-P-100) A-7 (without afterburning)	JA 37	Tornado	Jaguar (with afterburning) Hawk (without afterburning) T-2, F-1, Japan	Mirage 2000

Table 6.1 **Characteristic variables and data of combat aircraft engines.**

6.2.3.2 Specific Thrust

The **specific thrust** is that thrust which a gas mass flow rate of 1 kg per second (2.2 lb/s) generates:

$$F_{sp} = \frac{F}{m} \quad \frac{N}{kg/s}$$

The specific thrust indicates the degree of utilization of the working medium. It serves as a relative value for the comparison of jet-propulsion systems with one another.

Making simplifying assumptions (neglecting fuel flow rate, complete expansion, stationary case), the following results from the thrust equation for specific thrust:

$$F_{sp} = c_j [m/s]$$

This is the exhaust velocity from the nozzle, however. For modern engines with low bypass ratios (such as the General Electric F404) these values, with afterburning, lie above 1100 m/s (3600 ft/s) and without afterburning above 700 m/s (2300 ft/s). A comparison is contained in Table 6.1. In it daN/kg/s is given as the dimension. If it is multiplied by ten, the exhaust velocity in m/s according to the following conversion is obtained:

$$1 \frac{daN}{kg/s} = 10 \frac{N \times s}{kg} = 10 \frac{m \times kg}{s^2} \times \frac{s}{kg} = 10 \frac{m}{s}$$

6.3 **Gas Generator**

The central unit of every gas turbine engine is the gas generator, which is composed of the compressor, combustion chamber and turbine. However, an effective propulsion unit results only when the inflow and outflow sections are designed in a suitable way.

6.2.3.3 Specific Fuel Consumption

The specific fuel consumption (SFC) represents that quantity of fuel which is necessary to generate a unit of thrust for the duration of a particular period of time. In SI units the fuel consumption per hour in kg is related to 1 N or daN:

$$SFC = \frac{m_f}{F} \quad \frac{kg}{daNh}$$

SFC = specific fuel consumption
m_f = fuel flow per hour (kg/h)
F = engine thrust [daN] or [N]

In assessing the efficiency of an engine, the specific fuel consumption is the most important characteristic variable. The specific fuel consumption is particularly high during afterburning: engines having high bypass ratios being in a less favourable position with afterburning than pure turbojet engines or those with low bypass ratios. For combat aircraft engines, the consumption values with afterburning lie between 2 and 2.8 kg/daNh, and without afterburning at 0.7 kg/daNh (see Table 6.1).

In the simplest case there is power equilibrium between the turbine and compressor, which is, for example, approximately true for the turbojet engine. In turbofan engines the turbine power output is greater than the consumed compressor power, so that excess mech-

anical power is available. This excess power is used to drive the low-pressure compressor or fan and is converted into propulsion power.

In Fig. 6-6 the assembly groups of General Electric's famous J79 turbojet engine are shown (engine for the F-4 and F-104, and also for the Kfir and several other aircraft). In the following the components of the gas generator will be described, while the afterburning system, also depicted, will be dealt with separately.

6.3.1 **Compressor**

In the jet engines for modern combat aircraft only axial compressors are used. The advantage of this kind of compressor lies in the fact that high mass flow rates and pressure ratios are attainable. The main flow runs parallel to the axis, so that no deflections occur as is the case with radial compressors. Because of the small frontal area the aerodynamic drag is relatively small. Disadvantages are the complicated construction and high proportion of the total weight of the engine.

6.3.1.1 Construction

An axial compressor is composed of several characteristic components, i.e.:
− front compressor case
− stator casing with guide vanes
− rotor with rotor blades
− rear compressor case (see Fig. 6-6).

The air flowing into the gas generator first of all passes through the **front compressor case,** whose task is to carry the front mounting of the rotor and to conduct the bearing forces via the struts into the outer casing.

The front compressor case is followed by the **stator casing,** divided into two half shells. The stator casing carries the guide vanes, whose task it is to give the flow a particular direction. Modern com-

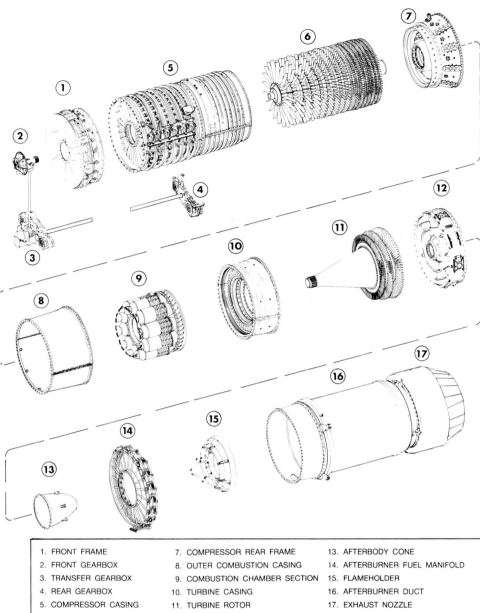

1. FRONT FRAME	7. COMPRESSOR REAR FRAME	13. AFTERBODY CONE
2. FRONT GEARBOX	8. OUTER COMBUSTION CASING	14. AFTERBURNER FUEL MANIFOLD
3. TRANSFER GEARBOX	9. COMBUSTION CHAMBER SECTION	15. FLAMEHOLDER
4. REAR GEARBOX	10. TURBINE CASING	16. AFTERBURNER DUCT
5. COMPRESSOR CASING	11. TURBINE ROTOR	17. EXHAUST NOZZLE
6. COMPRESSOR ROTOR	12. TURBINE FRAME	

6-6 Assembly modules of General Electric's J79 engine.

reduce the flow speed the flow duct is designed in the shape of a diffuser (the cross-section thus increases in the direction of flow). The rear compressor case has a particularly important function in handling the forces generated within the engine; the engine suspension is located here, and thus the transmission of the thrust force onto the aircraft. In the interior of the rear compressor is the rear bearing of the rotor which, as the fixed bearing, absorbs the thrust forces of the rotor.

6.3.1.2 Compressor Characteristic Variables

The conversion of mechanical energy into pressure energy within the compressor is described by means of characteristic variables which indicate the capacity of the compressor. The most important characteristic variables are:
– compression ratio
– efficiency
– mass flow rate

The pressure ratio is defined as the ratio of the total pressures at the compressor outlet (P_3) and at the compressor inlet (P_2):

$$\text{pressure ratio } \Pi_K = \frac{P_3}{P_2}$$

Practically all properties of propulsion, such as thrust, fuel consumption, and efficiency, are decisively influenced by the compression ratio. The weight is also dependent on the pressure ratio. An increase in the design pressure ratio usually demands more stages of blading.

For combat aircraft engines the pressure ratios lie between 9:1 and 25:1; the lower range is assigned to relatively robust engines without long range requirements. Among these are interceptors and fighter-bombers; in this case a

pressor designs make it possible to adjust the guide vanes and thus permit better matching to the particular load condition of the engine.

Inside the stator casing is the rotor, which – just like the stator casing – carries a large number of blades, and is one of the components which is mechanically under the greatest stress. The shapes of the rotor and stator blades

resemble small wings with a typical aerofoil profile. The blade length decreases with increasing compression of the air in the axial direction, so that the longest blades are always at the front.

The final part of the compressor assembly or module is the **rear compressor frame,** which feeds the 'compressed air' generated by the compressor to the combustion chamber. In order to high specific thrust is gained at the expense of an unfavourable (i.e. high) specific fuel consumption. On the other hand, a high pressure ratio is necessary for long range combat aircraft which need low fuel consumption. The modern lightweight fighters also carry out their air superiority missions with low fuel consumption in order to save fuel weight. The highest pressure ratios are necessary for this (see Table 6.1).

One of the most important characteristic variables of the compressor is its **efficiency.** This states how much of the available energy, supplied via the compressor shaft as mechanical torque, is converted into compressor work. The efficiency μ of axial compressors is between 85 and 90%. Losses arise primarily in the gap between the blade tips and the casing due to equalizing flows (pressure equalization between upper and lower surface of profile).

The **mass flow rate,** as the third important parameter, characterizes the rate at which air is processed and permits comparisons of the overall size of the engine.

In a modern axial compressor immense power is transformed in a very small space. A simple example will provide an idea of this. The loss-free specific (thus related to the mass flow rate 1 kg/s) compression work H_{Vis} is given by the relation:

$$H_{Vis} = c_p \, T_2 \left\{ \frac{P_3}{P_2} ^{\frac{\kappa - 1}{\kappa}} - 1 \right\}$$

c_p = specific heat at constant pressure
(for air $c_p = 1.004 \; \dfrac{kJ}{kg \times K}$)

T_2 = total temperature at compressor inlet [K]
P_2 = total pressure at compressor inlet [bar]
P_3 = total pressure at compressor outlet [bar]
κ = ratio of specific heats [–]
(for air: $\kappa = 1.4$)

By multiplication with the mass flow rate, and taking into account the efficiency, the necessary power for driving the compressor is:

$$N_v = m \, \frac{K_{Vis}}{\eta_v} \; [kW]$$

Example:

$P_3/P_2 = 23$
$m \quad = 60 \; kg/s$
$T_2 \quad = 288 \; K \; (15C)$
$\eta_v \quad = 0.9 \; (efficiency)$
$N_v = \dfrac{1.004}{0.9} \times 288 \times 60 \left\{ 23^{0.286} - 1 \right\}$
$\quad \quad = 27,983 \; kW = 38,056 \; hp$

6.3.2 Combustion Chamber

One of the components under maximum stress in a turbine engine is the **combustion chamber.** In it the fuel, after being mixed with the air coming from the compressor, is burnt, with a hot-gas flow of high energy being generated to expand in the turbine and in the exhaust nozzle.

To use the fuel effectively a combustion chamber must fulfil numerous design and performance criteria. Among these are:

– combustion efficiency
– total-pressure loss
– durability
– exit temperature profile
– altitude relight
– size (overall length)
– weight
– emissions.

In combustion chamber design the trends since the 1950s have been towards a continual increase in inlet pressure and inlet temperature: the exit temperatures, which at the same time are the inlet temperatures for the turbine also rose sharply, from 1100 K to over 1700 K. These advances became possible due to the application of modern cooling techniques in the turbine, as well as to improved turbine materials. In contrast, the entry speed has remained constant for years. This is because, with increasing flow speed, the pressure drop in the com-

bustion chamber increases, which influences the efficiency and fuel consumption.

6.3.2.1 COMBUSTION PROCESS

The compressed air coming from the compressor has a pressure of up to 30 bar on entering the combustion chamber, a temperature between 600 K and 800 K and a velocity of up to 150 m/s (500 ft/s). This velocity is much too high for the combustion process, so that the flow must first of all be decelerated. For this purpose the front section of the combustion chamber is designed as a diffuser (duct cross-section increasing in downstream direction, Fig. 6-7).

A further task of the combustion chamber is the formation of the fuel-air mixture. Corresponding to the changing conditions of flight operations the ratio of injected fuel to the air mass flow rate lies between 1:45 (2.2%) and 1:130 (0.8%) The stoichiometric (ideal) mixing ratio lies, however, in the region of 1:15 (7%). The result is that only a part of the volume of air flowing in can contribute to the mixture formation. The front section of the combustion chamber accordingly has the additional task of metering the air in a suitable way, so that as complete a combustion as possible takes place. This is achieved by a small diffuser-like duct within the diffuser section of the combustion chamber, at the exit of which a system of drag bodies further reduces the flow speed.

Fuel under high pressure (up to 100 bar) enters the combustion chamber via numerous injection nozzles set in the direction of the circumference. The task of the injection nozzles is to generate a homogeneous fuel-air mixture by means of extremely fine atomization or vaporization, so that effective combustion is ensured.

The actual combustion takes place in a relatively small part of the flame tube termed the primary zone (see Fig. 6-7). Here the temperatures lie between 2100 K and over 2400 K. Any combustion chamber material would melt if sufficient wall cooling were not ensured.

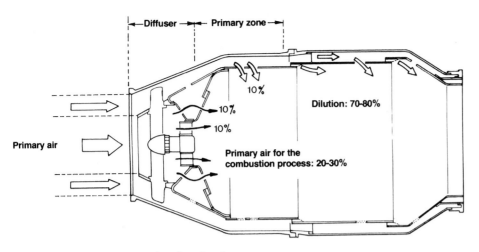

6-7 **Flow process in the combustion chamber.**

The proportion of air used for combustion is relatively small. By far the larger part of the volume of air flowing in is conducted into the space between the outer casing and the combustion chamber and is partly used for the generation of the cooling film for the combustion chamber wall. For this purpose numerous holes are arranged around the circumference through which it is possible to meter the air out exactly.

The remainder is added to the hot gases through larger inlets in the **secondary** zone. Here the combustion process must be completed so as to keep temperature peaks away from the next stage, the turbine.

The combustion process is started by electric ignition and is then self-sustaining.

6.3.2.2 ASSESSMENT OF COMBUSTION PERFORMANCE

The requirements set for the combustion system of an aircraft engine must be met under all conditions of flight operations. The criteria used for assessment will be discussed in the following.

COMBUSTION CHAMBER EFFICIENCY

The fuel supplied does not burn completely, and thus generates less heat than would be theoretically possible. The cause lies in obtaining an optimum fuel-air mixture, which is difficult to control and adjust to changing operational conditions.

Combustion chamber efficiency η_c is used to characterize fuel utilization. This states how much of the heat Q_0 (theoretically) contained in the fuel is actually released through combustion as heat Q_{eff}:

$$\eta_{th} = \frac{Q_{eff}}{Q_0}$$

It is also usual to give a definition of the thermal efficiency in which the effectively attainable temperature difference is expressed in proportion to the theoretical maximum possible temperature difference:

$$\eta_{th} = \frac{T_4 - T_3}{T_{4\ theor.} - T_3}$$

T_4 = total temperature at combustion chamber exit
T_3 = total temperature at combustion chamber inlet
$T_{4\ theor.}$ = theoretical, i.e. maximum possible total temperature at combustion chamber exit

Recently developed combustion chambers attain thermal efficiencies of 98% and more (η_{th} = 0.98), which became possible above all because of the increased exit temperatures.

Of particular importance is the temperature profile at the combustion chamber exit, influenced by the arrangement of cooling air supplied. The more air that has to be made available for cooling purposes, the more unfavourable is the temperature profile.

As the temperature at the combustion chamber walls is limited by the materials to about 1150 K, but the flame temperatures are in the region of 2450 K, the cooling air requirement is very much dependent on the design of the holes.

TOTAL PRESSURE LOSS

Pressure losses in the combustion chamber impair the efficiency of the gas turbine process. Due to turbulence as well as frictional influences, pressure losses are, however, inevitable. The pressure loss coefficient Π_b serves to characterize this:

$$\Pi_b = \frac{P_4}{P_3}$$

P_4 = total pressure at combustion chamber exit
P_3 = total pressure at combustion chamber inlet

With good annular combustion chambers the losses lie between 3% and 6% (Π_b = 0.94-0.97), depending on the inlet Mach number, with higher Mach numbers causing greater pressure losses.

EXIT TEMPERATURE PROFILE

The highest engine performance is attainable when the gas temperature approaches, as near as possible, the permissible temperature of the blades.

OPERATING BEHAVIOUR

Over the engine operating range, which lies between idling and full thrust as well as between high pressure on the ground and low pressure at high altitude, an extinction of the flame must be prevented. Depending on the different operating conditions, inlet pressure, inlet temperature and inlet Mach number vary in the combustion chamber. This has repercussions on the stable operating range.

The air pressure, decreasing with altitude, and the resulting drop in combustion chamber inlet pressure, limit the stable operating range. The high-compression ratio engines of air superiority fighters are less affected than others. In the case of a stoichiometric proportion, combustion is also possible under less favourable circumstances.

The combustion process is sensitive to inlet flow speed. If this is too high then there is a possibility that the combustion flame may be carried away.

EXHAUST EMISSION

Because the combustion process is not 100% efficient, there are gaseous and solid elements in the exhaust jet which may have adverse consequences. With civil engines, there has to be consideration of the environment. With military engines it is the military considerations which play the most important part. In particular unburned carbon, on reaching a particular particle size, can escape as visible smoke and is a clearly recognizable sign for an opponent.

The agreement between civil and military needs, although for different motives, has led to combustion chamber designs whose emissions are practically invisible. The problem of visible smoke occurs when pressures of over 10 bar exist in the combustion chamber and the fuel-air mixture is too rich. This was particularly the case with the earlier engines, where the altitude relight was critical.

6.3.2.3 TYPES

In gas turbine engine design the types of combustion chamber are classified according to shape into
- can-type combustors
- can-annular combustor and
- annular combustors.

The **can-type combustor** is one of the older types. The individual combustion chambers are arranged in a circle around the engine axis, with each combustion chamber being fed through its own air supply duct from the compressor. The disadvantages of this type are poor use of space, large overall length and limited mass flow (Fig. 6-8).

The **can-annular combustor** is, in relation to the number of civil and military engines at present in use, the most widespread type. Secondary air is supplied from a common external casing, while the primary air needed for combustion flows through individual inlets. The advantage, apart from good use of space, lies in the greater mechanical stability of the design.

The most effective use is made of the available engine volume by the **annular combustor** (see Fig. 6-8). This type

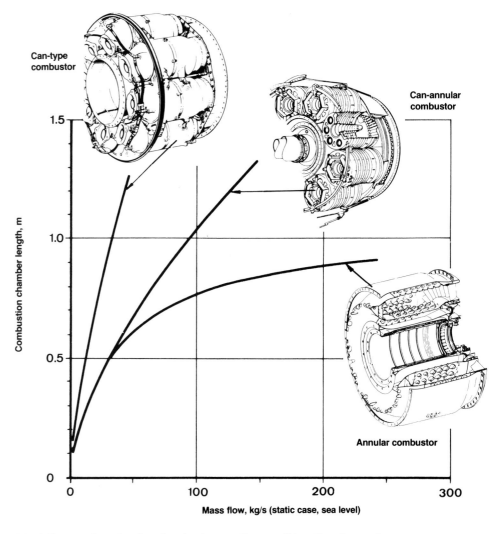

6-8   **Influence of combustion chamber type on the overall length and mass flow rate.**

permits a considerable reduction of the overall length and is the most common type in modern engines.

6.3.3 Turbine

The primary function of the turbine in a jet-engine is to drive the compressor. Moreover, mechanical energy must be generated for the operation of accessories. The mechanical and thermal loads which occur make the turbine the most critical component of an engine.

6.3.3.1 CONSTRUCTION AND MODE OF OPERATION

The mode of operation of the turbine is basically no different from that of the compressor. However, while the compressor releases energy to the air flowing through and thereby transforms mechanical energy into pressure energy, the turbine abstracts energy from the gas and converts this into mechanical torque.

In aircraft engines the axial type of turbine is exclusively used because of

the high mass flow: the design may be single-stage or multi-stage. For combat aircraft engines the number of stages usually lies between two and four (see Table 6.1).

By a stage is meant the combination of a (fixed) stator and a following (rotating) rotor (in a compressor the sequence is reversed). The stator is composed of a number of wing-like vanes set at a particular angle to the flow direction. In the nozzle-shaped (i.e. contracting) duct between two adjacent vanes, the flow is accelerated and leaves the guide vanes with increased speed and changed direction (Fig. 6-9), with pressure and temperature dropping. Because of the nozzle effect the stator is also called the **turbine nozzle** and the vanes **nozzle guide vanes.**

The rotor also has flow ducts which contract and therefore have a nozzle effect, so that the expansion of the hot gas is continued there. Analogous to the lift at the wing, reaction forces arise at the rotor blades which set the turbine rotating.

The number of stages of a turbine is dependent on various factors and is determined by:
– the number of compressor shafts

– the amount of energy to be taken from the gas
– the number of revolutions per minute
– the turbine diameter.

6.3.3.2 COOLING

The direction of development in military and civil engine construction has been towards turbofan engines with high temperatures and pressures in the gas generator. In order to minimise specific fuel consumption the turbine inlet temperature has to be raised along with the compression ratio.

The greatest influence on engine power is turbine inlet temperature. An increase of turbine inlet temperature from 1600 K to 1850 K raises the specific thrust by 40%. Thus, with the same thrust the mass flow rate can be correspondingly reduced, which will permit a reduction of engine diameter by 20%, along with all the positive consequences with regard to weight and aerodynamic drag.

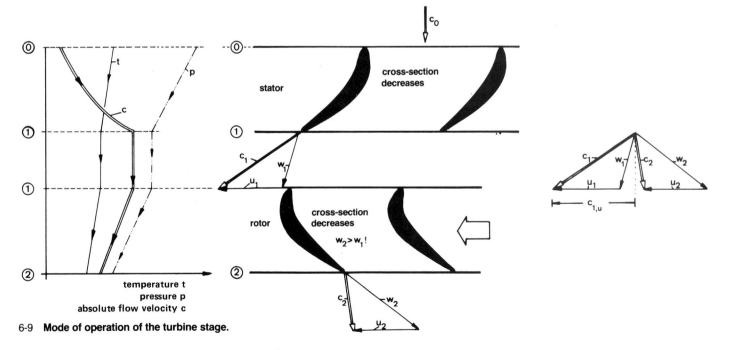

6-9 **Mode of operation of the turbine stage.**

The hot gases coming from the combustion chamber enter the turbine with temperatures of 1600 K to 1800 K. The melting temperatures of metallic turbine materials available today are about 1400 K. The only way to operate the turbine at these temperatures is to cool the blades.

The different cooling methods employed in practice will be described in the following (Fig. 6-10). The least complicated is **convection cooling.** Heat absorbed by the vane from the hot gas is carried off by cooling air within the blade, which is equipped with special ducts for this purpose. In order to increase the surface swept by the cooling air, cooling fins are often present (see Fig. 6-10a). The heat carried off by convection depends on the surface exposed to heat flow, the temperature difference between wall and cooling air, and the so-called heat-transfer coefficient.

A variation of convection cooling is **impingement cooling,** in which cooling air jets are directed against the inner wall at points under particularly heavy stress (see Fig. 6-10b). This cooling method is more intensive than the normal convection cooling. A considerable improvement of the cooling effect can only be achieved when partial film cooling is added to convection cooling. In this method cooling air escapes from the blade interior via tangential holes or slits and puts a film between the metal and the hot gas. Due to convection effects heat is first carried off from the holes, which directly reduces the wall temperature. After the escape the cooling film then insulates the blade wall (see Fig. 6-10c). As the cooling effect wears off after a short flow length, the film must be renewed downstream by means of a further row of tangential holes. In this kind of convection and film cooling, hot gas temperatures of up to 1800 K can be kept under control.

The most effective cooling effect is reached by letting cooling air escape through porous walls and putting a continuous cooling jacket around the blade (see Fig. 6-10d). With this so-called transpiration cooling temperatures of up to 2000 K can be allowed; provided that suitable porous surfaces can be successfully manufactured.

As the air taken from the compressor for cooling is withdrawn from the gas turbine process, the cooling air proportion must be as small as possible. In addition the holes must not become obstructed in operation under any circumstances, because the lack of cooling effect would lead to the turbine blades burning through and thus to turbine destruction.

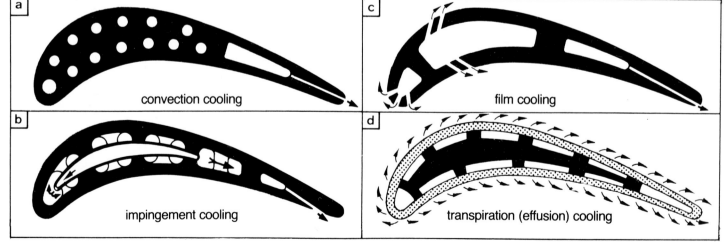

6-10 **Cooling methods with turbine blades.**

6.4 Exhaust Nozzle

During the expansion process in the turbine a part of the energy of the gas is removed, that is, exactly as much as is needed to drive the compressor and various accessories, such as fuel pump, oil pump and electric generator. In the case of jet engines, however, the energy reserves of the gas are still not exhausted. It is the task of the **exhaust nozzle** to convert the potential energy still present in the gas into velocity energy.

6.4.1 Accelerated Gas Flow

The acceleration of the gas is a necessary condition for the generation of thrust. This, in turn, is directly proportional to the exit velocity (see thrust equation).

In order for acceleration to take place at all, there must be a sufficiently large pressure at the nozzle entrance. Only in this way is it possible for the speed of sound or even supersonic speed to be achieved at the nozzle exit. The characteristic variable for this is the nozzle pressure ratio (NPR), which is the ratio of the pressures at the nozzle entrance and exit.

The extent of the acceleration is determined not only by the nozzle pressure ratio, but also by the temperature. The higher the gas temperature at the nozzle, the higher the exhaust velocity. This can be explained by the fact that hot gas has low density, so that the gas particles can easily be accelerated to a high velocity.

During the acceleration process, while the gas is flowing through the nozzle, the gas variables change: pressure, density and temperature fall. The most significantly changed is the pressure potential,

because at the nozzle exit the jet has practically reached the pressure of the surrounding atmosphere. The temperature potential cannot be fully exploited during the expansion. The exiting jet still contains a relatively large amount of heat which must be regarded as loss.

6.4.2 Velocity of Sound and Mach Number in the Exhaust Process

The velocity of sound (symbol: a) of a gas is proportional to the root of the absolute temperature and is described by the equation:

$$a = \sqrt{\kappa R T}$$

κ = ratio of specific heats (for air in the normal state $\kappa = 1.4$, for hot gas 1.33)
R = gas constant (for air R = 287 J/kgK)

As the temperature drops during acceleration, the local velocity of sound also becomes lower. On the other hand, the Mach number, as the ratio of flow velocity to the velocity of sound, increases for two different reasons:
1. the flow velocity rises;
2. the velocity of sound decreases.

If M is less than 1 (M < 1) the gas flow is called subsonic flow, if M > 1, supersonic flow. If the gas velocity is the same as the velocity of sound, then the Mach number M = 1. This state in the nozzle is called **critical**, and the cross-sectional area in which the velocity of sound just appears is called the critical cross-section.

It can now be simply proved by calculation that the gas pressure has decreased by 47%, the temperature by

17% and the density by 36% up to the critical cross-section, always referring to the conditions at the nozzle inlet.

We will see in the following that critical conditions – or equivalent, the velocity of sound – cannot be reached at any arbitrary point in the nozzle, but that the nozzle must fulfil special conditions for this with respect to its shape.

6.4.3 Design of the Duct Cross-section

The gas flow in a duct is characterized by the fact that at any arbitrary point the same number of gas particles per second pass through the duct cross-section. If the cross-sectional area is small, the gas flows through at high velocity, while in the case of a large section the velocity is low. This fact is based on the physical principle of the conservation of mass (continuity). On the basis of this principle, namely that the quantity flow per second or mass flow (symbol: m) must be the same at all points in the duct, statements about the design of a nozzle can be made.

First, the mass flow rate is to be understood as the product of gas density ρ, flow velocity w and area flowed through A:

$$m = \rho w A \quad \left(\text{dimension } \frac{kg}{s} = \frac{kg}{m^3} \times \frac{m}{s} \times m^2\right)$$

From this a simple relation can now be derived which reflects the dependence of the cross-section development on the flow Mach number[33]:

$$\frac{dA}{dw} = -\frac{A}{w}(1 - M^2)$$

A = respective duct cross-section
dA = differential change of cross-section area
dA > 0 duct cross-section becomes larger
dA < 0 duct cross-section becomes smaller
w = flow velocity
dw = change of flow velocity
dw > 0 acceleration (nozzle)
dw < 0 deceleration (diffuser)

---

[33] derivation in the relevant physics textbooks

From this is can be seen how a flow duct must be shaped which, as a nozzle, accelerates the flow or, as a diffuser, decelerates the flow.

On entering the nozzle subsonic velocity can always be assumed. According to this the duct cross-section in accelerated flow (dw > 0) must become smaller (dA < 0, Fig. 6-11). If the exit velocity does not need to exceed the velocity of sound, a cross-section development of this kind is fully adequate. In fact, the **convergent nozzle,** with which at best the velocity of sound can be reached at the exit, is found in all jet-propelled subsonic aircraft.

If the velocity of sound or supersonic velocity has already been reached in the nozzle (M ≥ 1), in the case of further acceleration (dw > 0) the cross-section must become larger (dA > 0). In practice this is the divergent part of a supersonic nozzle which, particularly in the case of rockets, has a distinct shape.

The condition that in the cross-section exactly the velocity of sound (M = 1) occurs is fulfilled by dA = 0, i.e. the duct wall runs parallel to the axis. In the flow duct this is always the narrowest cross-section, which is also called the **critical cross-section** or throat. Because of this, the flow in the supersonic nozzle is divided into two fundamentally different sections.

In the case of the diffuser the situation is reversed. In order to decelerate (dw < 0) the flow entering at subsonic velocity must find a duct which expands in the direction of flow (divergent duct). A supersonic diffuser (see Fig. 6-11, bottom right) cannot be realized because a vertical compression shock develops at the duct inlet which instantaneously brings the flow down to subsonic velocity with losses (the way to slow down a supersonic flow with smaller losses is described in Chapter 7).

6.4.4 Conditions for the Attainment of the Velocity of Sound and Supersonic Velocity

From the dependence of the gas parameters, particularly the gas pressure, on the flow Mach number the conditions can now be investigated which must be met if the velocity of sound and supersonic velocities are to be attained.

In order to accelerate the gas, the pressure at the nozzle entrance must be greater than at the nozzle exit, where normally atmospheric pressure is present. If the pressure difference is only small, the exit velocity also remains small because of the low expansion of the gas. Only in the case of a sufficiently large pressure gradient are high exit velocities attainable.

A critical velocity in the throat (= local speed of sound) corresponds to precise values for the gas parameters (pressure, temperature, density), which in turn are related to the state variables at the nozzle entrance. Thus the pressure drops up to the critical section by 47%. If the pressure gradient is smaller, the local velocity of sound cannot be reached at the nozzle exit. This means that the pressure at the nozzle entrance must be at least 1/0.47 times (i.e. 2.13 times) as high as the pressure at the nozzle exit (example: when flowing out into the surrounding air on the ground [air pressure 1 bar] the gas must have a pressure of about 2 bar, so that the velocity of sound is reached at the exit).

The **first** condition for attaining the velocity of sound is thus as follows:

$$p_{crit} \geq p_0 .$$

The **second** condition is that the critical velocity occurs in the smallest cross-sectional area of the flow. This condition is met by a duct which contracts in the direction of flow (convergent flow duct).

If the exit flow is to take place at **supersonic velocity,** the pressure in the

duct type	flow speed w	flow state in the duct	
		subsonic (M < 1)	supersonic (M > 1)
nozzle	w increases dw > 0 accelerated flow		
	example:	convergent exhaust nozzle	divergent section of a supersonic nozzle
diffuser	w decreases (dw < 0) decelerated flow		
	example:	inlet duct (subsonic diffuser)	cannot be realized

6-11 **The design of the duct system for nozzle and diffuser.**

6-12 **Subsonic aircraft have a convergent non-variable exhaust nozzle (Vought A-7).**

critical cross-section must be greater than the ambient pressure in which the exit flow takes place. Only by means of a further expansion, from critical pressure to ambient pressure, is acceleration to supersonic velocity possible. Hence, the first condition is as follows:

$$p_{crit} > p_0$$

The second condition is that the gas first flows through a **convergent** nozzle section, where it is accelerated up to the velocity of sound, and directly afterwards through a divergent nozzle section, where, reaching supersonic velocity, the expansion takes place up to external pressure, with increasing flow velocity.

6.4.5 Nozzle Shapes in Practical Operation

6.4.5.1 CONVERGENT NOZZLES

For aircraft which do not exceed the speed of sound, or only slightly, the convergent exhaust nozzle, whose exit area is not adjustable, is completely adequate. This nozzle shape is to be found, therefore, in fighter-bombers, which, because of their numerous underwing stores, have so much drag anyway that supersonic Mach numbers cannot be attained (Fig. 6-12).

6.4.5.2 CONVERGENT-DIVERGENT NOZZLE

Greater exit flow velocities can be reached with a nozzle shape in which a convergent section is followed by a divergent section (Fig. 6-13). Such nozzle shapes are already familiar from steam turbine construction in the last century and are called (after their Swedish inventor) Laval nozzles.

In the convergent section the flow behaves as previously described, with the velocity of sound occurring in the narrowest cross-section (critical pressure). The subsequent area increase in the divergent section makes a further

137

pressure drop below the critical value, and the acceleration of the gas to supersonic velocity, possible.

In practical use a supersonic nozzle with rigid geometry is unsuitable, because the exit cross-section of the nozzle cannot be adapted to the changing ambient pressures and power settings. In addition, such nozzles would have to be relatively long. For this reason supersonic nozzles for aircraft are always adjustable (in contrast to rocket nozzles), which permits short overall lengths but also leads to relatively complicated constructions.

Among the numerous convergent-divergent nozzle shapes, two types above all have been generally adopted in combat aircraft design, namely the **ejector nozzle** and the **iris nozzle**.

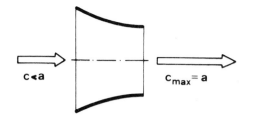

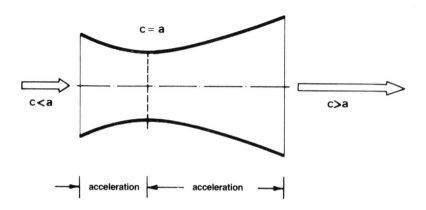

| c | flow speed |
| a | speed of sound |

6-13   **Convergent and convergent-divergent nozzle.**

EJECTOR NOZZLE

The ejector nozzle is the most frequently applied form of the supersonic nozzle. It always consists of a convergent primary nozzle which is concentrically surrounded by a duct acting as a secondary nozzle (Fig. 6-14). The primary flow, which constitutes the actual engine flow, reaches the velocity of sound ($M = 1$) in the narrowest cross-section, i.e. at the nozzle exit. This is, of course, the highest velocity which can be attained with a convergent nozzle. Because of its high pressure the jet continues to expand after leaving the nozzle, however, and accelerates to supersonic velocity ($M_I > 1$). Due to the suction effect of the primary jet a secondary flow is set in motion whose task is to contain the primary jet and to provide steady acceleration to supersonic velocity. Without the presence of the secondary flow the primary jet would, as a result of its high pressure at the nozzle exit, abruptly expand to ambient pressure. This would even lead to over-expansion of the jet and would involve high losses and less thrust. The secondary flow has a damping effect on the

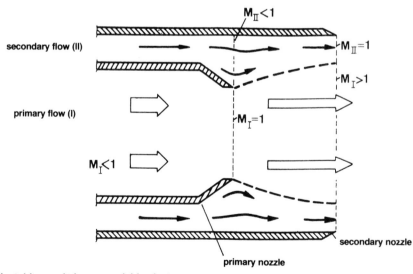

6-14   **Adjustable nozzle in non-variable ejector.**

primary jet and ensures gradual expansion to supersonic velocity. At the same time it is accelerated and reaches the velocity of sound at the exit ($M_{II} = 1$).

In an ejector nozzle the divergent section of the Laval nozzle is virtually replaced by gaseous boundary walls. Thus the second important task is fulfilled. The primary flow generally has a relatively high temperature, in particular with the afterburner in action. The secondary flow ensures the necessary cooling of the walls and prevents the hot exhaust jet from coming into contact with the outer casing.

Numerous variants of the ejector nozzle are in operation. In its simplest form of construction it consists of a non-adjustable slightly divergent flow duct (fixed ejector) surrounding the adjustable primary nozzle. A nozzle configuration of this type is, for example, attached to the afterburner duct of General Electric J85 engine (Fig. 6-15). The variation of the nozzle cross-section is effected by displacing the ring-shaped ejector axially by means of a hydraulic actuator. Rollers on the ejector ring run in guide rails on the nozzle segments. This arrangement is easily controlled mechanically.

When the ejector is completely extended the nozzle reaches its narrowest cross-section (Fig. 6-16, top), whereas, when the ejector is fully retracted, the largest flow cross-section is obtained (Fig. 6-16, bottom). The advantages of this shape are the low weight and uncomplicated construction. The characteristic is to a large extent that of a convergent nozzle with limited performance in the supersonic range. For this reason its application is limited to relatively simple combat aircraft (as in the case of the F-5).

An ejector which has a more complicated construction, but is also considerably more effective, is the fully variable ejector nozzle (variable flap ejector). The convergent nozzle section consists of a number of overlapping segments, while the divergent section is formed by the secondary flow (Fig. 6-18). Due to the

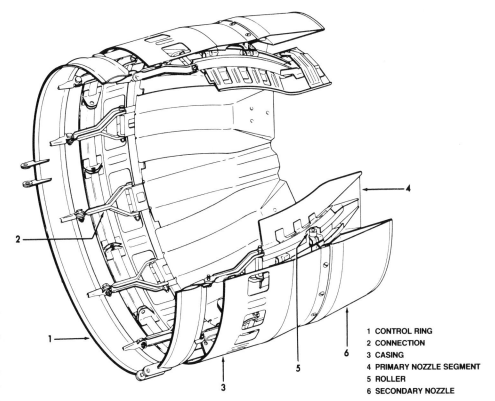

6-15   **Ejector nozzle (General Electric J85).**

1 CONTROL RING
2 CONNECTION
3 CASING
4 PRIMARY NOZZLE SEGMENT
5 ROLLER
6 SECONDARY NOZZLE

combined action of the two adjustable nozzles, the area ratio can be adapted to the particular flight conditions in an almost ideal way. On the other hand, however, a more complicated construction of the secondary nozzle, and much greater weight, has to be accepted. A further disadvantage is the need for a lot of secondary air which increases drag. The variable flap ejector is found, for example, on General Electric's J79 engine (Fig. 6-17).

A further form of ejector has in addition inlet doors to influence the cross-sectional area; through these doors tertiary air is sucked in from the external flow near the engine (blow-in-door ejector, BIDE, Fig. 6-19). At high supersonic speeds the inlet doors are closed because of the increased internal pressure, while the secondary nozzle simultaneously achieves the largest exit area. If the airspeed now decreases to low

supersonic speed, then the falling internal pressure automatically causes a gradual reduction of the exit area. This process continues until the segments reach their stops, which prevents further cross-section decrease. In this case the aircraft is in the transonic speed range (flight Mach number in the range between 0.5 and 1.2).

At subsonic speeds, as well as during take-off and landing, the spring-loaded doors are opened so that air from outside can enter. In general the ejector has good properties in the subsonic and supersonic range and is therefore in widespread use, as, for example, in the F-111, Viggen and SR-71 aircraft (Fig. 6-20).

6-16 Smallest flow cross-section (top) and largest cross-section (bottom) are generated by adjusting the ejector ring (Northrop F-5E).

6-17 Variable ejector nozzle of the J79 engine.

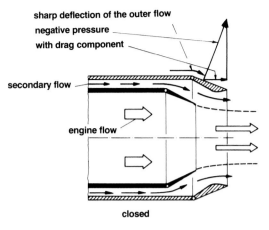

sharp deflection of the outer flow
negative pressure
with drag component
secondary flow
engine flow

closed

afterburner position

6-18　Variable ejector nozzle of the J79 engine.

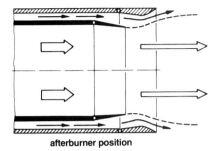

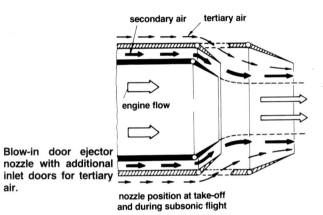

secondary air　tertiary air

engine flow

spring-loaded, closes
during internal
positive pressure

can move freely, position is
determined by pressure
equilibrium on the inside
and outside afterburner
position

mechanically adjusted
via controller

6-19　Blow-in door ejector
nozzle with additional
inlet doors for tertiary
air.

nozzle position at take-off
and during subsonic flight

afterburner operation

6-20　Ejector nozzle with open inlet doors for tertiary air (Lockheed SR-71).

Mechanically rather complicated, but extremely favourable from an aerodynamic point of view; these are the features which distinguish the **iris nozzle.** The axial displacement of the individual segments is effected by means of push rods, which are controlled via adjusting cylinders or spindle drives. As a result any required sectional area can be set (Fig. 6-21).

In general all nozzles designed for high Mach numbers generate considerable drag in the subsonic area at the expense of thrust. This drag arises as a result of the strong deflection of the external flow in a closed nozzle position. As a result negative pressures arise which act on the segments and act against the flight direction (see Fig. 6-18). The favourable outer contour of the iris nozzle avoids negative pressure peaks of this kind, however, and conducts the flow smoothly and free of separation along the wall.

The iris nozzle is the result of extensive research work at NASA as well as in the American aviation industry and is considered a particularly effective nozzle shape with high thrust performance. For this reason it is used on the latest combat aircraft, e.g. F-14 (Fig. 6-22).

6.4.6 Afterburning

Afterburning or **reheat** (or thrust augmentation) is a very effective way of increasing the thrust of a jet engine. The need to do this results from the requirements for improved manoeuvre performances, which are essentially dependent on adequate thrust reserves. Moreover, the take-off run can be considerably shortened by afterburning (Fig. 6-23).

As the name implies, the concepts reheat and afterburning mean the re-supply of heat to the gas. It has already been explained that the exit velocity from the nozzle depends on the one hand on the nozzle pressure ratio and on the other hand on the temperature of the gas. The aim of afterburning is to raise the gas temperature. Advantage is taken of the fact that the gas still contains enough oxygen on leaving the turbine, to permit fresh combustion when extra fuel is supplied.

The afterburner is fundamentally a duct attached behind the turbine of the basic engine (Fig. 6-24). The front part is designed as a diffuser to lower the flow Mach number from 0.5 to about 0.2. This is necessary so that the flame is not carried away.

What is noteworthy is the simple construction of the afterburner, which virtually consists of only four essential parts:
– afterburner duct
– injection system
– flameholder
– variable exhaust nozzle.

The exhaust nozzle with its variants has already been discussed. When the afterburner is turned off the exhaust nozzle is set to the smallest cross-section. Unintentional opening leads to pressure drop and immediate thrust loss.

The central component of the afterburner unit is the **afterburner duct,** in which the combustion takes place. Because of the high temperature numerous slots are provided, through which the cooling air flows in from the annular space between the outer casing and the flame duct. As further protection against oxidation the flame duct is provided with a ceramic coating.

The variable exhaust nozzle is attached to the afterburner duct. The outer casing generally carries the servo-cylinders for adjusting its area.

The injection system ensures that the fuel quantity needed for afterburning is distributed evenly in the flow and mixes homogeneously with it. This is taken care of by several circular distribution con-

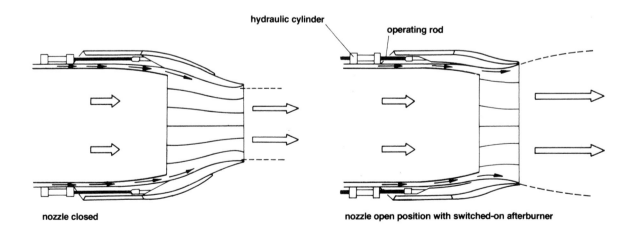

hydraulic cylinder

operating rod

nozzle closed

nozzle open position with switched-on afterburner

6-21 **Iris nozzle**

6-22 The iris nozzle makes a design possible which is favourable for flow and contributes to reduction of afterbody drag (F-14 combat aircraft, smallest exit cross-section left, afterburner position right, take-off with afterburner top right).

6-23 The thrust increase due to afterburning shortens the take-off run considerably (F-14).

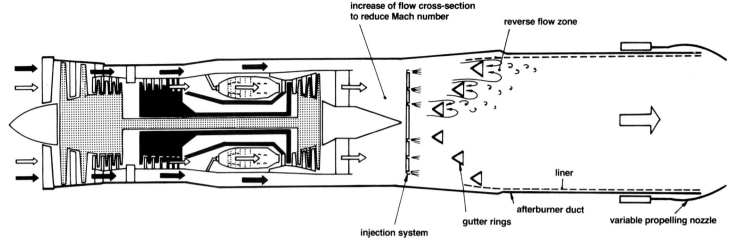

increase of flow cross-section to reduce Mach number

reverse flow zone

liner

afterburner duct

variable propelling nozzle

gutter rings

injection system

6-24 **The afterburner is a duct which is attached behind the engine (example: Volvo RM8).**

duits, from which injection ducts branch off radially inwards. Fuel flows out at right angles to the main flow through numerous holes in the injection ducts.

The **flameholder** lies behind the injection nozzles and consists of several circular rings with a V-shaped cross-section.

In spite of the deceleration effected in the diffuser the flow velocity of the gas is higher than the speed of propagation of the combustion. The shape of the flameholder, which is unfavourable with regard to flow, prevents the flame from being carried away. This is taken care of by the V-shaped cross-section, behind which standing vortices and reverse-flow zones form (see Fig. 6-24). In order to ensure effective combustion, several flameholder rings are provided, placed behind one another to prevent the flow from choking.

To ensure reliable functioning complicated engineering is necessary for the operation of the afterburner. This includes a separate fuel system consisting of fuel pump, filter, fuel control unit and distributor, as well as an ignition system. It is switched on automatically when the pilot selects the afterburn position on the throttle lever.

Ignition of the mixture does not take place by itself, in spite of the high gas temperature. In addition, the readiness to ignite is dependent on flight altitude and Mach number. For this reason spark or flame ignition is always used.

The increase of thrust by means of afterburning depends on the airspeed. The higher this is, the more strongly the thrust increase grows. It is lowest at rest on the ground. The specific fuel consumption increases with rising temperature more quickly than the engine thrust.

When the thrust increases by 30% the specific fuel consumption increases by about 55% under the assumption made. Thrust increases which can be attained for military engines currently available lie in the range of 100 to 75% for the static case. This performance increase is at the expense of fuel consumption, which increases two-fold to five-fold; turbofan engines with relatively high bypass ratios are in a particularly unfavourable position. The cause of this is the lower pressure at which the heat is supplied. Less heat can thus be converted into kinetic energy.

If the engine runs without the afterburner in action, its thrust drops, due to aerodynamic losses in the afterburner duct, by about 2 to 3%.

6.4.7 Reverse Thrust

Most military aircraft require long landing runs. The causes of this are the high landing speed, the weight of the aircraft as well as in the limited power of the mechanically acting wheel brakes. It is therefore obvious to exploit the principle of jet propulsion to shorten the braking distance. This idea led to the development of thrust reversers. These are usually integrated with the exhaust nozzle and are components of the exhaust systems.

The mode of operation is as follows: the escaping jet strikes baffle plates which can be swung into the flow path. The flow is diverted outwards by this means, but with some forward direction. The resulting thrust component directed forward provides a braking effect (Fig. 6-25).

While thrust reversers are the rule with commercial aircraft, they are the exception with combat aircraft. In fact, only two of more recent aircraft types are equipped with thrust reversers, namely the Tornado and Viggen. The essential reasons which make the use of the thrust reverser with combat aircraft so rare lie in the increase of weight, cost and complexity. Added to which there is usually a

144

6-25 **The thrust reverser shortens the required runway length (Tornado).**

deterioration of other important parameters. Moreover, when it is remem-
bered that the thrust reverser is used only
in an extremely short phase of a flight,
then very convincing reasons have to be
brought forward for its introduction. Their
great value, however, is obvious.

7 Integration I: The Design of the Air Intake

7.1 **The Problem of Integration**

The significant increase in the performance of modern combat aircraft is due largely to considerable advances in individual fields of technology, e.g. in engines with greater thrust, or, however, in improved aerodynamics of the wing. A further fundamental reason is, moreover, to be seen in the fact that better control of complex flow processes in the interplay of engine and airframe has been developed. This resulted from the need to extend the operating spectrum so that one single aircraft type can meet several operational tasks.

Above all the requirement of higher

manoeuvrability in the transonic speed range shifted the centre of interest from the capability of supersonic flight, which had up to then been favoured, to the considerably more difficult operating range close to the speed of sound. There the complicated flow processes, characterised by a large increase in drag (see Chapter 4), highlight the problem of integration.

Integration essentially means the search for an optimum trouble free and low-drag interplay of engine and airframe over the entire flight range.

The problems which occur are the

result of the special method of design used for combat aircraft. In contrast to subsonic commercial aircraft, where the engines are suspended under the wing or are on fuselage support struts, the engines of modern combat aircraft are usually integral with the fuselage (Fig. 7-1). The intake of air needed to generate thrust is through side or ventral air inlets immediately next to the fuselage. The intake flow is, as a result, strongly influenced by adjacent parts of the fuselage and even subject to considerable disturbance during some conditions of flight.

In the tail area it is the propulsive jet

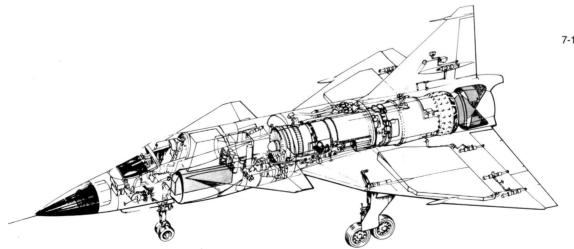

7-1 **Compared with commercial and transport aircraft, where the engines are attached to isolated wing or fuselage support struts, the engines of combat aircraft are normally integrated into the fuselage. Opposite page above left: Airbus A300, above right: DC-10, below: F-15; drawing on the left: AJ37, Viggen.**

146

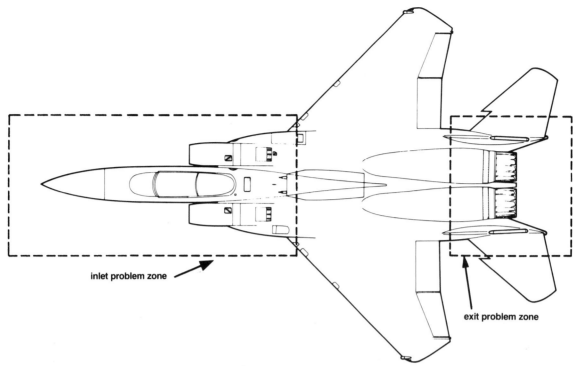

7-2 Integrating the engines with the airframe reveals two problem areas: namely the fuselage nose with the inlet and the tail cone with the exhaust nozzle and tail unit (F-15).

which reacts on the flow around the aircraft, particularly around the tail surfaces. The alteration of the nozzle sectional area by adjusting the nozzle and the distance between the nozzles in the case of twin-jet aircraft are factors which influence aircraft drag.

The essential problem areas for integration are discernible: namely the flow over the forward part of the aircraft with fuselage nose and inlet (forebody flow-field) as well as in the region of the aircraft afterbody with exhaust nozzle and tail (afterbody flow-field, Fig. 7-2).

7.2 **Air Intakes for Combat Aircraft**

Combat aircraft have one or two engines, which are almost without exception integral with the fuselage. Supplying them with the necessary quantity of air for generating thrust takes place by means of specially designed inlets, through which air is taken from the external flow and supplied to the engines by inlet ducts. These inlets are termed **air intakes;** they are arranged as side or ventral openings immediately next to the fuselage (Fig. 7-3).

As the inlet flow reacts very sensitively to disturbing influences, the operational behaviour of the inlet must be investigated in the early development stage of the aircraft. This has to be done in order to assess the operational limits in good time and, if necessary, to make alterations; that is, as long as the costs of these are still justifiable. For example oblique flows occurring in a sideslip or at high angles-of-attack is a source of disturbance.

148

7-3 Inlets for modern combat aircraft. Above: normal shock diffusers for a maximum of double the speed of sound; on the left, ventral inlet (F-16), on the right side-mounted D-shape inlet (Viggen).
Below: multiple-shock diffusers, suitable for flight speeds of more than twice the speed of sound; on the left: variable-geometry axisymmetric inlet (Mirage); on the right: variable-geometry two-dimensional inlet (F-14).

Because of individual requirements inlet designs are as numerous as the aircraft types themselves. There are designs which have proved to be very successful, but also those which were so complicated and susceptible to trouble that the success of the entire project has been jeopardized.

Basically, the task of every inlet is to supply the engine with a uniform, stable, low-loss flow. These conditions must not only be capable of fulfilment during flight, at different speeds and altitudes, but also on the ground, when the aircraft takes off and requires maximum thrust. The operational spectrum for which satisfactory performance must be produced includes the following flight conditions:
- take-off and landing (including the static case);
- low-speed flight;
- high-speed flight (subsonic);
- manoeuvring flight (transonic);
- high-speed flight (supersonic).

The different flow behaviour at subsonic and supersonic speeds also affects the properties of the inlet, so that the inlet configuration is dependent largely on the Mach number range for which the aircraft is designed. Combat aircraft which fly at a maximum speed less than double the speed of sound will, therefore, have different – and usually simpler – inlets than aircraft which can reach two and a half times the speed of sound and more (see Fig. 7-3). Above all, the difference lies in the inlet geometry and in the use of a more or less complicated adjustment mechanism needed for the higher Mach number range. Mastering the variable geometry mechanism involves considerable effort in terms of control engineering. Adverse consequences also result for cost and weight.

7.2.1 Normal-Shock Diffuser

The inlet configuration with the simplest structure is the **normal shock diffuser,** or **pitot intake.** The term 'normal shock diffuser' derives from the shock form which occurs at supersonic speeds. The alternative term 'pitot intake' is used in honour of the French physicist Henri Pitot (1695-1771), who discovered the pitot tube for the measurement of flow speed which is named after him.

The following aircraft are equipped with a pitot intake: the F-16, F-18 and AJ37 Viggen combat aircraft as well as all subsonic transport aircraft (see Fig. 7-3, top). Typical is a cross-section shape which has numerous intermediate stages between full circle, semi-circle and semi-ellipse. This affords many design possibilities. Using an example of an inlet of this kind, its behaviour will first of all be explained in the subsonic range, and then in the supersonic range.

PITOT INTAKE IN SUBSONIC FLOW

All current engines require subsonic flow for entry into the compressor. In supersonic flight the flow must therefore be reduced to the specified entry Mach number for the engine, which lies between 0.4 and 0.7. Conversely, the flow in the inlet duct has to be accelerated when the flow speed is too low, as for example when static and during low-speed flight.

The static case is distinguished by the fact that the inlet takes in the air, which is at rest, from a wide area of its surroundings, which also includes the area behind the inlet lip (Fig. 7-4, left). The flow coming from behind is forced into a strong deflection at the inlet lip; here there is a danger of local separation which impairs the quality of the inlet flow. As a remedial measure, a well-rounded inlet lip is aimed for.

With increasing flow speed the flow pattern changes fundamentally in front of the inlet. As long as the speed of the aircraft is not high enough to generate the required flow speed at the compressor inlet, the inlet speed must be allowed to accelerate. This process means a **contraction** of the streamlines immediately in front of the inlet, with the limiting streamlines on the outer casing of the inlet cover forming stagnation points which move forwards when the speed increases (Fig. 7-4, centre). A certain amount of separation is also to be

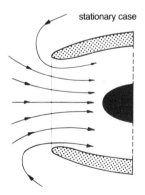
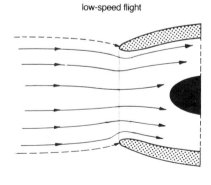
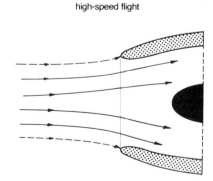

stationary case   low-speed flight   high-speed flight

7-4   **Inlet flow at take–off, low-speed flight and high-speed flight (subsonic).**

expected here, which despite rounding of the nose is similar to the static situation.

The air requirement of the engine determines the flow speed (c_2) at the compressor face and at the same time the speed (c_1) at the intake cross-section A_1. At low airspeeds ($c_0 < c_1$), the necessary flow acceleration leads to contraction of the streamtube. A higher airspeed ($c_0 > c_1$), on the other hand, produces dynamic pressure in front of the inlet, with kinetic energy being converted into pressure energy. In this case the cross-section A_0 of the approaching streamtube in the undisturbed state is smaller than the entry cross-section A_1 of the inlet (Fig. 7-4, right).

The exploitation of the kinetic flow energy to gain pressure is continued in the inlet duct. This is designed in such a way that the cross-section in the direction of flow expands gradually and steadily (see Fig. 7-35). A divergent air duct with the capacity to decelerate a subsonic flow in this way and, at the same time to build up pressure, is called a **diffuser**[34].

PITOT INTAKE IN SUPERSONIC FLOW

Up to flight Mach numbers of $M = 1.5$, the pitot intake functions stably and efficiently enough to make more complicated inlets with variable geometry superfluous. The increased performances of today's engines make this intake type operable even up to airspeeds corresponding to Mach 2 (F-16, F-18), but, because of the shock losses which occur, this is the upper limit.

Now how does the pitot intake work in the supersonic flow? After exceeding the speed of sound a shock front builds up in front of the intake which runs perpendicular to the approaching flow and decelerates the flow instantaneously from supersonic to subsonic speed; however high the supersonic flow Mach number (Fig.

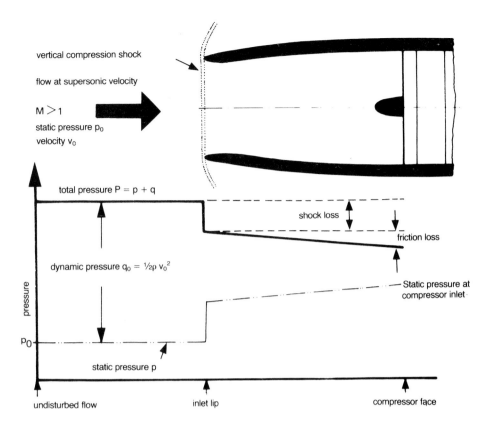

vertical compression shock

flow at supersonic velocity

$M > 1$
static pressure p_0
velocity v_0

total pressure $P = p + q$

shock loss

friction loss

dynamic pressure $q_0 = \frac{1}{2}\rho\,v_0^{2}$

Static pressure at compressor inlet

pressure

p_0

static pressure p

undisturbed flow   inlet lip   compressor face

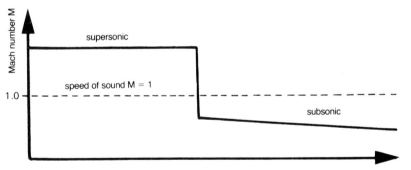

Mach number M

supersonic

speed of sound $M = 1$

1.0

subsonic

7-5   **Pressure changes of the air at a normal shock diffuser; supersonic flow.**

7-5). As a result there is a rise of pressure and density, for which reason this phenomenon, which is typical of supersonic flows, is called a **normal compression shock.** The passage through a shock front of this kind means that the kinetic energy taken away from the flow is not completely regained as pressure energy. On the contrary, a part of it is to be seen as loss which increases with increasing flight Mach number. This also explains why the upper operating limit of

the normal shock diffuser is around Mach 2. Other inlet types are used for higher supersonic flight Mach numbers.

A shorter diffuser duct and better use of aircraft space are achieved by designing a side-mounted axisymmetric air inlet. This inlet type is found, for example, on the Mirage III, V and F1 (all Dassault, France) as well as on the Starfighter F-104. The inlets are designed in an almost semi-circular shape and have half-cones as central bodies (see Fig.

[34] The converse process, i.e. the exploitation of pressure energy to accelerate the flow, is achieved with a convergent duct, called a nozzle (see Chapter 6).

7-7, top and bottom left). A further step was taken in the case of the F-111 (General Dynamics, USA), where the conical inlet appears only as a quadrant, with a translating and collapsing centre body (see Fig. 7-7, bottom right).

To avoid the low-energy fuselage boundary layer getting into the engine flow, the inlets are always separated somewhat from the fuselage. The resulting gap is used to extract the boundary layer.

The design as a side-mounted inlet makes corresponding changes of direction in the diffuser duct necessary, especially in the case of single-jet aircraft, so that at particular places on the curving duct walls there is a tendency to flow separations which have adverse effects on engine flow. In the case of twin-jet aircraft, the semi-circular or quadrant-shaped cross-section must, in addition, be increased to a fully circular cross-section at the compressor inlet. For this reason the diffuser duct cannot be kept arbitrarily short.

7.2.2 Oblique-Shock Diffuser

The main disadvantage of the normal shock diffuser is its inefficiency. This becomes worse when the flight Mach number increases; it also leads to increased total pressure loss even in the case of the shock attached to the intake lip. To avoid this disadvantage, the oblique-shock diffuser first of all decelerates the flow over one or several oblique shocks, which are relatively low-loss. Only then does the inevitable normal shock follow, which brings the flow down to subsonic speed. The reduced shock intensity of the diminished normal shock causes only a slight total pressure loss.

Such a shock configuration can be attained, for example, by inserting a conical centre body into the previous normal shock diffuser. In this way a conical shock front arises which has the desired loss-reducing properties. In cross-section the shock front appears sloped, which is why it is called an oblique shock (Fig. 7-6). The number of oblique shocks and their position is determined by means of kinks on the centre body.

Fig. 7-6 shows how much the losses are reduced by this step. A normal shock diffuser (N = 1) generates at Mach 2 a pressure recovery of only 70% (P_2/P_0 = 0.7), while with a four-shock diffuser (of which three are oblique shocks) over 95% can be attained.

PRACTICAL EXAMPLES

For combat aircraft which operate mainly in the supersonic range, and for which manoeuvrability is of secondary importance, the axisymmetric conical inlet is a good solution of the inlet problem. In the fifties and early sixties supersonic capability was in the foreground, so that this inlet shape is found mostly on interceptor aircraft developed at that time.

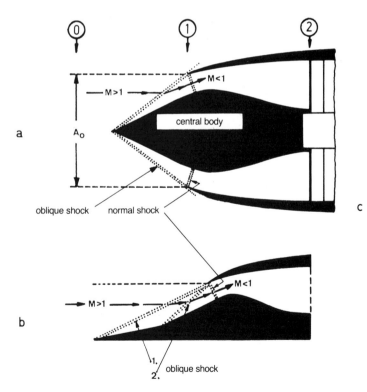

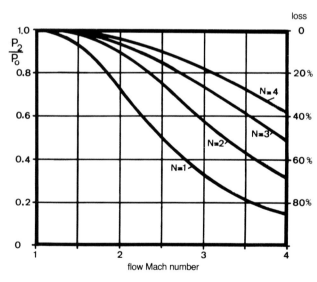

a) two-shock diffuser
b) three-shock diffuser
c) maximum possible total pressure recovery P_2/P_0

N = number of shocks

7-6 Oblique-shock diffuser.

7-7 **Combat aircraft with axisymmetric conical inlets – top left: Mirage 5, top right: Lightning, bottom left: Mirage F1, bottom right: F-111.**

The classic axisymmetric conical inlet with fully circular cross-section and translating centre body is found on the types MiG-21 (first flight 1955), Su-7, Su-11 (all USSR) and BAe Lightning (UK, first flight 1957) (Fig. 7-7, top right). The position of the inlet in the fuselage nose requires a long air supply duct up to the compressor inlet, for which greater frictional losses must be accepted. The advantage of this inlet position is the undisturbed flow field in which the intake functions.

The angle formed by the oblique shock with the flow direction is dependent on the Mach number and the angle of aperture of the cone in such a way that, with increasing Mach number, the conical shock wave becomes acute and the angle of inclination of the shock front becomes flatter. It is important, however, for the efficiency of the axisymmetric conical inlet, that the shock coming from the apex of the cone should always pass close to the inlet lip. With a fixed geometry inlet this condition can be met only for one particular Mach number (Fig. 7-8). If the airspeed is lower, the oblique shock moves ahead of the intake lip as a consequence of its less acute inclination. This raises the external drag of the inlet.

153

If the airspeed is too high, then the shock moves into the inlet duct because of its greater angle of inclination and causes a strongly distorted flow. The Starfighter has a non-adjustable diffuser of this kind, which does have the advantage that it weighs little and is simple in operation.

With a variable-geometry inlet the centre body translates axially: at high flight Mach numbers forward, because of the greater inclination of the shock front; at low Mach numbers accordingly to the rear (see Fig. 7-8, right). This process takes place automatically via a control unit which determines the required position from various flow data, such as static pressure, dynamic pressure and temperature, and gives the commands to translate the centre body.

A variable geometry inlet, although in strongly simplified form, in which the centre body can assume three different positions, is used on the MiG-21.

Compression in the supersonic range is effected by means of one or several oblique shocks as well as by a final normal shock which brings the flow to subsonic speed. Up to medium super-sonic Mach numbers (about $M = 2.5$), this compression process is concluded on the entry of the flow into the inlet, with the final normal shock, leading to subsonic speed, lying immediately behind the inlet lip. As the compression takes place outside the intake duct, it is termed **external compression.** At flight Mach numbers over 2.5 the sole use of external compression leads to relatively large inlet diameters with high drag. For this reason the alternative is used with very fast aircraft by using only a part of the deceleration process as external compression and transferring the remainder as internal compression into the annular duct of the inlet. This form is called **mixed compression.** An inlet with mixed compression is used on the Lockheed SR-71 (USA) long-range reconnaissance aircraft. This operates at extreme altitudes and can exceed Mach 3 (Fig. 7-9).

For an inlet with mixed compression it is necessary for the incoming clustered oblique shocks to be guided very accurately by displacing the centre body so that they strike the inside of the inlet cover directly behind the sharp lip. Here they are reflected as a single oblique shock. Behind the last oblique shock, which is set off by the kink in the inner contour, the supersonic flow is decelerated so far that the final oblique shock has still only low intensity and is thus relatively low-loss.

Exact adherence to the shock positions, which is necessary in the case of inlets with mixed compression, is impaired by the boundary layer arising on the centre body and in the intake duct, so that costly design steps are needed to eliminate them.

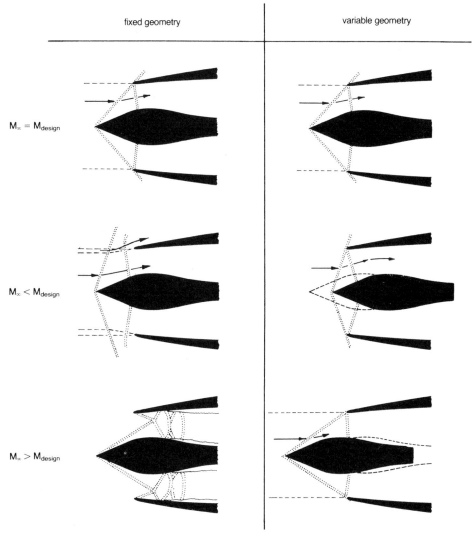

fixed geometry variable geometry

$M_\infty = M_{design}$

$M_\infty < M_{design}$

$M_\infty > M_{design}$

7-8 **Shock configurations in the case of a fixed geometry and variable geometry inlet.**

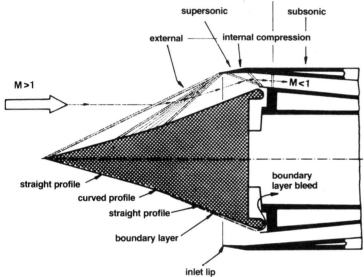

7-9 **Axisymmetric inlet with mixed compression (Lockheed SR-71).**

7.2.3 **Two-dimensional Intakes**

However advantageous an axisymmetric inlet may be for optimum pressure recovery, it turns out to be equally unfavourable when the flow is not symmetrical to the axis of the cone but is at an angle to it. This state, which occurs, among others, during sideslip and turning flight manoeuvres, leads to severe distortion causing the compressor to operate in the dangerous surge limit area.

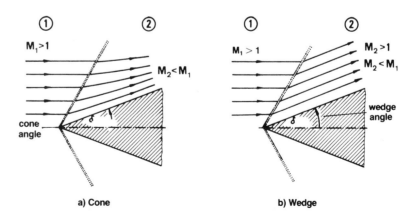

7-10 **Comparison of supersonic flow at cone and wedge**

In contrast, the two-dimensional intake reacts considerably less sensitively to oblique flow, even if the pressure recovery which can be attained is less favourable. As the wedge is an important element in the inlet design of modern supersonic aircraft, its behaviour will be dealt with briefly here.

Due to the presence of the wedge, the supersonic flow is compelled to change direction, as in the case of the cone. This causes the familiar oblique shock, across which the flow changes direction and the Mach number drops. In distinction to the cone, which produces a conical (axisymmetric) shock front, the wedge produces a plane (two-dimensional) shock front. This is emphasised by the flow pattern (Fig. 7-10). Whereas with a wedge the streamlines immediately run parallel after the shock has passed through, the streamlines of the cone are slightly curved after passing through the shock. The compression process, indicated by the narrowing space between the streamlines, is thus continued on the cone.

PRACTICAL EXAMPLES

Numerous modern combat aircraft designs are equipped with inlets which act as two-dimensional air intakes, such as the F-14, F-15, MiG-25, and Tornado. However, this inlet shape is also found on the Concorde and Tu-144 civil supersonic aircraft.

What is distinctive about the designs mentioned is the **horizontal** position of the compression ramp, to give a particularly favourable effect at high angles-of-attack. The **vertical** ramp has also been successfully applied, but is less effective at high angles-of-attack.

The Northrop F-5 combat aircraft has a fixed geometry two-dimensional inlet with the compression ramp placed vertical to the fuselage side wall (Fig. 7-11). The oblique shock is generated at the sharp edge of the ramp and extends in the

7-11 **Northrop F-5 with side-mounted fixed geometry two-dimensional inlet, ramp in a vertical position.**

7-12 **F-4 Phantom with adjustable inlets.**

design case, i.e. at a particular flight Mach number, to the outer inlet lip.

Up to Mach numbers of 1.5 a fixed geometry inlet is sufficient, so that adjustment mechanisms are not needed. In addition, the vertical wedge matches the fuselage contour relatively well and this makes integration easier.

Fixed geometry inlets tend, during acceleration from low flight Mach numbers up to the design Mach number, or during sudden throttling of the engine, to behave unstably; the normal shock in the narrowest cross-section is squeezed out of the inlet within milliseconds. This causes high flow losses which instantaneously cause the compressor to surge. In order to reduce this so-called **inlet unstart,** perforated walls, inlets with bypass apertures, as well as half-open inlets are used.

A way out of these difficulties is provided by the variable intake, as in the case of the F-4 (Fig. 7-12). By this means a better adaptation of the shock fronts to the particular flight Mach number is achieved.

The two-dimensional air intake with **horizontal** compression ramp has the advantage that high angles-of-attack can be flown without the fear of too much distortion of the inlet flow. Because of their particular importance for modern high-performance combat aircraft, the features of these inlets will be dealt with in greater detail (see Chapter 7.6).

157

7.3 Operational Behaviour of Supersonic Inlets

At supersonic speeds the compression process takes place in two stages:
1. The flow is decelerated when passing through the shock either instantaneously (normal shock) or progressively (multiple shock), to subsonic speeds, while the pressure builds up at the same time.
2. Subsequently, the deceleration process is continued in the divergent flow duct (subsonic diffuser) while pressure continues to build up.

In order for the propulsion system to reach its highest effectiveness, the inlet must be adjusted to the engine in such a way that the former functions over the entire permissible flight range, and when the engine is under considerable load, close to its optimum conditions.

Such an optimum point is reached when, in the case of the normal shock diffuser, the normal shock lies at the inlet lip, or when, in the case of the multiple shock diffuser, the oblique shock runs immediately in front of the inlet lip and the terminating normal shock leading to subsonic speed lies in the narrowest cross-section (Fig. 7-13a). In this case, when the engine needs all the air taken in, the cross-section of the stream tube approaching at supersonic speed is exactly as large as the **capture area** of the diffuser. The air quantity flowing in has reached its maximum value. This state is termed **critical.** It often corresponds to the **design point** as determined by a flight Mach number, a flight altitude and a typical engine throttle setting.

If the engine power is altered, such as by varying the rpm, then this reacts on the entire upstream flow field, including the shock position. If, for example, the engine requires a lower mass flow due to reduction of the rpm at the same flight altitude, then the back-pressure in front of the compressor rises and causes a part of the originally required air quantity to be spilled around the outside of the

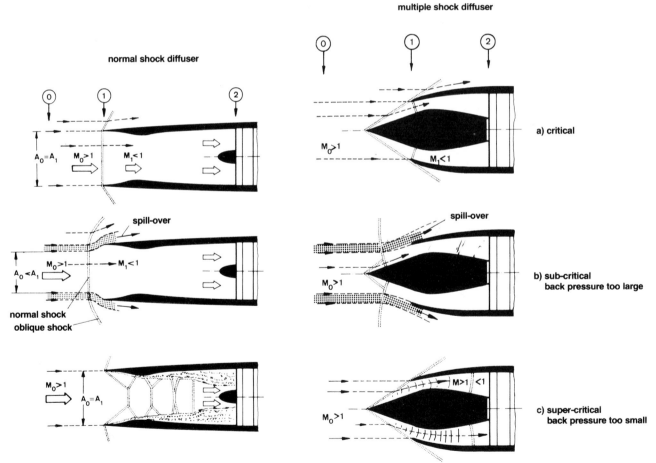

7-13 **Operational conditions of normal and multiple shock diffuser.**

inlet as **spill-over** (Fig. 7-13b). At the same time the shock system shifts upstream and the cross-section of the stream tube approaching the intake is smaller than the capture area. This state is called **sub-critical.** In the case of the normal shock diffuser, the section of the shock passed through by the intake flow continues to act as a normal shock, i.e. it decelerates to subsonic speed, while the edges of the shock surface become increasingly inclined. The oblique shocks maintain supersonic flow, although with reduced Mach number behind the shock.

The situation can also occur in which the air requirement of the engine exceeds the capacity of the inlet. In this case the back-pressure drops first of all in front of the compressor, the shock is absorbed and assumes a more or less stable position further downstream in the duct (Fig. 7-13c). This **super-critical** state generates a complicated system of oblique and normal shocks which interacts with a wall boundary layer, becoming thicker in the direction of flow and therefore providing poor flow characteristics.

This is no longer applicable, however, if characteristic supersonic shocks occur. During flow through the shock front the static pressure rises sharply, and at the same time the flow is decelerated to subsonic speed (see Fig. 7-5). The resulting dynamic pressure drop is greater, however, than the increase of static pressure. If both pressure components are combined in the usual way to form the total pressure, then this is now less than before the shock. With increasing flight Mach number the total pressure loss due to shocks rises, and, in the case of the normal shock diffuser, reaches 28% at Mach 2 ($P_1/P_0 = 0.72$), at Mach 3 even 67% (see Fig. 7-6). The proportion which can be recovered as total pressure from the flow thus becomes smaller and smaller. Although the static pressure rises behind the shock to 4.5 times at Mach 2, and even to 10 times at Mach 3, this pressure rise cannot compensate for the loss of kinetic energy (dynamic pressure). The consequence is reduced thrust generation and higher drag).

A further source of total pressure losses is the **friction** of the flow at the walls of the inlet duct. The cause of this is the property of fluid **viscosity.** Because of this a transitional area forms between the duct wall, to which the flow adheres, as it were, and the free flow; the special feature of this area is the increasing velocity drop approaching the wall. This layer is called the **boundary layer.** Boundary layer problems form a particularly difficult chapter in fluid mechanics.

A flow with rising pressure, such as is present in the diffuser, favours the growth of the boundary layer, as do deflections leading to flow separation. For this reason an effort is made to prevent the angle of aperture of the diffuser increasing above 6°, so as to avoid large changes of direction and also to provide the duct walls with as smooth a surface as possible.

7.4 **Inlet Characteristic Variables**

The compression process by means of precompression is a considerable gain for the operation of the entire propulsion system, particularly at high flight Mach numbers. In order to be able to exploit the full energy potential of the flow, deceleration must be conducted in such a way that an optimum increase of pressure over a wide operating range is achieved. To assess how successfully the inlet manages this task, characteristic variables are used which can be determined from measurements of the physical flow properties, particularly the pressure. In this **pressure recovery, flow distortion, turbulence** and **mass flow ratio** can be determined.

7.4.1 **Flow Loss in Inlet Duct**

The value of the air volume flowing to the compressor directly affects the thrust generated. Inevitable losses in the inlet duct as well as shocks during supersonic flight always result in a reduction in engine performance. Losses also rise during flight manoeuvres which involve high angles-of-attack or sideslip angles. A successful inlet design can keep these adverse effects as low as possible. An important assessment parameter for this is **pressure recovery.**

In the undisturbed state the stream tube approaching the inlet has a static pressure p, which is equal to ambient pressure, as well as a dynamic pressure q, which results from the flow speed v. The sum of both forms the total pressure P:

$$\text{total pressure P} = \text{static pressure p} + \text{dynamic pressure q}$$

As long as no losses occur, an increase in static pressure leads to a speed and dynamic pressure drop to such a degree that the sum always yields the same total pressure (P remains constant).

7.4.2 Distortion

The experience gained from test flying the F-111 (USA), a billion Dollar project, showed that the aircraft could not achieve the design performance. This applied particularly to manoeuvrability at high subsonic speeds and in the supersonic range. One of the causes was found to be irregular flow coming from the inlet, resulting in compressor surge so considerably reducing engine power. This incompatibility between inlet and engine in the F-111 was the motive for an extensive investigation programme, with the aid of wind tunnel and flight test data, to determine quantitatively the reasons for compressor surge, and to derive measures to overcome it. Since then intensive investigations of intake/engine compatibility have become an integral part of every new combat aircraft development.

The starting point of the analysis is a study of the flow field at the compressor inlet. In general there is not a uniform distribution of speed and pressure at this point. But at particular parts of the compressor inlet cross-section there are zones with larger or smaller total pressures which depend on the particular power setting of the engine and the conditions of the flow in their position and extent. The flow field therefore shows a **distortion** which can considerably impair the efficiency of the turbomachinery. In addition to the **magnitude** of the compression the **quality** also has a considerable influence on the engine thrust.

Distortion is represented in the form of lines of equal pressure (isobars) which are plotted over the compressor inlet cross-section (Fig. 7-14). By means of this graphic method it is possible to recognize critical zones more easily and to attempt to initiate design steps to limit their expansion. Particular dangers come from areas in which, due to flow separation, the total pressure is lower than in other areas. This is usually the case when high angles-of-attack are flown, such as are usual with present-day aircraft. This results, as a rule, in separations at the lower inlet lip, found in the isobar diagrams as zones of low total pressure recovery. With increasing angle-of-attack these areas extend from the duct wall to the hub (see Fig. 7-14, right). The most effective remedial measure turns out to be a better rounding of the inlet lip in the critical separation. This always results, however, in higher drag in high-speed flight. Where the compromise finally lies will depend on the aircraft requirements.

The guarantee that an engine also actually produces the stated performance is usually given by the manufacturer, however with the qualification that a particular degree of flow distortion may not be exceeded. The inlet must therefore be designed in such a way that the distortion which actually occurs lies within the permissible tolerance limits in every case. To produce evidence of this, extensive measurements are carried out over the plane of the compressor inlet. This takes place first of all in the wind tunnel model; in a later development phase the comparison is then made with the large-scale model.

A substantial number of **total pressure probes** are used for measuring, which can be compared to a **rake** (Fig. 7-15). A rake of this kind consists of several streamlined faired arms whose number may lie between two and 24. Each arm is equipped with five or six total pressure probes. This method has been used successfully for many years. It allows radial scanning of the flow field. As the flow field has to be covered as completely as possible, rakes which have only a few arms must rotate but this requires a great deal of experimentation and involves high cost.

Fundamentally, as many arms as possible is desirable, because this lowers the required time for testing. Thus a two-armed rake equipped with six probes can provide only six test data at **one** angle position, while with a 24-armed rake

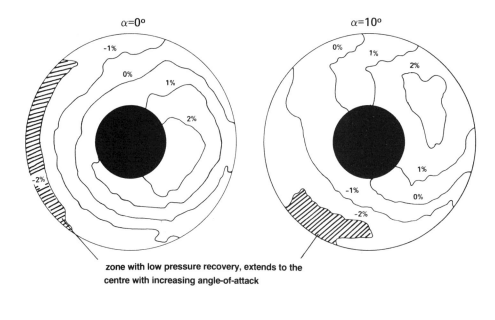

zone with low pressure recovery, extends to the centre with increasing angle-of-attack

$$\text{isobars:} \quad \frac{P_2 \cdot \bar{P}_2}{\bar{P}_2}$$

P_2: probe measured value

$\bar{P}_2$: mean value of all measured values

7-14 **The representation of flow distortion by means of lines of equal total pressure over the compressor inlet cross-section (left: angle-of-attack 0 degrees, right: angle-of-attack 10 degrees; model: Grumman F-14, flow at Mach 2.5).**

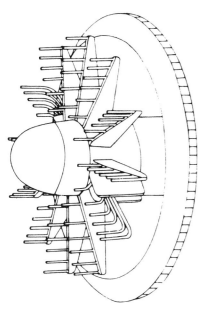

7-15 **Rakes to determine the total pressure distribution at the compressor face.**

the contrary, this form of distortion is to be seen as a steady mean value formation over a longer period of measurement, and is suitable only up to a point as a criterion for predicting the sudden occurrence of disturbances in the compressor. For this reason, in addition to the steady-state recovery pressure, the pressure fluctuations are recorded at every probe[35]. It can be seen from this that areas with high steady pressure recoveries show relatively small pressure fluctuations, whereas zones with low pressure recoveries are characterized by

more intensive fluctuations. The greatest pressure fluctuations always appear where the boundary layer of the fuselage gets directly into the inlet.

If the mass flow is formed as the product of density ρ, flow speed v and cross-section area A, then the mass flow ratio is given as follows:

$$\mu = \frac{m_1}{m_{1max}} = \frac{\rho_0 \, v_0 \, A_0}{\rho_0 \, v_0 \, A_1} = \frac{A_0}{A_1}$$

From this it is clear that mass flow ratio and capture area ratio are one and the same.

There is a close connection between mass flow ratio, or capture area ratio, and pressure recovery (Fig. 7-17). In critical operation the normal shock lies in the

---

[35] Note: There are several possibilities in Anglo-American usage to describe non-steady pressure: oscillatory pressure, transient pressure, dynamic distortion, transient disturbance, turbulence.

twelve times as many data result in the same time. On the other hand, the rake itself acts as a perturbation to the flow. This can lead to blockage of the flow even at a compressor inlet Mach number of 0.5, when the area taken up by the rake only amounts to 2% of the total area. The resulting data from the measurements are so extensive that they must first of all be stored on magnetic tape. They are then evaluated using electronic data processing with the help of suitable software programs. At the same time these permit automatic plotting of the measured results.

7.4.3 Turbulence

The difficulties experienced with the inlets of the F-111 led to the realization that the determination of flow distortion in the way previously described is not enough by itself to explain completely the tendency of the compressor to surge. On

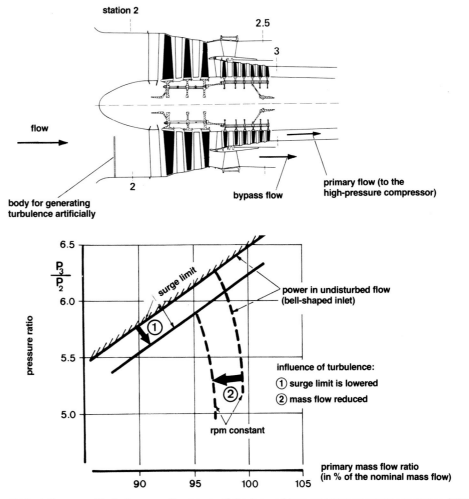

7-16 **Influence of turbulence on the power of the fan and low pressure-compressor stages (TF30 engine in F-111A combat aircraft).**

161

area of the narrowest inlet cross-section, which normally corresponds to the design point and produces good pressure recoveries. In this case the mass flow ratio lies near its maximum (see Fig. 7-17, point A). Also in the case of slightly sub-critical operation (back-pressure too large), a higher pressure recovery may arise in spite of reduced mass flow. This is the range of stable flow in which the inlet is normally operated.

In super-critical operation (point B) the engine's capacity is greater than the mass flow which can be supplied by the inlet, which cannot exceed a maximum value. As a result the shock moves into the inlet duct and, due to its intensity, causes an increase in turbulence. This results in greater losses and a smaller total pressure recovery.

Turbofan engines, which are in widespread use in modern combat aircraft, are particularly sensitive to high-frequency pressure fluctuations. The detrimental consequences are expressed in a reduction of mass flow rate (displacement of the rpm lines to the left) as well as in a lowering of the surge limit (Fig. 7-16). An effort is therefore made to increase the tolerance of the engines to inlet flow fluctuations and to design the inlets in such a way that any turbulence generated remains within limits and does not lead to a restriction of the flight range.

7.4.4 Mass Flow Ratio

A further important variable for the characterization of the interplay between inlet and engine is acquired by means of the mass flow. In the explanation of inlet operation behaviour, it was shown that the mass flow made available does not always match the engine requirement: it may be either too high or too low.

If the compression shock is adjacent to the intake lip (critical state), or has even moved into the duct (super-critical state), the stream tube flowing towards the inlet with cross-section A_0 gets through the inlet cross-section A_1 completely. In this case the **capture area ratio** A_0/A_1, formed from both cross-sections, has the value 1, the maximum possible mass flow rate being reached. However, if the shock is in front of the inlet (sub-critical state), then a part of the oncoming flow is conducted around the outside of the inlet as **spillage flow.** In this case the capture area ratio is correspondingly reduced, and the mass flow coming into the inlet is smaller than the maximum possible. A **mass flow ratio** (MFR) μ is therefore defined which states how large the mass flow m_1 – (what is actually absorbed and required by the engine) – is in comparison with the maximum possible mass flow m_{1max}:

$$\text{mass flow ratio } \mu = \frac{\text{actually absorbed mass flow rate } m_1}{\text{maximum absorbable mass flow rate } m_{1max}}$$

If the back-pressure exceeds a certain amount (strongly sub-critical), the flow in the inlet becomes unstable (point C). Due to the position of the shock far in front of the inlet the mass flow decreases more strongly than is in keeping with the engine requirement. Because of this more mass flow is required for a short time than the inlet is able to supply, and the shock jumps into the inlet duct (point B). This now means significant super-critical operation. This mass flow is too large for the engine requirement, however, so that the shock is squeezed out again and the process starts afresh. Periodic pressure fluctuations of this kind lead, in the case of sufficiently high intensity, to compressor surge, with the

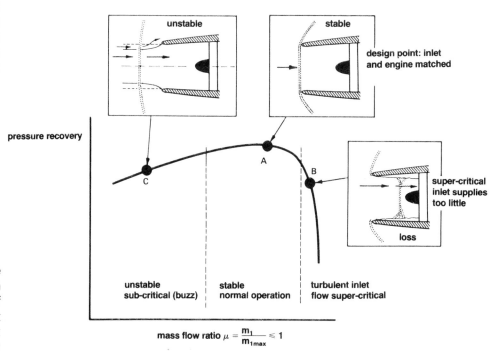

$$\text{mass flow ratio } \mu = \frac{m_1}{m_{1max}} \leq 1$$

or capture area ratio A_0/A_1

7-17 **Characteristic inlet behaviour in supersonic operation.**

result that the flames in the combustion chambers may be extinguished. The pressure fluctuations are called **buzz** because of their intense sound, and cause great concern. It is also possible for high turbulences to appear in the stable operational range. For example, when an insufficiently bled boundary layer alters the position of the shock.

7.5 **Inlet Drag**

The thrust of an engine in the aircraft is always smaller than on the test bed. The most important reason for this is that in test bed running an inlet shape is chosen which, although it ensures a particularly good flow due to its bell shape, is however unsuitable for installation in aircraft. By adapting the inlet shape to the given specifications of the aircraft and the conditions of the operational spectrum, adverse deviations inevitably result which are reflected in the thrust power. In practice it is usual to list thrust losses of this kind as drag components, either separately as single contributions of the total inlet drag or as a modification of the drag polars of the total aircraft.

The following drag components are emphasized:
– additive drag due to intake spillage;
– bypass drag;
– boundary-layer bleed drag;
– diverter drag.

The additive drag is of great importance in this connection, because, especially in off-design conditions, drag increases occur which may account for 10% or more of the total aircraft drag. Aircraft manufacturers pay great attention to these problems, for every percentage point of drag gain is immediately reflected in the flight performance; be it as an increase of radius of action or as an extension of combat time.

The additive drag is the force which the inlet exerts in high-speed flight on the incoming stream tube. This drag could be avoided if it were possible to design the inlet geometry so that it adapts the capture area so as to match the air requirement of the engine. In the case of non-adjustable inlets this is true only for the design point, i.e. for the design Mach number and maximum engine power. At all other flight Mach numbers and with off-design power settings, additive drag appears. In order to minimise it a variable inlet would be one possibility, but its advantages must be seen in relation to increasing complexity and additional weight. It was with good reason that variable inlets were dispensed with in the case of the F-16 and F-18 lightweight fighters and the disadvantages in the off-design area deliberately accepted. This view is entirely justifiable, as long as the airspeed does not exceed Mach 2. However with faster aircraft a variable inlet is always the aim.

Fixed geometry inlets also offer the opportunity to reduce the additive drag noticeably, at least at particular airspeeds. As the additive drag arises from the fact that superfluous flow, but of high-energy, is conducted around the outside of the inlet, it is obvious that this energy should not escape unused. In fact, a suitable design of the inlet fairing leads to the decelerated flow at the lip being accelerated again. This causes a negative pressure area to build up which counteracts the additive drag with its component acting in the direction of thrust. In certain cases this 'lip suction' is even able to make a considerable contribution to drag reduction. In the case of pitot inlets the additive drag can be reduced in this way in the subsonic and transonic range by up to 80%. Although these high values cannot be attained with multi-shock diffusers because of the sharp inlet edge, improvements are, however, also possible here.

Because of the close interplay between additive drag and lip suction, both components are frequently combined under the concept **spillage drag.** This drag component is always effective when the cross-sectional area of the incoming stream tube is smaller than the capture area of the inlet. The losses occurring are

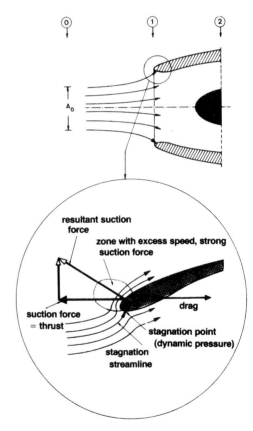

7-18 **With correct flow at the inlet lip, a suction force can arise due to acceleration of the spill-over. This acts in the thrust direction and reduces drag.**

all the greater, the more the air mass has to be conducted around the outside of the inlet, i.e. the smaller the capture area ratio is.

However, there is a way of reducing the spillage drag by first of all allowing a higher mass flow than is needed by the engine to flow through the inlet. Before reaching the compressor this spillage air is led away again and is either released into the free atmosphere or, as secondary air, mixed with the exhausting jet. This procedure is frequently employed with aircraft which are faster than Mach 2 in order to place the shock waves in such a way that critical inlet operation can be maintained throughout the entire supersonic range.

The excess air is drawn off by means of outlets specially designed for this purpose; these are often located, however, at places which are unfavourable for the flow about the aircraft, such as near the suction side of the wing (Fig. 7-19). The disturbances which result generate undesirable rolling and pitching moments which may have an adverse effect on flight behaviour. The definition of bypass drag does not take these effects into account. On the contrary, bypass drag is understood mainly as momentum loss undergone by the component of the air mass flow which is first absorbed but not required; the pressure loss occurring on passing through the outlets is counted as a further component of impulse loss. Bypass drag rises with increasing capture area ratio, because the impulse loss increases with mass flow. In order to attain a minimum intake drag, the influences of bypass and spillage drag have to be weighed against each other, and the bypass apertures varied in such a way that the inlet can always function near its optimum conditions.

Particular importance is attached to the boundary-layer development in the case of supersonic intakes. The boundary layer is known to be a transitional area between the free flow (potential flow) and the walls of the aircraft. Its particular feature is the velocity decrease towards

the wall, which is a function of the viscosity of the air and is the cause of friction drag. The boundary layer acts as if it were a solid body superimposed on the contour and displacing the free flow. This process is to be observed particularly where the flow is decelerated and has to overcome a pressure increase, or where there are large contact lengths which favour the thickening of the boundary layer. As the inlets on modern combat aircraft are almost always positioned immediately next to the fuselage and behind the cockpit – for reasons of good visibility for the pilot – the flow proceeding near the relatively long fuselage nose must cover a great distance to the inlets, so that, depending on the flight condition, a considerable boundary layer is to be expected there. A fundamental aim of inlet design is to prevent this low-energy flow, which causes the dreaded

diffuser buzz, from getting into the compressor. A relatively simple remedy turns out to be the splitting of the boundary layer by moving the inlets away from the fuselage, so that the side of the inlet near the fuselage still lies in 'healthy flow' under normal conditions (Fig. 7-20). The boundary layer is led away in a narrow duct between fuselage and inlet.

This measure is not enough by itself in the case of recent high-performance fighters with normal shock diffusers to attain acceptable inlet flows even in extreme flight conditions. On the contrary, an additional **diverter** is employed which is located upstream of the inlet and prevents the boundary layer from entering the engine. In the case of the F-16 this diverter consists of a 25cm-long plate which forms a 9cm deep aperture with the underside of the fuselage and is an integral part of the inlet lip (Fig. 7-21).

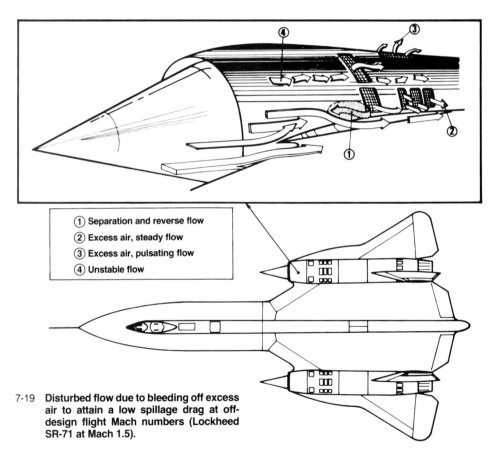

① Separation and reverse flow
② Excess air, steady flow
③ Excess air, pulsating flow
④ Unstable flow

7-19 **Disturbed flow due to bleeding off excess air to attain a low spillage drag at off-design flight Mach numbers (Lockheed SR-71 at Mach 1.5).**

7-20 **In order to prevent the low-energy boundary layer from getting into the compressor, the inlets are positioned clear of the fuselage (top: Saab Viggen with normal shock diffuser, bottom: Mirage III with oblique shock diffuser).**

The momentum loss is then seen as the drag of the boundary layer diverter arising from the air flowing off through the aperture as boundary layer.

In flights at supersonic speed the additional function of the diverter is to keep the shock in front of the inlet away from the boundary layer. Shocks which travel into the boundary layer mostly disintegrate locally into several individual shocks and lead to a complicated shock system involving heavy losses.

The pressure jump during the shock passage causes, moreover, a further sharp increase of the boundary layer, which, on the other hand, is not without repercussions on the position of the shock itself and requires more or less expensive remedies. These consist of removing the boundary as far as possible. A widespread method, which is simple to apply, is **boundary layer bleed** through a number of small holes. These

165

are used, for example, on the YF-17/F-18 diverter (Fig. 7-22). In contrast to the single-engined F-16, where the position of the inlet below the fuselage has led to a solution favourable for flow and ensures good inlet efficiencies even in the high angle-of-attack range (Fig. 7-21), the inlets of the twin-engined YF-17/F-18 were arranged on the side of the fuselage. Although they cannot profit by this means from the directional effect exerted by the fuselage on the flow, as in the case of the F-16, however favourable direction is also achieved by means of the strakes. Thus this lightweight fighter is also in a position to fly at high angles-of-attack.

The use of boundary layer bleed also costs energy, which is expressed in **boundary layer bleed drag.** According to definition, this means above all the momentum loss of the bled air quantity. This drag component is always active when aircraft fly at supersonic speed and have to keep to exact shock positions in order to achieve a favourable pressure recovery. Multiple shock diffusers are considerably more sensitive in this respect than normal shock diffusers with only one single shock, so that, for aircraft with the typical two-dimensional or the

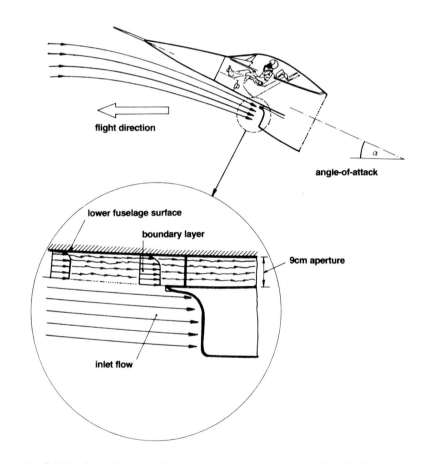

7-21 **In the F-16 the boundary-layer diverter consists of a 25 cm-long (10 in) plate.**

166

axisymmetric inlets, bleeding off the boundary-layer requires considerably more effort.

At the two-dimensional intake of the F-15, which has a shock configuration consisting of three oblique shocks and a normal shock, the boundary layer is bled on the second and third compression ramp and on the intake side walls. When looked at more closely, numerous holes can be detected to drain off the boundary layer. The bled air escapes via laminated outlets specially designed for this purpose on the upper surface of the inlet and on the side walls (Fig. 7-23), see also Figs. 7-29 and 7-30).

At an airspeed above Mach 2.5 the need to attain maximum pressure recoveries and minimum inlet losses intensifies. A typical aircraft of this speed range is the Lockheed SR-71 (maximum speed above Mach 3), which axisymmetric inlet with a translating centre body (Fig. 7-24). The bleed takes place on both the cone and on the duct wall.

The spindle-shaped centre body has a number of small slots in the throat area of

7-22 **By means of a large number of small holes the boundary layer ahead of the diverter is bled off immediately in front of the inlet. The boundary layer is directed into the duct between the diverter and the fuselage (YF-17).**

7-23 On the F-15 the boundary-layer air bled from the intake is dumped through laminated apertures on upper and side surfaces of the inlet body.

the flow channel (largest body diameter). The boundary layer is bled to the outside through louvres located at the ends of the centre body support struts. In contrast, the boundary layer coming from the inner duct wall is absorbed and is conducted to the ejector nozzle together with a part of the bypass air. The bypass flow must be regulated in such a way that the bleed is maintained and inlet unstarts are avoided.

On the way to the ejector nozzle the bled air flows around the engine and thereby has, in addition, a cooling function.

All measures shown to reduce the inlet losses, which involve a greater or lesser degree of effort, are a consequence of the different behaviour of engine and inlet. On the engine side, the broad operational range of modern combat aircraft means that the mass flow ratios have to be varied in a large area, with the power setting playing no less a part than flight altitude and Mach number. For the inlet it follows that this should be designed in such a way that a shortage of air cannot occur under any circumstances. With a non-adjustable inlet with fixed geometry (Starfighter), this is possible only for **one** particular Mach number. If, for example, the inlet is matched for supersonic flight at extreme altitude, then the various characteristics of engine and inlet lead to a considerably greater mass flow being made available in the transonic range than the engine needs. Therefore, in order to achieve maximum efficiency of the propulsion system in all flight conditions, the inlet has to be matched to the engine in such a way that it always functions close to its optimum conditions. This requires critical operation in particular over the supersonic range, i.e. terminating normal shock in the throat (narrowest cross-section). In this respect this is called a **matched inlet.** The matching is carried out by means of variable geometry and always means the intake of a greater air mass than required. A part of this excess airflow is required, as shown before, to bleed the boundary layer, to ventilate the cockpit and in particular electronic equip-

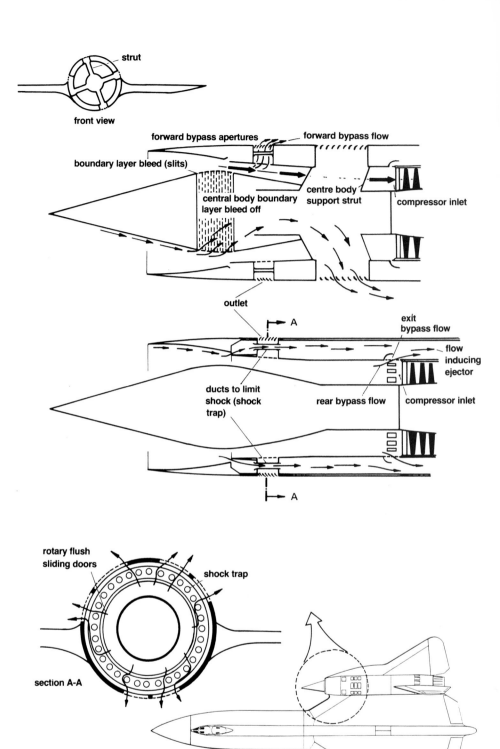

7-24   In the SR-71 the boundary layer is bled from both the centre body and the duct inner wall.

168

ment (environmental control system, ECS), as well as to cool the engine bay.

The entire excess airflow, whether used or bled, undergoes a momentum loss which has to be generated by the propulsion system. The aim of a good inlet design is to keep these losses low.

7.6 **Inlet Systems**

Solving the problems connected with matching the inlet to the air requirement of the engine led to more or less complicated air inlet control systems (AICS). By these are meant functional units which automatically carry out the matching and take into account both the airflow requirement of the engine and the flight condition.

A system of this kind normally includes the adjustable inlet with the controls, a controller, as well as sensors to measure certain physical variables (pressure, temperature, rpm).

The decisive factor for the amount of instrumentation employed is the operational spectrum of the combat aircraft as well as the excess weight that a sophisticated air inlet control system involves. However, cost takes precedence, towards which the system feasibility has to be orientated.

For this reason subsonic combat aircraft are restricted to having an inlet with fixed geometry whose inlet cross-section is at best increased by means of auxiliary inlets in the lower speed range and at take-off.[36]

In the transonic range an inlet with fixed geometry is also sufficient, provided that a simple bypass system is available for matching to the air requirement of the engine. However, high-performance aircraft like the F-14 and F-15, whose operational range requires large variations in mass flow ratios, have a control system which has to react to changes in flow very quickly. As an example, the air inlet control system of the F-14 will be explained.

The inlets of the F-14 combat aircraft are attached to the side of the fuselage as two-dimensional air intakes with basically horizontal orientation (Fig. 7-25). In order to match the air requirement of the engine an adjustable ramp system is used which reduces the inlet cross-section in supersonic flight, but in low-speed flight and at take-off, provides the full flow cross-section (Fig. 7-26).

In supersonic flow a shock system builds up consisting of three oblique shocks and a terminating normal shock. The first oblique shock is generated at the fixed ramp leading edge, while the positions of the following oblique shocks result from the positions of the movable ramps. The two front ramps are connected with each other by hinges and with the inlet structure. The second ramp has its centre of rotation in the subsonic section of the flow duct. Its position determines the throat cross-section as well as the geometry of the subsonic diffuser; at the same time the slot height for the excess air to be discharged and the boundary layer is determined by this means. These are discharged aft from a variable exit door atop the wing glove which simultaneously serves as an auxiliary inlet.

Every adjusting element has its own hydraulically operated servocylinder for exact positioning.

A basic design goal of the F-14 inlet was to keep the number of variable input parameters to the control unit as small as possible, so as to simplify the design of the unit. The following are unavoidable as inlet variables: the flight Mach number, the angle-of-attack and the airflow requirement of the engine. Taking into account all three variables would, however, lead to a three-adjustable-ramp intake system requiring a considerable amount of effort in terms of control engineering. This would be out of all proportion to the attainable performance improvements. Therefore the ramp adjustments were successfully carried out only as a function of the Mach number, i.e. the controller makes a ramp adjustment only when the aircraft accelerates or decelerates. The inlet geometry control schedule was established in the wind tunnel and confirmed by flight tests.

In the F-14 inlet the bleed exit door plays an important part: by adjusting the aperture the required proportion of excess air is determined so that it is diverted before it enters the subsonic diffuser and is conducted to the outside. Its position depends above all on the angle-of-attack, but also on the flight Mach number and the engine rpm. Thus a system which looks relatively simple turns out to be essential for achieving good inlet efficiency. The intake control unit is the core of the system. It is one of those many 'black boxes' essential to a modern aircraft. The control unit requires as input variables Mach number, angle-of-attack, total temperature and rpm of the low pressure compressor.

The flight Mach number is determined by means of a normal **pitot-static probe** which measures the static pressure p and the total pressure P, from which with air temperature, and Mach number can be calculated.

---

[36] Note: This is not contradicted by the fact that this inlet shape is also encountered on supersonic fighters such as the F-16 and F-18. Here the pressure of costs and the need to save weight dictated a solution which, aerodynamically, was not the optimum.

7-25 **The inlets of the F-14 are arranged as two-dimensional side-mounted air intakes with basically horizontal orientation of the compression ramps.**

Angle-of-attack is derived from the pressure difference measured at two holes perpendicular to each other in two alpha sensors, the pressure difference being applied as a measure of the angle-of-attack.

Total temperature is necessary for the determination of the mass flow. It is measured with a commercial platinum resistance thermometer and together with the speed N of the low pressure shaft gives the corrected engine speed $N/\sqrt{T}$. The speed is measured with a tachogenerator or pulse probe.

The intake control unit is an electronic computer which carries out pre-programmed functions. In this way input signals are operated to provide outputs used to adjust the three ramps and the bleed exit door. As the computer understands only **electronic** signals, the measured variables (analog signals) have to be digitized (A-D). Conversely, the command signals to operate the actuators have to be converted in a digital-analog (D-A) transducer into hydraulic pressure. The high computation

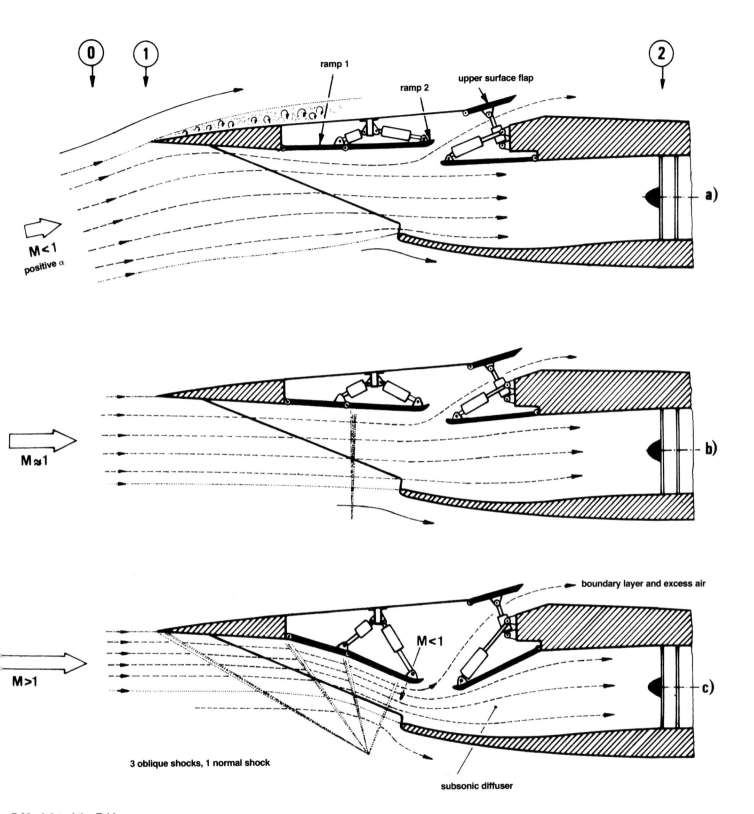

ramp 1

ramp 2

upper surface flap

M<1
positive α

a)

M≈1

b)

boundary layer and excess air

M>1

M<1

c)

3 oblique shocks, 1 normal shock

subsonic diffuser

7-26 **Inlet of the F-14**
Ramp positions and flow at various flight conditions: a) subsonic speed and high angle-of-attack (typical manoeuvre case); b) transonic flow;
c) supersonic flow.

171

speed makes up to 100 subsequent adjustments per second possible for each movable element of the intake system.

The accuracy requirements for ramp adjustment are ±0.3 degrees in high-speed flight and ±0.6 degrees at low speeds. In this connection various sources of error are taken into account: such as inaccurate installation during maintenance work between flights, slight damage due to foreign objects as well as deflections under loads.

For safety reasons both inlet systems are completely separated from one another. In the case of controller failure the ramps adjust so that the engines remain functioning for subsonic cruising flight and for landing.

The air-inlet control system of the F-14 is designed as open-loop control, i.e. the adjustments take place according to functions which are determined for the particular flight conditions derived from wind tunnel tests. The control output is not corrected to match changes in shock configuration. By adopting an open-loop system a simpler control unit results and one which provides both operational safety and low cost.

The use of a simple, low cost, control is directly connected with the inlet type. The inlet of the F-14 functions according to the principle of outer compression, which is preferred up to airspeeds corresponding to Mach 2.5. In particular, the position of the terminating normal shock is not a problem with this type of inlet: the normal shock moves only over a very small area and has hardly any effect on pressure recovery and distortion. In the case of inlets with mixed compression, such as the SR-71, the position of the terminating normal shock is critical, however, for which reason exact adherence to the shock position is always necessary. The subsequent correction takes place through determination of the particular shock position (actual value) and by comparison with the desired value. A closed-loop control is necessary for this, i.e. the shock configuration obtained feeds back to the adjusting elements.

covery which the inlets produce, as well as on inlet/engine compatibility.

7.7.1 Flow Field at the Fuselage Forebody

The most important point in the development of inlets for highly manoeuvrable combat aircraft concerns the flow field to which the inlet is exposed. During extreme flight conditions local flow conditions occur which deviate considerably from the idealized uniform flow, and, depending on the position of the inlet, have different values of the local angle-of-attack, the total pressure and the Mach number. As inlets always have to ensure a steady flow for the engine under these conditions, an understanding of the flow field in the area of the fuselage forebody and at the position of the inlet is necessary for all flight conditions. This will provide realistic data for inlet design.

During the **preliminary design** stage the position of the inlets is established at the same time as the basic configuration of the aircraft. The first results can be immediately applied to the selection of the inlet type. If the inlet is, for example, shielded by the wing or fuselage (shielded inlet), it is enough to use an inlet type which need only provide good performance at relatively low angles-of-attack. This is because of the shielding effect of the airframe, that higher local angles-of-attack are not to be expected, even at high angles-of-attack of the aircraft. If, on the contrary, the inlets lie in the free flow or in areas with possibly high local angles-of-attack or Mach number gradients, then the inlet design must make allowances for these extreme conditions.

Which factors are to be taken into account? The answer to this is derived from the position of the inlet with reference to the fuselage. In the case of lateral inlets (F-14, F-15, F-104, F-4, MiG-23) the following, for example, have to be considered:

7.7 Integration of the Inlet

So far the different types of inlet and their characteristic features have been discussed. It will now be shown how intake and aircraft are matched with one another, and what influencing variables are to be taken into account in this connection. The propulsion efficiency is critically dependent on the solution of this problem. This dependence has a particularly serious effect in the highly manoeuvrable air superiority fighter and the interceptor. The extensive operational spectrum of these aircraft, which is characterized by large Mach number and altitude excursions as well as large variations of attitude and engine power, requires an inlet which can safely deal with the specific disturbances which occur. Propulsion gases from missiles, muzzle gases from guns and other sources of disturbances lying in front of the inlet produce additional flow disturbance.

In the past few years numerous efforts have been made to determine the decisive factors for the efficiency of a supersonic inlet; both qualitatively as well as quantitatively. The investigations concentrated primarily on the total pressure re-

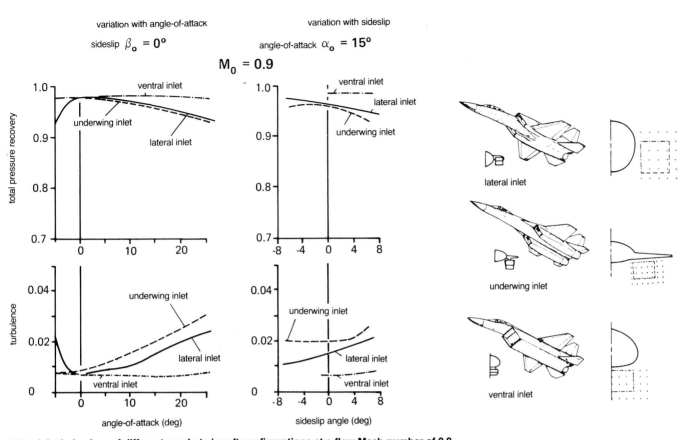

7-27 **Inlet behaviour of different combat aircraft configurations at a flow Mach number of 0.9.**

- the design of the fuselage nose
- the shape of the lower fuselage surface (flat or rounded)
- the design of the cockpit canopy
- the inlet position relative to the cockpit
- the inclination of the fuselage forebody relative to the aircraft longitudinal axis
- the camber of the fuselage
- the fineness ratio of the fuselage.

An understanding of the influence of the cockpit canopy on the inlet flow is important, because in present-day combat aircraft a large field of view for the pilot is required. This predicates a cockpit providing all-round visibility. But, because of its size, the cockpit is a body which disturbs the fuselage flow.

The design of the lower fuselage surface also has a considerable influence on the adjacent lateral inlets at high angles-

of-attack. Investigations have shown that a flat lower fuselage surface causes strong cross-flows in the inlet area, whereas a well-rounded lower surface is considerably more favourable. This is why the F-15 has a fuselage cross-sectional shape which, in the area of the inlets, is similar to an upright ellipse.

With ventral inlets (example: F-16) the lower fuselage surface is assigned a primary inlet flow function: here the directional property of the fuselage has a positive effect on the inlet flow (see Chapter 7.7.2.2).

Which assessment criteria are important for inlet integration?

The assessment of different inlet configurations is done by representing the parameters of total pressure recovery, turbulence and distortion in a realistic

range of angles-of-attack and sideslip angles (Fig. 7-27). In this example the total pressure recovery and turbulence were plotted for an angle of attack range from $-5°$ to $+25°$ at a sideslip angle of $0°$ as well as for a sideslip angle range of $-8°$ to $+8°$ at an angle-of-attack of $15°$, valid for the Mach number of 0.9[37]. This selected example is representative of typical manoeuvre situations.

It can be seen that for the flows in the compressor inlet plane (the parameters are, of course, drawn up for this) there is no essential difference between underwing and lateral inlets. The fuselage-shielded inlet, such as on the F-16,

---

[37] Note: The curves are based on an investigation carried out by the USAF under the name 'Project Taylor-Mate'.

173

shows a considerably higher pressure recovery as well as lower turbulence values than comparable configurations.

Lateral and underwing inlets react very sensitively to changes in the sideslip angle. The curve development is in both cases distinguished by a clear drop in total pressure recovery, whereas the fuselage-shielded (ventral) inlet remains uninfluenced (see Fig. 7-27, diagram top right).

The fuselage-shielded inlet is also superior in turbulence behaviour: over the sideslip angle range described practically no change of turbulence level

occurs, while lateral and underwing inlets reveal a strong increase.

In their flow distortion behaviour lateral and underwing inlets come near the permissible threshold values with increasing angle-of-attack. In connection with sideslip angles, the limits are exceeded at relatively low angles-of-attack. By way of contrast, the distortion index of the fuselage-shielded inlet is far enough removed from the danger area in the entire angle-of-attack and sideslip angle ranges.

FUSELAGE FOREBODY INFLUENCE FACTORS

The following results come from investigations carried out by the Boeing company in the framework of a combat aircraft study on a fuselage-inlet model. The model used consisted of a forebody and a detachable two-dimensional lateral inlet with horizontal compression surfaces. The position of the inlet relative to the fuselage could be altered; the inlet could also be measured by itself. This made it possible to determine both the inlet behaviour in the presence of the

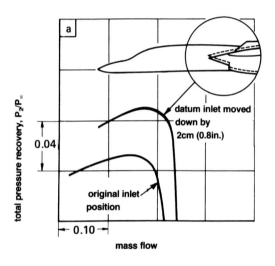

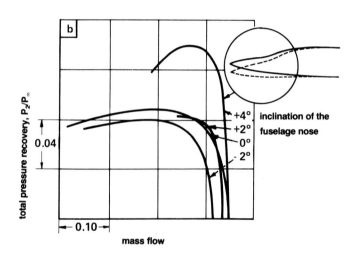

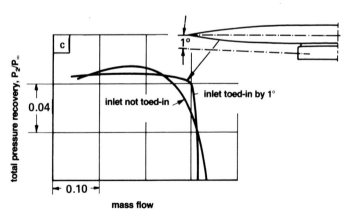

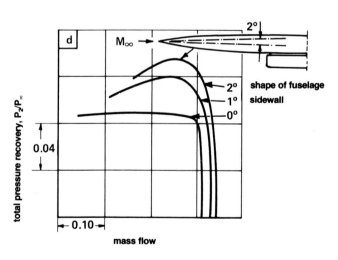

7-28 **Fuselage design measures to improve inlet efficiency.**

a) lowering the inlet
c) toe-in of the inlet aperture

b) raising the fuselage axis
d) inlet in the compression field of the fuselage

174

fuselage and the behaviour of the undisturbed inlet.

The results described will show that with relatively simple geometrical variations considerable improvements in inlet behaviour can be obtained (Fig. 7-28).

Among these simple steps are:
- displacement of the inlet position upwards and downwards
- vertical displacement of the fuselage nose,
- rotation of the inlet in the most favourable flow direction,
- utilization of the fuselage shape for pre-compression.

The particular influences are described in their effects on the total pressure recovery, for a Mach number $M = 2.2$ (this manner of representation is explained in Fig. 7-17). Even slight lowering of the inlet out of its basic position led to considerable improvements in total pressure recovery (Fig. 7-28a). Above all this is due to the lower local Mach number distribution at the inlet. A further improvement resulted from inclining the axis of the fuselage nose by four degrees upwards (Fig. 7-28b). Because of this the expansion of flow at the nose could be largely avoided, which led to a lowering of the local Mach number level, so that the operating point of the inlet lay closer to its design point. The reverse step, i.e. an inclination of the fuselage axis by two degrees downwards, led to greater losses and turned out to be unfavourable. However, this may not be true of every project. For example, the F-4 Phantom has a nose which is noticeably inclined downward, by means of which the inlet flow is improved. However, the F-4, with vertical compression surfaces, has a different inlet arrangement, which would be less favourable for modern combat aircraft.

A comparison of pressure recoveries at the isolated inlet and at the configuration with fuselage shows, in general, a lower total pressure level with the combined configuration. The attempt to reduce these losses was successful in the present example by means of a rotation of the inlet by one degree inwards (toe-in), so as to give a better alignment to the local flow (Fig. 7-28c).

A favourable fuselage shape is one in which the fuselage side wall in the area of the inlet is not parallel to the flow, but forms a slight angle with it. The resulting flow displacement causes precompression, which in the present example, at two degrees angle of inclination, improves the total pressure recovery by 4% (Fig. 7-28d).

These examples show that even comparatively simple steps are enough to obtain considerable improvements in the effectiveness of the propulsion system. Up to now even the major aircraft companies have not been able to predict reliably the demonstrated influences with theoretical methods. As a rule, use is made of semi-empirical approximation procedures which can be derived from a multitude of preliminary tests and which are always subject to an uncertainty factor. However, proof of the determined values will always be dependent on wind-tunnel experiments.

7.2.2 Design of the Inlet in Practice

After the previous remarks on design measures at inlets, the importance of the configuration of the inlet on the design of a modern combat aircraft will now be shown using examples of actual systems. The inlets of the F-15 and F-16 will be cited as examples. The relevant data has been provided with the cooperation of the companies concerned.

7.7.2.1 F-15 INLET DESIGN

The performance requirements of the F-15 have risen considerably in comparison with earlier combat aircraft. In particular, one of these is the ability to carry out air superiority operations successfully requiring use of excess thrust over the entire operational spectrum. On the other hand a high supersonic Mach number (at least 2.3) must be attainable in order to fulfil the interception mission.

As a result the F-15 has made an impression with its remarkable performance. A considerable contribution to this was provided by the well thought-out design of the propulsion system. Distinguishing features are:
- two-dimensional inlets with variable capture area which are arranged at the sides of the fuselage, in front of the wing,
- powerful Pratt & Whitney F100 engines with high thrust/weight ratio,
- low-drag integration of the two convergent-divergent exhaust nozzles in the airframe (Fig. 7-29).

The propulsion system was designed over a period of five years; three characteristic phases are discernible:
- Concept formulation phase,
- Contract definition phase,
- System development phase.

In the concept formulation phase a large number of possible aircraft configurations was investigated in relation to their suitability for air superiority missions. From these was selected the best possible inlet configurations.

INLET CONFIGURATIONS

The essential configuration criteria for the inlets of the F-15 are as follow:
- high performance in the manoeuvre phases and at maximum Mach number;
- minimum distortion in all flight conditions as well as acceptable distortion behaviour in extreme manoeuvre cases;
- minimum weight.

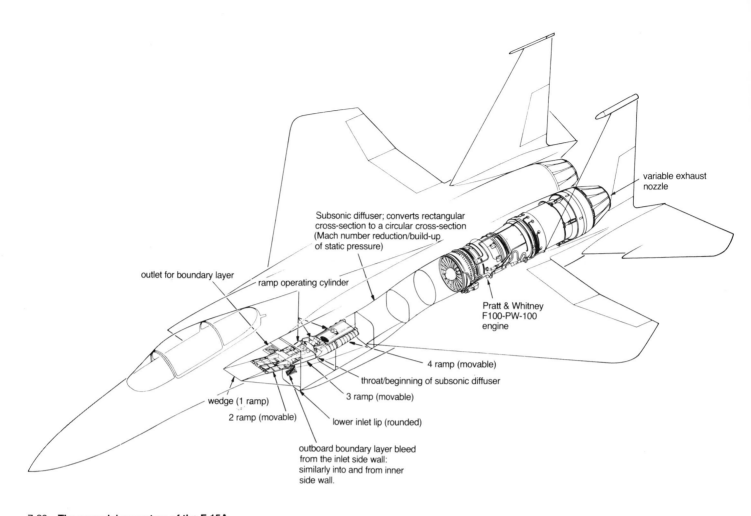

variable exhaust nozzle

Subsonic diffuser; converts rectangular cross-section to a circular cross-section (Mach number reduction/build-up of static pressure)

outlet for boundary layer

ramp operating cylinder

Pratt & Whitney F100-PW-100 engine

4 ramp (movable)

throat/beginning of subsonic diffuser

3 ramp (movable)

wedge (1 ramp)

2 ramp (movable)

lower inlet lip (rounded)

outboard boundary layer bleed from the inlet side wall: similarly into and from inner side wall.

7-29 **The propulsion system of the F-15A.**

In order to determine the optimum inlet configuration, parametric studies were carried out in the wind tunnel on a large number of model inlets. The range of configurations included fuselage-integrated engine locations as well as separate engine locations below the wing. Twin-engine arrangements with a common inlet module were also considered, but this solution was ruled out because the immediate proximity of both inlets led to undesirable reciprocal flow interferences.

Individual suspension of the engines at underwing stations also appeared tempting, because in this way a straight and relatively short subsonic diffuser can be realized, which has the advantage of a good overall length/weight ratio. However, the relatively high drag and the unfavourable behaviour when an engine fails told against this solution.

Hence only fuselage-mounted inlets were put on the short-list. All conceivable configurations were examined, for instance, two-dimensional intakes with single compression ramps as well as opposed ramps, axisymrnetric intakes with translating full spike as well as half spike, and so on. All inlets were investigated with regard to total pressure recovery and distortion at high flight Mach numbers and angles-of-attack as well as with regard to drag and weight.

External compression flow was selected for the supersonic speed regime, be-cause the alternative to this, i.e. mixed compression, would have brought additional difficulties and greater manufacture costs. Axisymmetric inlet shapes (Mirage, MiG-21) were ruled out because of their sensitivity to oblique flow. This is particularly important for an air superiority fighter, which must frequently fly manoeuvres in the high angle-of-attack range. Because of the suitability of two-dimensional inlets, further experiments therefore were concentrated on this type of inlet, which has a better pressure recovery and little flow distortion. A further advantage is the relatively low development risk.

Now the important thing to establish was the number of shocks to be used to

7-30 **Inlet of the F-15 with variable capture area.**
Above: the adjustment of the complete ramp system at high angles-of-attack reduces the capture area and decreases the inlet drag.
Below: in the high-speed flight position the ramp system pivots upwards.

decelerate the supersonic flow. The three-shock diffuser (two oblique and one terminating normal shock), as chosen for the Tornado, as well as the more costly four-shock diffuser were considered. The three-shock diffuser, i.e. with fixed compression ramp and a hinged ramp, turned out, however, in the course of the investigations to be unsuitable in meeting the manoeuvring requirements at Mach 2.2 and therefore was ruled out of further consideration.

CHOICE OF FINAL CONFIGURATION

After the decision was taken in favour of the four-shock diffuser, ways of determining the final configuration had to be found. In particular, it was a matter of keeping the structural weight low.

An inlet with variable capture area seemed favourable for achieving low drag and for matching to the engine. However, four-shock diffusers with constant capture area were also investigated. The aim was to discover the configuration which could best meet the performance requirements.

For this purpose, four different inlets were designed as four-shock diffusers and investigated in a parametric study in the wind tunnel. The inlets differed in the size of the capture area, which was variable in the case of two inlets, as well as in the position of the shocks with relation to each other. Shock position depends on length and the angular adjustment of the compression ramps. The configurations had different bypass systems which diverted the excess air either immediately in front of the compressor inlet or in the throat.

The variable capture area was designed in such a way, in the case of one of the four inlets, that the compression wedge lying in front was movable, while the angular adjustment of the second and third ramps depended on the flow direction. As an alternative solution, an inlet was investigated with variable capture area, three compression ramps, all ramps rotating with angle-of-attack and Mach. For typical missions and maximum performance at the design points, this configuration turned out to be superior to the other competing inlets and was therefore adopted for quantity production. Since then this type of inlet with its pivoting ramp system has been one of the characteristic features of the F-15 (Fig. 7-30).

INTEGRATION

According to the previously described methods flow-field investigations were carried out on fuselage-inlet models of the F-15 in order to ensure the integration of the inlet with the complete aircraft. As a result of these investigations the following modifications were made to the fuselage:
- better rounding of the lower fuselage surface;
- avoidance of flattened fuselage side walls (a rectangular cross-section is unfavourable);
- raising of the fuselage nose line;
- raising forebody maximum width above inlet level.

The effectiveness of the last-named measure becomes clear from a comparison of the flow developments: the considerable downwind components in the upper inlet area disappear almost completely after the correction (Fig. 7-31).

MEASURES TOWARDS FURTHER INLET IMPROVEMENT

Further studies were carried out in order to improve the inlet configuration. Among these are:
1. The inlet geometry 'schedules' were optimized. This measure also served to improve handling qualities.
2. The trailing edge of the third ramp was raised somewhat, so that the excess air could enter the bypass duct more smoothly. The resulting advantage is a higher total pressure with low flow losses in the bypass system.
3. The lower inlet lip was reshaped and moved downwards slightly to prevent flow separations at high angles-of-attack. Test at Mach 1.6 and 2.2 are reported to have shown that no drag increases resulted.

The complete inlet system is controlled by an electronic digital computer (air inlet controller, AIC). The computer contains the preprogrammed inlet geometry schedules, which depend on angle-of-attack, the flight Mach number, the Mach number in the throat cross-section and the total temperature of the external flow.

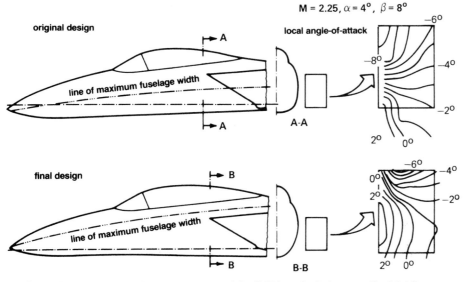

7-31 **Corrective measures at the fuselage nose of the F-15 in order to improve the inlet flow.**

SUBSTANTIATION OF INLET PERFORMANCE

The inlet performance was established on a full-scale model in the Arnold Engineering Development Center (AEDC) wind tunnel at Mach numbers 0.6, 0.9, 1.8, 2.0 and 2.2. The model consisted of an airworthy prototype inlet and a fuselage forward section mock-up at a scale of 1:1. At the same time, an F-15 served as a control test for the propulsion system. The port inlet of this aircraft was instrumented in exactly the same way for purposes of comparison as the large-scale inlet measured in the wind tunnel (Fig. 7-32).

EFFECTS ON FLIGHT CHARACTERISTICS

The movement of the inlet forward section is used in the first place to achieve a high total pressure recovery and improvement of distortion behaviour. However, the inlet configuration cannot only be seen in this context. The reason for this has to do with the size of the inlet relative to the entire aircraft. The upper surface of the movable section reaches about 30% of the horizontal tail surface and is located far enough forward of the aircraft's centre of gravity (about one reference wing chord), so that the aerodynamic forces acting on it, depending on the ramp angle, have noticeable effects on the pitching moment behaviour of the aircraft. In fact, this influence can amount to 10% of the horizontal tail effectiveness at subsonic speed, and at supersonic speeds even 30%.

The stability increase caused by lowering the inlet (nose-down moment) counteracts an insufficient stability of the basic configuration in critical cases, and makes the aircraft easier for the pilot to fly.

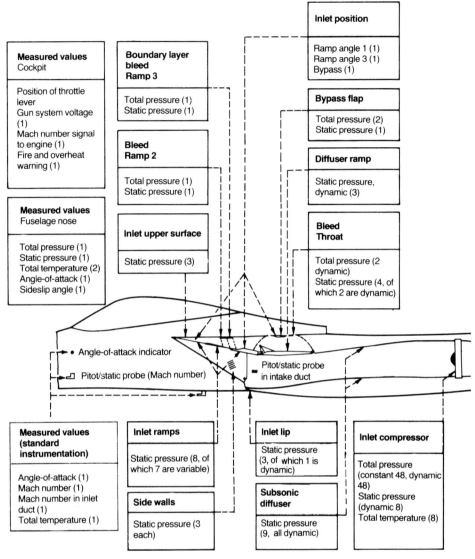

Numbers in brackets = number of test data pick-ups

7-32 **Instrumentation of the F-15 inlets for flight tests and comparative wind tunnel measurements.**

7.7.2.2 INLET DESIGN OF THE F-16

The F-16 is a tactical multi-purpose combat aircraft whose primary role is air superiority. Accordingly, the main operational range is in the subsonic and transonic regimes; supersonic Mach numbers up to a maximum of 2 can also be reached, however. The propulsion is effected by means of the same engine used in the F-15 (Pratt & Whitney F100).

The F-16 belongs to the new generation of highly manoeuvrable lightweight fighters.

The inlet of the F-16 differs fundamentally from the previously described inlet of the F-15. The requirement of simplicity led to an uncomplicated fixed-geometry normal shock diffuser which is arranged on the lower fuselage surface (ventral surface) (Fig. 7-33).

7-33 **F-16 lightweight fighter prototype with pitot type inlet.**

REQUIREMENTS

Corresponding to the F-16's role as an air superiority fighter, specific criteria were laid down for the design and arrangement of the inlet. Just as in every case, the assessment was also made with respect to pressure recovery, distortion, drag and inlet/engine compatibility. The particular requirements were:

1. Maximum ultilizable energy potential due to high total pressure recovery and low spillage drag in the manoeuvre range between M = 0.6 and M = 1.6.
2. No restriction of the flight range as a result of insufficient inlet/engine compatibility. Even in the limiting range of angles-of-attack and sideslip angles the engine must be completely capable of acceleration (snap throttle operation).
3. Although a maximum speed corresponding to Mach 2 should be attainable, it should not be at the expense of a reduced performance.
4. Minimum weight as a means of reaching performance targets and reducing costs.
5. Simple construction, in order to ensure high reliability with minimum maintenance.

First estimations of the angle-of-attack and sideslip angle ranges which could be flown were carried out empirically and the results obtained were then improved, taking into account the wind-tunnel experiments. These estimations were made with the aid of simulation techniques, with all conceivable flight manoeuvres being run through on the simulator. The improved estimated values obtained for the efficiency of the aircraft determined the angle-of-attack and the sideslip angle limits within which the planned inlet model was to be studied.

For the inlet design the required air mass flow of the F100 engine was important. The mass flow to be coped with by the inlet fluctuates between the maximum engine air-flow at take-off and the minimum mass flow at idling speed.

The distortion requirements were specified by the engine manufacturer for the low-pressure and the high-pressure compressor. In general, it appeared that the fan section (low-pressure compressor) reacts more sensitively to flow distortions and was therefore significant when establishing the maximum permissible degree of distortion.

DESCRIPTION OF INLET

The inlet of the F-16 is a fixed-geometry normal shock diffuser which is located beneath the underside of the fuselage. It is at a distance of about 4 metres (13 ft) from the fuselage nose. This inlet position ensures a uniform flow field at all angle-of-attack and sideslip-angle combinations within the manoeuvre range. The shielding effect of the fuselage on the intake flow turns out to be favourable (see Fig. 7-21). This makes it possible to fly angles-of-attack up to 30 degrees without a drop in total pressure recovery. Even at 40 degrees angle-of-attack stable inlet operation is still possible. The co-ordination of gun muzzle and inlet positions, moreover, prevents the intake of hot muzzle gases from the gun. The nose wheel is located behind the inlet aperture, so that debris thrown up cannot get into the engine (Fig. 7-34). In order to avoid flow separations at high angles-of-attack, the inlet lip is well rounded in the lower area. The upper section near the fuselage is, on the contrary, designed as a sharp-edged diverter whose edge is set forwards (see also Fig. 7-21). This prevents the compression shock located in front of the inlet at supersonic Mach numbers from penetrating the fuselage boundary layer. This prevents negative interactions between shock and bound-

7-34 **The inlet of the F-16.**

ary layer. A streamlined strut in the front inlet duct is intended to prevent deformations of the inlet, under load, and to give the lightweight design additional strength.

Auxiliary inlets are located near the fuselage and increase the intake area at take-off and in low-speed flight. The duct between diverter and fuselage is designed in such a way that the boundary layer is bled under minimum drag. This is the area in which the inlet apertures for the supply of the cabin ventilation system and the heat exchanger are also located.

The relatively long subsonic diffuser, equal to more than five engine inlet diameters, is an essential feature of the inlet system. The gradual increase in cross-section (diffuser effect) causes an almost linear Mach number drop between throat and compressor face, so that the diffuser losses remain low (Fig. 7-35). The inlet is sized in such a way that, with maximum mass flow, in the throat a flow Mach

number of 0.75 occurs. Between the inlet plane (capture area) and the throat the flow duct contracts accelerating the flow. This is caused by the rounding of the lip. On the other hand, contraction was deliberately aimed at, as an acceleration has a damping effect on the distortion. The relevant contraction ratio, from the capture area to the throat, is 1.16.

A characteristic of the maintenance-friendly design is the modular construction, which permits the replacement of the entire 2.63 metre-long (9 ft) inlet module in one piece. Moreover, there is the possibility of equipping later versions with larger or variable inlets, in case the operating range should be extended beyond Mach 2.

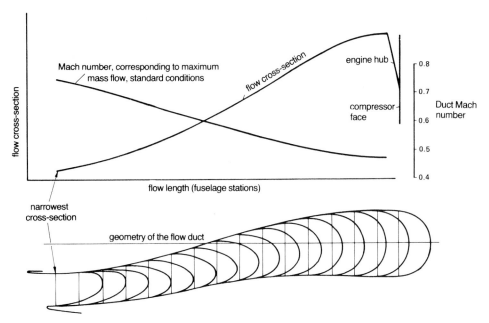

7-35 Geometry of the F-16 duct.
The gradual increase in cross-section makes an almost linear Mach-number drop possible between throat and compressor face.

inlet position. Compared with the lateral inlet and the freely moving inlet, the ventral inlet provides the lowest local Mach numbers and flow angularity at high angles-of-attack.

With a ventral inlet, the rounding of the lower cowl lip, which increases the drag in the supersonic range, can in addition be reduced in radius without the fear of flow separation at higher angles-of-attack. This results in advantages for the cowl size, which can be given smaller dimensions.

At supersonic speeds the precompression is expressed in a reduced local Mach-number level, which results in higher total pressure recoveries and improved manoeuvrability.

Finally, the ventral position of the inlet leads to a more favourable boundary-layer behaviour at high angles-of-attack. The relatively thin boundary layer makes a small diverter possible which largely prevents the ingestion of low-energy flow. A resulting advantage is the low additive drag of the diverter.

CHOICE OF FINAL CONFIGURATION

In the selection of the inlet, not only the normal shock diffuser was under discussion, but also oblique-shock diffuser, whose higher efficiency at supersonic speeds is well-known. The fixed-geometry oblique shock diffuser designed for Mach 2 and the variable-geometry diffuser designed for Mach 2.2 were compared in their performance with the normal shock diffuser, a typical long-range, air-superiority mission being taken as a basis for the calculation.

The fixed-geometry oblique-shock diffuser showed, in the altitude and Mach-number ranges under consideration, considerable disadvantages in turn rate and in the acceleration behaviour of the aircraft. The reason for this lies primarily in the greater weight of this inlet, because it is necessary to match the installation of a bypass system to the air requirements of the engine.

The variable-geometry oblique-shock

diffuser, as an alternative, has also, for the same reasons, worse turn rate and longitudinal acceleration behaviour. But it shows a gain in the specific excess power (P_s) at Mach 1.6 (see Chapter 9). The conclusion was drawn from these comparisons that the simple normal shock represents the optimum solution for the F-16.

SHIELDING EFFECT OF THE FUSELAGE

The arrangement of the inlet in the shielding field of the fuselage forward section raises the manoeuvre potential of the F-16 considerably. The lower surface of the fuselage exerts a shielding effect on the flow which ensures high pressure recovery and low distortion at high angles-of-attack. The investigation results of the previously mentioned experimental study 'Project Taylor-Mate' clearly show the advantage of the ventral

PERFORMANCE OF THE F-16 INLET

The inlet performance with regard to the total pressure recovery shows the advantage of the ventral inlet position of the F-16 (Fig. 7-36). At subsonic speeds the pressure recovery occurring in steady level flight remains up to angles-of-attack of 30 degrees, and drops at higher angles-of-attack only, because the flow starts to separate at the lip. As a result of the shock losses the pressure recoveries become smaller with increasing flight Mach number at $\alpha = 0°$. This effect can also be calculated by means of simple gas dynamic relations (see equation in Fig. 7-36 and the results obtained).

However, an advantage of the ventral inlet position is a considerable increase in pressure recovery with increasing angle-of-attack at supersonic speeds, which is due to the positive influence of the fuselage nose.

The parameters determined with rakes for distortion and turbulence show good

182

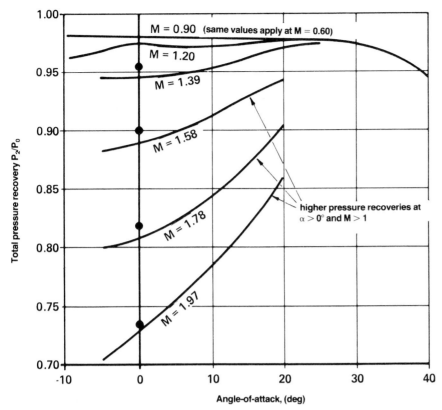

$$\frac{P_2}{P_o} = \frac{7M_o^2 - 1}{6} \left[\frac{1 - \dfrac{0.2M_o^2}{1+0.2M_o^2}}{1 - \dfrac{1+0.2M_o^2}{7.2M_o^2}} \right]^{3.5}$$

● calculated

M_o	P_2/P_o
1.2	0.99
1.39	0.96
1.58	0.90
1.78	0.82
1.97	0.73

7-36   **Influence of angle-of-attack and Mach number on pressure recovery.**

to satisfactory engine/inlet compatibility in the entire flight range.

The stability of the inlet flow at very low mass flows was also established. This case is important, for example, when the pilot throttles back the engine at high airspeeds and, as a consequence of the pronounced sub-critical operation, diffuser buzz occurs. In experiments the mass flow was throttled so far back that the flow conditions in the inlet were suf-ficiently subcritical to reach the limit of diffuser buzz. If the buzz did not occur, the inlet was fully blocked by the flow. These experiments were carried out for numerous angle-of-attack and sideslip combinations, from which the limits of stable inlet operation could be derived. It is the inlet control unit's task to set a lower limit for the engine speed, if nec-essary, to keep the mass flow always above the danger limit. The large range of stable inlet operation made the intro-duction of a separate bypass system to bleed the excess air unnecessary.

The normal-shock diffuser of the F-16 and its position in the shielding field is an excellent solution for a single-jet air superiority fighter and is optimum from the point of view of inlet/engine compati-bility.

8 Integration II: Problems in Tail Design

The problems arising from the interaction between exhaust nozzle and airframe turn out to be just as difficult to solve as inlet/airframe integration. The reciprocal interference between the flow field of the aircraft and the exhaust jet leads, as a rule, to a drag increase, which often conflicts with the predicted results.

The use of engines with afterburning requires variable exhaust nozzles which cause considerable changes in exhaust area. This leads to adverse aerodynamic effects; such as fuselage contours which are not the optimum, or – for twin-jet aircraft – non-optimum interfairings between the engines.

Also of great importance is the arrangement of control surfaces which are immediately next to the exhaust nozzles. In total these factors are critical for a more or less non-uniform flow field, which – due to exhaust jet interference – may cause a considerable alteration of the tail drag up to local flow separation. The consequence is always an increase of drag.

The behaviour of the universally employed symmetrical, circular nozzles has long been understood. That is provided that the nozzle is isolated from, and is not influenced by, the flow field of the aircraft. Until recently, relatively little was known, however, about the appropriate method of integrating the exhaust nozzle with the aircraft tail; particularly about the extent of installation losses and the effect of tail design on drag. This factor is particularly significant with twin-jet combat aircraft, because above all the space needed for the twin propulsion systems, with their large-area exhaust nozzle cross-sections makes it difficult to design an aerodynamically favourable tail.

The drag problem with tail design was investigated in particular in the USA at great expense; the airforce, industry and NASA participated with several large-scale programmes.

In Western Europe, too, experience was accumulated during the development of the Tornado. Investigations in optimizing tail drag are today part of the standard development programme of every aircraft.

Experimental programmes have proved that tail drag with single-jet and twin-jet combat aircraft configurations is influenced by numerous factors, for example:

- afterbody local flow separations,
- horizontal and vertical tail surfaces as well as their relation to each other,
- fairing of movable tail surfaces,
- projecting tail support booms,
- ventral fins.

Steps to reduce drag can be derived from the above. In the following, some important conclusions from these investigations will be reviewed.

8.1 Origin of Tail Drag

All nozzles designed for high flight Mach numbers generate, in the low-speed range, a noticeable tail drag which reduces net thrust. In unfavourable cases this drag can amount to 30% of engine thrust.

This negative effect is because modern high-performance aircraft are able to fly at subsonic and supersonic speeds. They not only have variable inlets but also variable exhaust nozzles. The limited fuel supply on board makes it necessary to fly a greater part of a sortie in the more economical subsonic range; with the exhaust nozzle set at its smallest area (Fig. 8-1). As a result of the body

8-1 **In subsonic cruising flight the exhaust nozzle is operated with its smallest exit cross-section (Grumman F-14).**

shape, which is unfavourable for flow, tail drag arises at the nozzle which depends on a number of factors, for example:
– nozzle length
– nozzle power setting
– nozzle pressure ratio
– gas properties
– airspeed.

To give an idea of the mechanism of drag formation, the flow around a body of revolution will be considered (Fig. 8-2).

Immediately in front of the body, the flow stagnates and then flows off uniformly to all sides. The stagnation streamline leads to the stagnation point S,

where the flow comes to rest completely (w = 0). At this point the pressure coefficient C_p (definition see Fig. 4-12) reaches its greatest possible value ($C_p = 1$). The final acceleration of the flow leads to maximum pressure decrease (pressure minimum) at the thickest point of the body. Beyond this point the flow is decelerated again as the pressure rises.

For an air particle close to the wall in frictionless flow, the kinetic energy at the point of maximum body thickness (point D) would just be enough to overcome the pressure rise to the aft stagnation point H. The air particle would thereby be able

to get from S via D to H, where it comes to rest and is then carried away with the external flow.

If all the pressure forces acting at the body in an **axial** direction are added up, in ideal (frictionless) flow, these would amount to zero drag. In real (friction-affected) flow the actual pressure distribution deviates from the ideal, so that the pressure integral assumes a value different from zero (Fig. 8-2, dotted line). The resultant force is called **form drag.**

This relationship can be demonstrated by a mechanical analog, as shown. A frictionless sphere rolls on the plotted

185

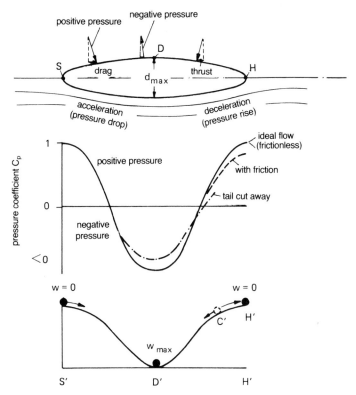

8-2 **Pressure distribution around a body of revolution to explain tail drag.**

path from S' to H'. However, if friction occurs, the sphere comes to rest at C' and rolls back again.

Now, let the assumption be made that a section of the body of revolution is cut off in the tail area. This results in the pressure distribution being changed once again in such a way that only a small thrust-increasing positive pressure zone can form at the tail (dash-and-dot line).

The summation of the pressures in the axial direction now yields a higher drag. This is caused solely by the altered geometrical proportions in the tail area.

This **afterbody drag** is usually split into two components, **base drag** and **boat-tail drag.** The base drag is the sum of all pressures over the rearward facing area normal to the freestream. That is with the exception of the jet exhaust surface. Boat-tail drag acts on the tapering side walls.

The aircraft constructor's problem is to establish the determining factors of boat-tail drag and to look for ways of reducing it.

8.2 **Drag of the Individual Nozzles**

The basic formation of tail drag has been discribed using a body of revolution. A better idea of drag behaviour is obtained with a model more closely related to reality. For this purpose a convergent nozzle contiguous with a cylindrical duct will be considered (Fig. 8-3).

At the transition to the convergent section the external flow must be accelerated in order to be able to follow the contour. This causes centrifugal forces on the air particles, generating negative pressure on the nozzle surface. The axial component of negative pressure acts as drag. At the end of the nozzle the flow

near the wall is automatically diverted into the axial direction again, the pressure rises, and its axial components produce thrust. The acceleration and deceleration processes on the nozzle surface are dependent on the profile of the nozzle contour and on the exhausting jet. The jet in particular has a continuous influence on the pressure distribution in two respects:

1. The jet acts like a solid body which displaces the external flow.
2. The jet entrains air from its immediate surroundings (mass flow entrainment).

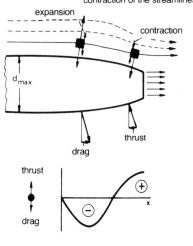

Centrifugal forces as a consequence of flow curvature cause expansion or contraction of the streamlines.

8-3 **Flow conditions at a convergent nozzle.**

186

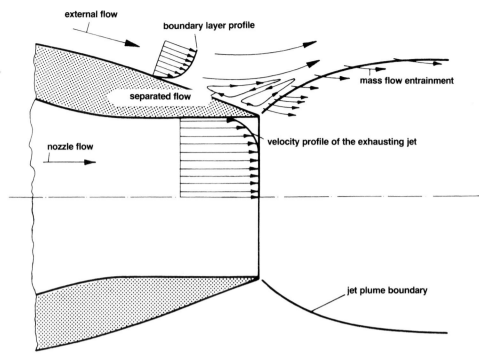

external flow

boundary layer profile

separated flow

mass flow entrainment

nozzle flow

velocity profile of the exhausting jet

jet plume boundary

8-4 **Suction effect of the jet.**

nozzle leads, on the contrary, with surface and nozzle pressure ratios constant, to the fact that practically no thrust force can act any more, but only drag (this description is for a nozzle pressure ratio $P_0/p = 3$, which is representative of combat aircraft engines with low bypass ratios).

These two influences conflict. Whereas the jet raises the tail pressure and thus reduces the drag – in particular when it expands after leaving the nozzle – the positive influence of the curvature effect in the rear area of the nozzle is reduced by entrainment (Fig. 8-4).

INFLUENCE OF TAIL GEOMETRY

An important factor in drag behaviour is the angle which the nozzle contour forms with the axis (Fig. 8-5). The comparison of nozzles with different angles shows that the expansion (acceleration of the flow) along the transition contour from cylindrical to conical section also takes place gradually. Therefore only a weak negative pressure with correspondingly low drag can build up. A short

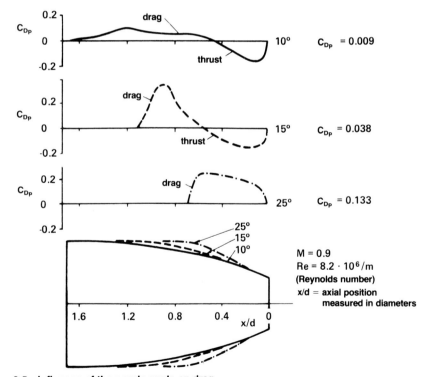

C_{D_P}

drag

thrust

$10°$ $C_{D_P} = 0.009$

C_{D_P}

drag

thrust

$15°$ $C_{D_P} = 0.038$

C_{D_P}

drag

$25°$ $C_{D_P} = 0.133$

$25°$
$15°$
$10°$

$M = 0.9$
$Re = 8.2 \cdot 10^6/m$
(Reynolds number)
$x/d =$ **axial position**
measured in diameters

1.6   1.2   0.8   0.4   0

x/d

8-5 **Influence of the nozzle angle on drag.**

187

8.3 **Afterbody Effects in Single-Jet Combat Aircraft**

The development of single-jet light-weight fighters has emphasised the need to reduce drag as much as possible, so that the performance potential can be fully exploited. Among the factors which particularly influence drag are:
- afterbody design
- shape of the nozzle in both open and closed positions
- nozzle pressure ratio
- tail configuration.

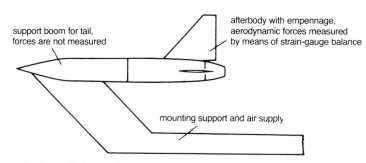

8-6　**Tail model for realistic simulation of the exhaust jet.**

TAIL INVESTIGATION USING EXPERIMENTAL MODELS

The optimum tail design of an aircraft can be determined in the wind tunnel. In this respect, it is sufficient to use only a part of the aircraft, namely the afterbody. Wings are normally not present, and even the fuselage nose usually does not correspond to the complicated contour shape of the real aircraft, but rather to an easily produced basic body. However, the fuselage nose provides a method of mounting the model and of supplying air (Fig. 8-6). The built-in nozzles are of the convergent/divergent type, provided that the full-scale model will also have this nozzle shape. As a rule, two extreme nozzle settings are investigated, namely the purely convergent setting with smallest area, which is 'run' with switched-off afterburner (dry operation), as well as the setting with fully-opened cross-section, which is necessary when the afterburner is switched on. Compressed air at ambient temperature is the principal method of simulating the propulsive jet.

The tail surfaces can usually be mounted in different axial positions.

In addition the horizontal tail can be displaced in the vertical direction. It is usually sufficient to use only two conventional tail surface positions: on the fuselage axis or a lower set position.

Aerodynamic forces on the afterbody-tail-nozzle combinations are measured with an internal strain-gauge balance. Forces which act on the model forebody are not measured, nor the thrust in most cases. Jet interference forces, which act on the tail configuration are, on the other

8-7　**Typical low-drag solution of the integration problem, the tail of the F-16.**

hand, taken into account and are included in the measured forces. The pressure distribution is determined by means of numerous static pressure-gauge holes on the surface, and the particular drag component calculated by integration of these pressures.

As a rule, an extensive experimental programme is necessary until a successful tail, such as that of the F-16, has been developed (Fig. 8-7).

8.4 **Afterbody Effects in Twin-jet Combat Aircraft**

An effective integration of nozzle and afterbody is a great deal more difficult with twin-jet than with single-jet aircraft. Apart from the variables which influence single-jet combat aircraft, already mentioned, there are important factors, namely **nozzle spacing** and **contouring** of the space between the nozzles, to be taken into consideration. Insufficient integration can, in certain conditions, lead to flow separations which can increase drag considerably.

Mathematical procedures to establish these influences are scarcely applicable, because of the complexity of the flow around the tail. This applies particularly in the transonic speed range, where the procedures fail even with simple afterbody configurations. Experiments in the wind tunnel are therefore all the more important. They are almost the only way to get reliable results. Here the problem arises, however, of their applicability to the full-scale design as well as the question of how close the simulation is to reality.

In parallel with the development of the new generation of combat aircraft, comprehensive experimental studies were carried out, particularly in the USA, on the problem of tail interference. The published technical data on the investigation results afford an insight into the aerodynamic relations.

EXPERIMENTAL TECHNIQUES

In order to determine the influences which occur at the integral nozzle and at the tail, the usual procedure is to compare the pressure distribution and the drag of the nozzle on the test stand with the values of the integral nozzle.

In the particular study reported here, the nozzle measured in isolation at the body of revolution was consequently the first step in determining the required tail configuration (Fig. 8.8, configuration A). By incorporating the nozzle pair into a wing/fuselage combination similar to a twin-jet combat aircraft, it could be investigated on a representative model (con-

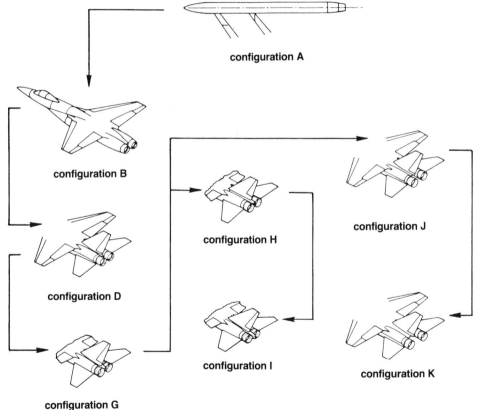

configuration A

configuration B

configuration D

configuration G

configuration H

configuration I

configuration J

configuration K

8-8   **Configuration buildup for the investigation of afterbody/nozzle effects on twin-jet combat aircraft.**

figuration B). By adding tail surfaces their influence also could be determined. Tails were usually used which did not have the full span. This was done in order to keep down the structural loading of the model. This procedure is permissible because the influence on the flow by that part of the tail surfaces which is cut away is small.

Various forms of interfairing were also investigated. Configuration D had a horizontal wedge-shaped interfairing which isolated the nozzles. In configuration G the interfairing was extended to the end of the nozzles. Configuration H also had an extended interfairing, but with a vertical wedge. With configuration I the vertical wedge interfairing extended beyond the end of the nozzles.

All the configurations mentioned up to now had a relatively small engine spacing. This is usually expressed by the ratio of the axial spacing s of the nozzles to the nozzle diameter d at the mounting flange. The measurement in the example examined amounted to an s/d of 1.25. In configuration J the ratio was enlarged to 1.625 and in configuration K to 2.0.

The experiments were carried out for two representative nozzle power settings, namely, the convergent setting, which characterizes subsonic cruising flight, and the convergent-divergent setting which is necessary in maximum afterburner for a Mach number greater than 1.

It is not possible within the limitations of this description to discuss the results individually. Moreover, it appears that many parameters are configurationally determined, which makes it difficult to make generally valid statements.

The intention has been to give only an impression of what needs to be examined during the design of a combat aircraft.

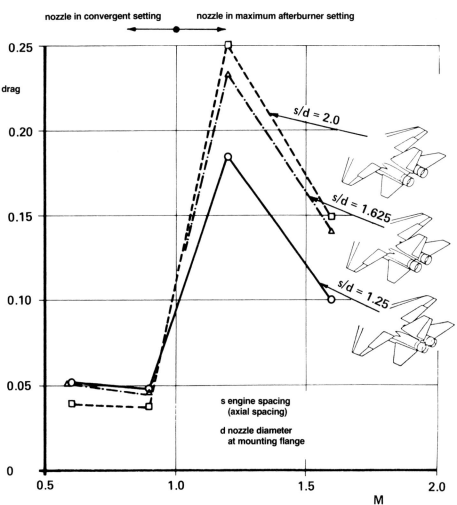

8-9 **Influence of engine spacing on drag.**

INFLUENCE OF ENGINE SPACING

Results of investigations on even simple models of engine spacing can be of value.

The relative position of the engines and thus of the nozzles with respect to each other is an important factor in the design of a twin-jet combat aircraft.

At subsonic Mach numbers the pressure rises at the afterbody, at the nozzles and at the interfairing with increasing engine spacing. This causes a decrease in drag of all components mentioned. For supersonic combat aircraft, which have to cover large distances in the subsonic range economically, a relatively large engine spacing is therefore advantageous (Fig. 8-9). These considerations may have played a part in the design of the F-14, which is distinguished by a noticeably large engine spacing (see Figs. 8-1 and 5-12, right).

At supersonic speeds, on the contrary, the drag is at its lowest when the nozzles are close together. The cause of this is the smaller wave drag as a result of the favourable cross-sectional area distribution.

8.5 **F-15 Afterbody Integration**

Using the example of the F-15, the design decisions and steps will be shown which led to the afterbody design of this outstanding combat aircraft.

The performance of the F-15 represents a considerable advance compared with earlier tactical combat aircraft. The successful integration of engine and airframe made an important contribution to the design (Fig. 8-10).

The afterbody design was based almost exclusively on wind-tunnel investigations, as theoretical procedures could not determine reliably the interaction of the exhaust jets with the (external) flow field of the aircraft. At the beginning of the F-15 programme only scanty data were available from previous experimental studies with which to design an advanced afterbody configuration. For this reason an extensive wind-tunnel experimental programme was carried out in order to increase the fund of knowledge related to the complicated flow conditions in the tail area. A basic design could be derived from this which was subsequently improved for the purpose of increasing performance. This was also intended to provide a reliable prediction of flight performance.

During the development of the afterbody numerous system studies and wind-tunnel experiments were carried out. Mainly conventional, axisymmetric nozzles were investigated, but also some rectangular nozzles. The essential elements of these studies will be described.

8-10 **A successful integration of the propulsion system into the airframe: the F-15 twin-jet combat aircraft.**

AFTERBODY WITH AXISYMMETRIC NOZZLES

The installation of axisymmetric nozzles in twin-jet combat aircraft leads to complicated interference phenomena, for which the following factors are decisive (Fig. 8-11):
– exhaust plume effects
– afterbody contour
– nozzle/afterbody closure
– tail support booms
– inter-nozzle fairing
– position of the tail surfaces
– engine spacing.

Determination of engine spacing was based on test results obtained by NASA. The essential finding from this was that for supersonic flight the smallest possible engine spacing is to be aimed at. It is even desirable for the nozzles to touch each other at their mounting flanges. However as this would have encountered structural difficulties, an engine spacing for the F-15 was chosen of 1.1 flange diameters, instead of one flange diameter (the engine spacing is stated as the distance between the axes of both engines).

An important investigation point concerned the influence which the tail booms have under cruise conditions. From NASA's measurement two fundamental findings could be derived for this:

1. Boom fairings increase drag, especially when they choke the flow in the duct between fairing and nozzle (Mach 1 in the duct).
2. The interference drag does not act on the fairings but at the nozzle.

To obtain a low-drag solution it was necessary to have the largest practicable distance between the tail support booms and the nozzles (Fig. 8-12).

The space between the jets was filled by a narrow horizontal wedge extending to the end of the nozzles (see also Fig. 8-10). By this means favourable flow guidance was attained and the danger of flow separation avoided.

Following the recognition of those cri-

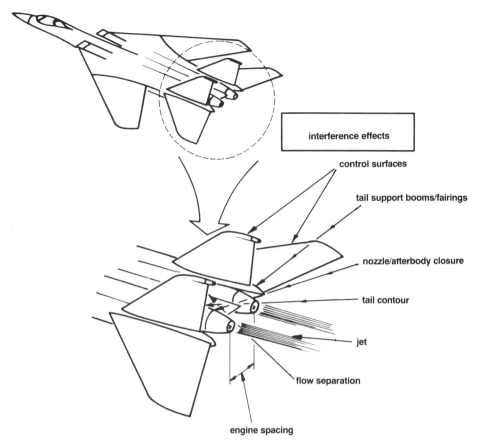

8-11 Factors influencing tail drag on twin-jet combat aircraft.

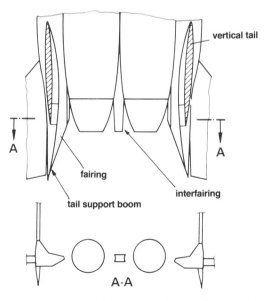

8-12 The tail support booms must have a large lateral distance from the nozzles to avoid flow blocking effects: tail configurations of the F-15 before optimization.

teria essential for the preliminary tail design, further studies had to be undertaken in order to establish the final tail configuration. Particular attention had to be paid to equating performance with weight. The minimum-weight solution turned out to be the least favourable because it would have needed a relatively blunt tail where consequent drag would have offset any weight-saving.

AFTERBODY WITH TWO-DIMENSIONAL NOZZLES

Two-dimensional or rectangular nozzles (2-D nozzles) can be well integrated with the tail, particularly when the engines are very close together. Such a solution suggests a low interference drag and is, therefore, well-suited for a tactical aircraft sensitive to drag (Fig. 8-13).

Together with the two major engine manufacturers General Electric and Pratt & Whitney an extensive experimental programme was carried out. The configuration selected for evaluation featured a double wedge mounted horizontally across the exhaust duct, thereby providing 'twin-throats' for each nozzle. This led to the name 'Twin Throat Nozzle'. A further advantage of this nozzle is the easily effected jet deflection (thrust vector control, thrust reversal), although this possibility was not contained in the design specification of the F-15.

CHOICE OF FINAL CONFIGURATION

The establishment of the final afterbody configuration and the selection of suitable nozzles was based on performance comparisons carried out with the aid of measured results. The two engine companies mentioned provided data for six convergent/divergent nozzle types with circular cross-section, while McDonnell's studies of rectangular nozzles were included in the final comparative evaluation.

The points of emphasis in the study were:
- installed performance,
- structural weight,
- development risk (state of the art),
- maintenance costs.

Flight performance was calculated ac-

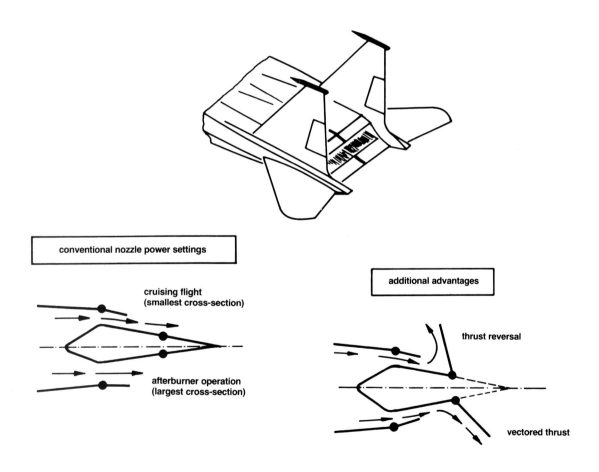

conventional nozzle power settings

cruising flight (smallest cross-section)

afterburner operation (largest cross-section)

additional advantages

thrust reversal

vectored thrust

8-13 **The ease with which a two-dimensional nozzle can be integrated with the afterbody makes this type nozzle particularly suited for tactical combat aircraft.**

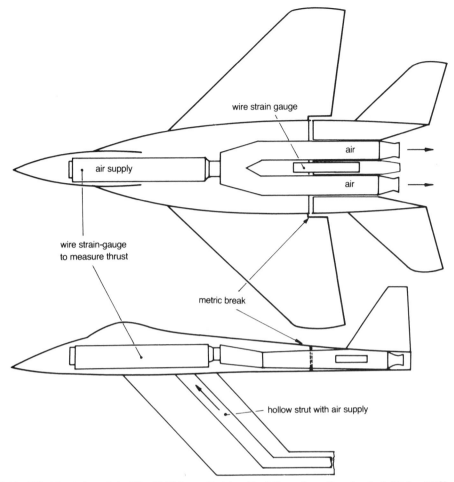

- influences of the metric-to-nonmetric splitline location.

The wind-tunnel experiments themselves included the effects of the following variables:
- nozzle fairing
- nozzle power setting (cruising and afterburner setting)
- nozzle pressure ratio
- position of the vertical tail
- ventral fins.

The tail configuration had, before its optimization, practically all elements of the production aircraft. However, differences were the use of vertical tails of smaller aspect ratio, as well as tail fins. By removing the ventral fins and simultaneously increasing the vertical tail surface by 10% a drag reduction of 5.5% was achieved (Fig. 8-15). This finding was immediately included in the 1971 production aircraft, which as a result does not have any ventral fins.

At the end of this primarily experimental investigation the F-15 afterbody appeared as a successful integration of the propulsion system into the complete aircraft (Fig. 8-16). Typical features are:
- closely adjacent engines to obtain low drag in the transonic and supersonic range;
- carefully contoured afterbody;
- tail support booms with large lateral distance from the afterbody to reduce interference drag;
- low-interference fairings of the tail support booms.

8-14 **Wind tunnel model of the F-15 for optimizing the tail configuration (scale 1:26, i.e. 3.8% of the large-scale model).**

cording to standard procedures, as is common practice in the aircraft industry (see Chapter 9). Each design was arranged so that a particular combat task could be fulfilled. For various manoeuvre points the specific excess power (P_s) was calculated.

The Twin-Throat nozzle was eliminated in spite of the ease with which it could be integrated with the tail, because at the time the weight and cooling problems had not been solved, and their installation would therefore have meant too great a development risk. However, it is certain that this type of nozzle will be developed for operational use and will be applied to future combat aircraft.

Following the decision in favour of the BBN-1.6 nozzle type, the resulting 'frozen' tail configuration was further investigated in the wind tunnel for the purpose of improving performance. A full-scale model was available mounted on a strut. In addition to the measurement of forces exerted on the tail, this also permitted measurement of the total forces (Fig. 8-14). The Mach number range for the experiments lay between $M = 0.6$ and $M = 2.5$, and the angle-of-attack range between $\alpha = -3°$ and $\alpha = +15°$.

Sources of error in the measurement which made correction necessary were above all:
- interference due to the model mounting support
- distortion of the true flow development due to the faired inlets of the jet model

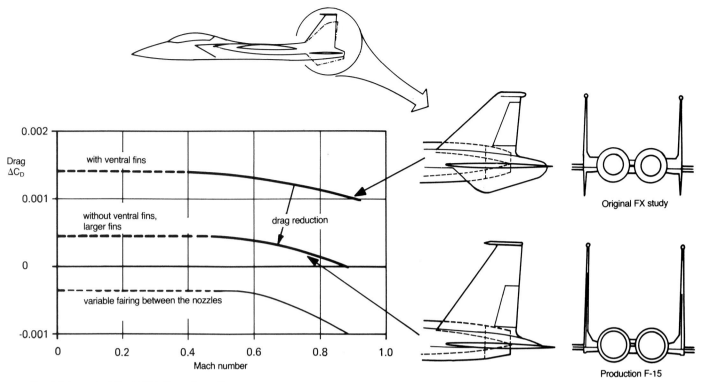

8-15 **Establishment of the F-15 tail configuration.**
Drag gains by removing the ventral fins and increasing the vertical tail surfaces by 12%.

8-16 **The tail of the F-15. Features: engines close together, afterbody favourable for flow, tail support booms with low-interference fairing.**

9 Performance

All investigations conducted during the design process, be they theoretical or empirical, are ultimately intended to answer the question: what can the aircraft do? How good is its performance in comparison to competing designs? The answer can be derived as numerical data using following variables:

- maximum Mach number or maximum speed
- service ceiling
- radius of action or range
- climbing speed
- turn rate
- acceleration
- take-off distance as a function of take-off weight
- landing distance.

The list can be continued indefinitely. As with every aircraft type, different performance variables are paramount at different times and assume different orders of importance. Thus, for combat aircraft used primarily against ground targets, what matters is manoeuvrability, military payload and flight duration; on the other hand maximum speed is less important. On the contrary, the essential criteria for an air superiority fighter are manoeuvrability and acceleration potential. The quantitative statement of the variables mentioned yields the **performance.** This can generally be divided into three groups:

1. manoeuvre performance
2. mission performance
3. field performance (take-off and landing).

The determination of the individual performance variables will be described in the following.

9.1 **Forces on the Aircraft**

When calculating performance the aircraft is considered as a rigid body moving through the airspace. The flight path is determined by the interial properties of the aircraft, gravitation, and thrust of the propulsion system, as well as aerodynamic forces and moments which arise as the air reacts to the motion of the aircraft.

When an aircraft is in unaccelerated (i.e. steady) level flight or climbing flight, the forces acting are in, so-called, **static** equilibrium; if the flight path is curved (turning flight) or the flight accelerated, the forces are in **dynamic** equilibrium.

First of all, consideration will be given to those forces which are effective in straight flight (Fig. 9-1). For this it is ex-pedient to introduce a system of co-ordinates and to resolve the forces in the direction of the axes. The x-axis is arbitrarily placed in such a way that it lies in the direction of flow, the z-axis is perpendicular to it and points downwards (the y-axis, which is not needed here, is perpendicular to the page and points in the clockwise direction to the starboard wing. It is also assumed that all forces act at the centre of gravity (c.g.).[38] The inclination of the flight path with the horizontal is termed γ, the angle between the flight path and the aircraft's longitudinal axis is the angle-of-attack α.

Equilibrium in straight flight and in symmetrical flow (no sideslip) means that in each case the sum of all forces K_x or K_z, with reference to the x-axis or the z-axis respectively, is zero (see Fig. 9-1):

$$\Sigma K_x = -W \sin \gamma - D + T \cos\alpha - m_{A/C}b_t = 0$$
$$(9.1)$$

$$\Sigma K_z = W \cos \gamma - L - T \sin\alpha + m_{A/C}b_n = 0$$
$$(9.2)$$

b_t is the tangential acceleration, b_n the normal acceleration; by multiplication with the aircraft mass $m_{A/C}$ the particular mass force results (as force = mass times acceleration).

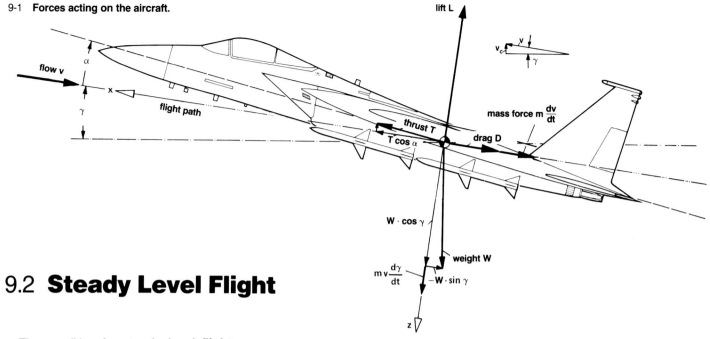

9-1 **Forces acting on the aircraft.**

9.2 **Steady Level Flight**

The condition for **steady level flight** ($\gamma = 0$) arises from the equations (9.1) and (9.2), when a small angle-of-attack[39] is also assumed (Fig. 9-2):

$$T = D \qquad (9.1a)$$
thrust drag

$$W = L \qquad (9.2a)$$
weight lift

Steady level flight forms the major part of any mission.

---

[39] At small angles-of-attack the approximation can be made $\cos\alpha = 1$ and $\sin\alpha = 0$.

lift L

thrust T

drag D

$$W = L$$
$$T = D$$

9-2 **Force equilibrium in steady level flight.**

weight W

9.2.1 Maximum altitude (Ceiling)

For steady level flight the following is derived from the lift equation:

$$W = L = \tfrac{1}{2}\rho \, v^2 \, S \, C_L$$

With Mach number $M = v/a$, the square of the speed of sound $a^2 = \kappa R t$ and from the ideal gas equation we get:

$$p = \frac{W/S}{\kappa/2 \, M^2 \, C_L} \quad (9.3)$$

As the air pressure p is a function of altitude there is a clear correlation between wing loading W/S, flight Mach number and lift coefficient. In particular the minimum pressure p_{min} is derived from the curve of maximum lift, $C_{L_{max}}$ against Mach number. From this we obtain the maximum altitude:

$$H_{max} = f \, (M, C_{L_{max}}, W/F) \quad (9.4)$$

In experimental aerodynamics there are procedures which provide approximate values of maximum lift against Mach number for a given wing geometry. After establishing the wing loading the equation 9.3, above, provides a simple method of calculating the limiting lift curve for the maximum altitude (Fig. 9-3).

The calculated curves show that a combat aircraft with high wing loading, such as the Starfighter, must raise its Mach number considerably as altitude increases in order to be able to fly at all. The relatively low wing loadings of modern lightweight fighters allow an extension of the flight envelope at lower Mach numbers toward greater altitudes.

Note: flying at the maximum altitude involves high angles-of-attack, particularly in the lower Mach number range. If this is neglected then the calculated altitude is too low according to equation (9.2a). Equation (9.2) shows that 17% of the thrust contributes to lift at an angle-of-attack of 10 degrees (sin 10° = 0.17). It is therefore more sensible to use equation (9.2) instead of equation (9.2a); provided that the thrust is a function of Mach number and flight altitude.

---

[41] The interested reader with a pocket calculator can determine the maximum level flight altitude from the $C_{L_{max}}$ curve and the relevant equations.

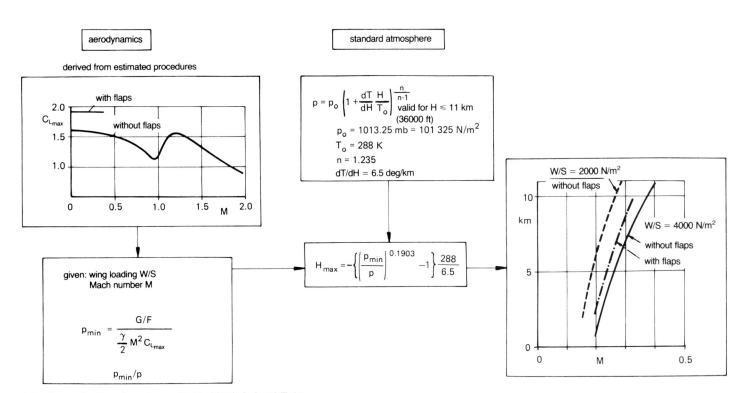

9-3 **Determination of maximum flight altitude in level flight.**

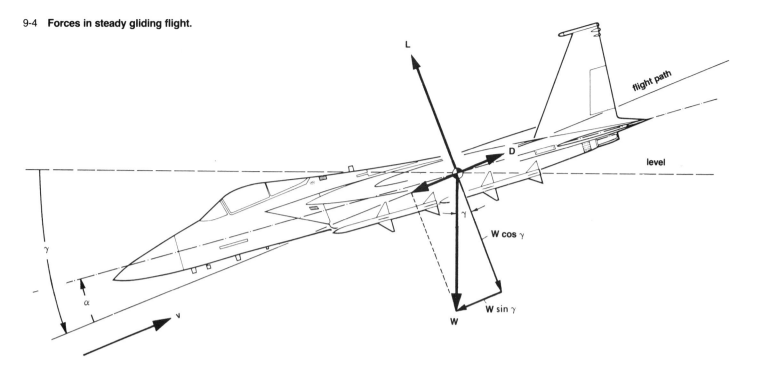

9.2.2 Lift/Drag Ratio

The downward motion of the aircraft in the power-off state takes place as if on an inclined path under the influence of weight (Fig. 9-4). The lift acts perpendicular to the flight path, and the drag acts opposite to the flight direction. As the flight condition is steady, the acceleration terms disappear in equations (9.1) and (9.2). Under these conditions the following holds:

$$- W \sin\gamma = D$$
$$W \cos\gamma = L$$

By dividing both equations it follows that

$$\tan\gamma = - \frac{D}{L} = - \frac{C_D}{C_L}$$

This equation shows that the angle of glide, and therefore the distance covered in gliding, depends only on the lift/drag ratio L/D. The greatest distance is achieved when the lift/drag ratio is a maximum. This lies, in the case of combat aircraft, between five and eight, commercial aircraft reach 12 to 15, gliders even reach 50 (i.e. for an altitude loss of 1m the aircraft flies 50m in gliding flight).

It can be shown that, with correlations of C_D and C_L which correspond to the optimum lift/drag ratio, the minimum drag is reached in horizontal flight.

Hence, the most economical flight always takes place under these optimum conditions, which for combat aircraft lie between M = 0.8 and M = 0.9, depending on the design.

9.2.3 Thrust and Drag

The flight performance results from the interaction of aerodynamics and propulsion. In order to obtain a quantitative statement for this, the thrust needed to meet the aerodynamic factors is compared with the thrust **available** from propulsion.

The thrust required arises from the drag characteristics and is dependent on Mach number, altitude and configuration. Drag development is determined in the early stage of a project with the aid of current assessment procedures. As the project advances the calculated drags are supplemented or corrected by wind-tunnel experiments. In particular, effects may be taken into account which are not amenable to mathematical procedures, such as inlet flow, tail contour, hard points (pylons) and so on (see Chapter 7 and 8).

The **thrust required** for use in performance calculations appears as a set of drag polar curves with the Mach number as parameter (Fig. 9-5, centre left). The **thrust available** (engine) is given by the engine manufacturer (see Fig. 9-5, top right). As a rule it is in the form of maximum engine airflow curves with and without afterburning. These were determined on the test stand and converted into specific altitudes and Mach numbers; taking the standard atmosphere into account (see Appendix I). In the first approximation the curves are usable in this

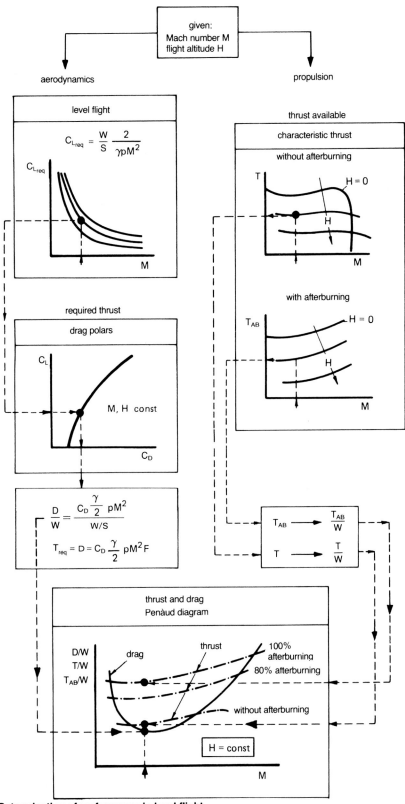

9-5 Determination of performance in level flight.

form. A realistic performance analysis must, however, make allowance for the changed installation conditions in the actual aircraft (as against the ideal conditions of the test stand). Estimating procedures are available which take into account pressure recovery, boundary-layer bleed, or nozzle efficiency. These results can be improved by means of wind-tunnel tests as the project progresses. It is particularly important that the thrust and drag components resulting from the integration of propulsion be recorded with a 'book-keeper's' accuracy in a thrust-drag balance.

The next step in the performance calculation is to plot the thrust **required** (drag) and the thrust **available** (engine) for **one** specific flight altitude at a time. In this way the so-called Penàud diagram results (see Fig. 9-5).

It is expedient to relate thrust and drag to the aircraft weight W. Also, several engine power settings, at least the maximum power curves with and without afterburning (AB), will always be entered.

First of all, the Penàud diagram shows that steady level flight is possible only when the co-ordinates of thrust required and thrust available coincide (Fig. 9-6). That is usually the case for two flight Mach numbers established by means of the points of intersection of the drag curve with the particular thrust curve. This yields, for a particular engine power setting and flight altitude, a minimum and a maximum Mach number with which unaccelerated horizontal flight is possible (point A or point B respectively). In the Mach number range between the two derived points the thrust available is greater than the thrust required. This **excess power** can be used for manoeuvring (turn, climb, pull-out). At the equilibrium points A and B there is no manoeuvrability potential. At Mach numbers outside the excess power range, i.e. smaller than M_{min} and larger than M_{max}, the thrust required is greater than the thrust available. The deficit in thrust can be compensated for by the potential energy of the aircraft. In this regime the flight can be continued only with loss of altitude (descending flight), provided that this is aerodynamically possible (danger of stall at $M < M_{min}$) or permissible from the point of view of structural strength (strength limit at $M > M_{max}$).

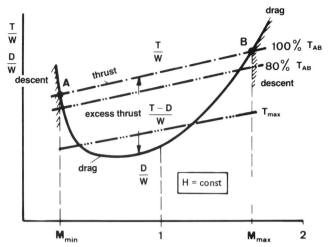

9-6 **Penàud diagram.**

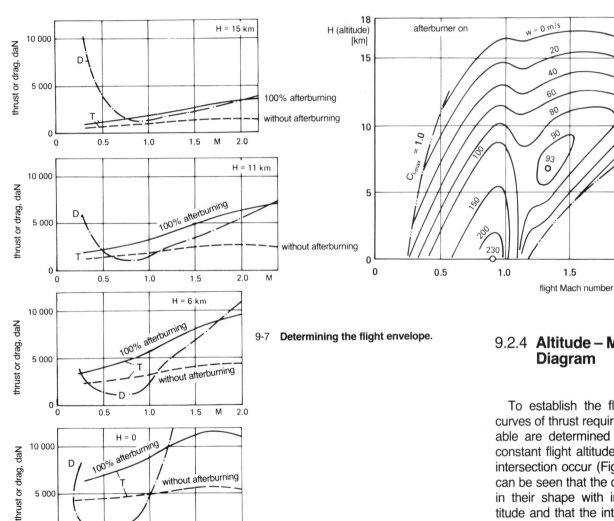

9-7 **Determining the flight envelope.**

9.2.4 Altitude – Mach Number Diagram

To establish the flight envelope, the curves of thrust required and thrust available are determined for every arbitrary constant flight altitude in which points of intersection occur (Fig. 9-7). From this it can be seen that the curves approximate in their shape with increasing flight altitude and that the intersections become less well-defined. The maximum altitude is reached when both points merge to a

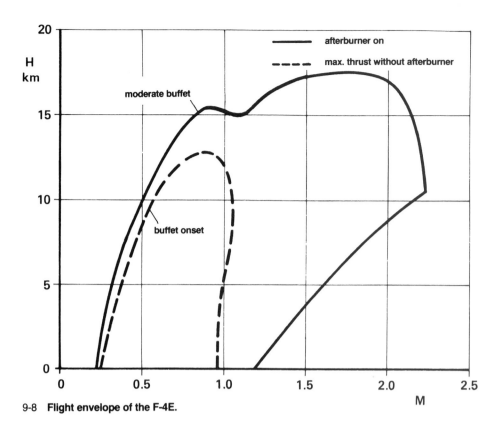

9-8　**Flight envelope of the F-4E.**

(graph labels: H km vertical axis 0–20; horizontal axis M 0–2.5; legend: afterburner on / max. thrust without afterburner; labels: moderate buffet, buffet onset)

single point or the curves are identical in parts.

From the thrust/drag curves a mini- mum and a maximum Mach number is obtained for every flight altitude permitted by the engine running at maximum r.p.m.

in steady level flight. If these values are plotted as flight altitudes against Mach number, then the **flight envelope** results. This defines the conditions in which **unaccelerated horizontal flight** is met. This range is often reduced by the fact that other limits are reached first. Among these are, for example, the $C_{L_{max}}$ curve mentioned in Chapter 9.2.1, which describes the lower limit of Mach numbers which can be flown (see Fig. 9-7). In the upper Mach number range there may be a limit due to structural strength. This is given by a curve of constant static pressure, such as $q_{max} = 100$ kN/m^2 (2045 lb/sq ft). Finally, the **materials** from which the aircraft is constructed can lead to the establishment of a heat limit. This is given by the stagnation point temperature, which in turn is dependent on Mach number (Fig. 9-7).

The flight envelope determined in this way represents the theoretical limit of the aircraft's performance. On this curve there is no manoeuvring potential, unless flight altitude of Mach number are reduced; but **within** this range the aircraft is more or less manoeuvrable. Fig. 9-8 reproduces the flight envelope of the F-4E, in each case at full throttle with and without afterburning.

9.3 **Manoeuvrability**

The most important property of a combat aircraft is its ability to manoeuvre.

This can be expressed by:
- climbing capacity
- tangential acceleration
- normal acceleration (pull-up)
- turn.

9.3.1 **Climbing**

The climbing speed v_c, as shown by Fig. 9-1 is the sine of the trajectory angle γ. On the other hand, this value can be expressed by equation (9.1) as the forces acting on the aircraft.

For unaccelerated flight and at small angles-of-attack ($\cos\alpha = 1$), the following applies:

$$\sin\gamma = \frac{T - D}{W} = \frac{v_c}{v}$$

If the airspeed v is replaced by the product of Mach number and speed of sound ($v = M \cdot a$), the following results for climb speed:

$$v_c = M \cdot a \cdot \frac{T - D}{W} \qquad (9.6)$$

Equation 9.6 contains as a factor the specific excess thrust (i.e. excess thrust

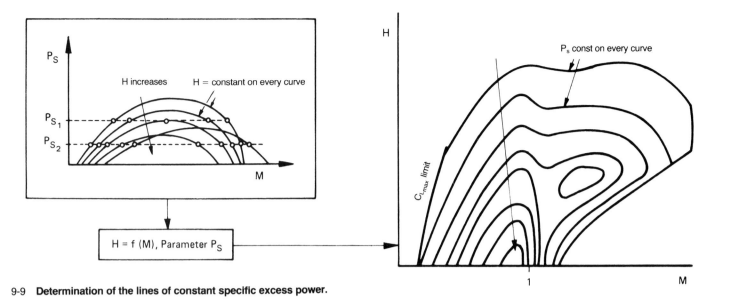

9-9   **Determination of the lines of constant specific excess power.**

related to aircraft weight W) shown in the Penàud diagram (see Fig. 9-6). The climbing speed is therefore also termed **specific excess power** (SEP, symbol: P_s). It has the dimension of a speed.[42]

For every altitude the curve of specific excess power can now be taken from the Penàud diagram and plotted against the Mach number (Fig. 9-9, left). It is necessary to recognize the point in the flight regime at which an aircraft produces particularly good climb performance. This is expressed by the specific excess power P_s. Where this is less pronounced, lines of constant excess power must be calculated and entered into the altitude/Mach number diagram. The co-ordinates of the line P_s = constant result from the curves P_s = f(M) with altitude as the parameter, from which, for given values of P_s a point cluster is obtained:

$$H = f(M), P_s = \text{constant (see Fig. 9-9)}$$

A fighter aircraft which enters combat at a higher energy level – expressed by flight altitude and flight Mach number – and is able to maintain this superiority on the strength of greater excess power – has the advantage. If, on the other hand, it enters combat at a lower energy level than its opponent, it will use the higher excess power in moving to a higher energy level within a very short period of time, so as to outmanoeuvre its opponent. This way of considering energies is known as energy manoeuvrability (EM) and is an essential part of a pilot's training.

9.3.2 Pull-up

The transition from a more or less steep glide into a climb is called **pull-up**. Similar conditions also exist at landing.

Pull-up is the accelerated motion of the aircraft along a curved path (Fig. 9-10). The lift of the wing has to balance the weight of the aircraft **and** the centrifugal force. The centrifugral force Z is given with the aircraft mass m_{AC} and the

normal acceleration[43] $b_n = v^2/r$ according to Newton's first fundamental law, (force = mass times acceleration); by the following:

$$Z = m_{AC}\frac{v^2}{r} = \frac{W}{g}\frac{v^2}{r}$$

The equilibrium condition (9.2) thereby provides the lift required for pull-up, with small values being assumed again for γ and α ($\cos\gamma = 1$, $\sin\alpha = 0$):

$$L = W + \frac{W}{g}\frac{v^2}{r} = W\left(1 + \frac{v^2}{gr}\right)$$

The expression in brackets is also called the **load factor** n.[44] Depending on the role and speed of the aircraft acceleration forces of various values are assumed, and the airframe strength required for these is taken into account. Combat aircraft are designed for load factors of 8 to 10.

Considering the load factor, the following equation results for the lift coefficient:

---

[42] Power is defined as 'the product of force, distance and time' with the dimension

$$\frac{Nm}{s}$$

If this is divided in the present example by the aircraft weight W (dimension: N), the specific power, i.e. power related to the unit of weight, has the dimension of a speed.

---

[43] normal = vertically to flight path.

[44] The load factor is also defined as the ratio of lift to weight: n = L/W. In steady level flight L = W and consequently n = 1. When manoeuvring (for example turning flight) the lift must also balance the centrifugal force in addition to weight, so that L > W and n > 1 applies.

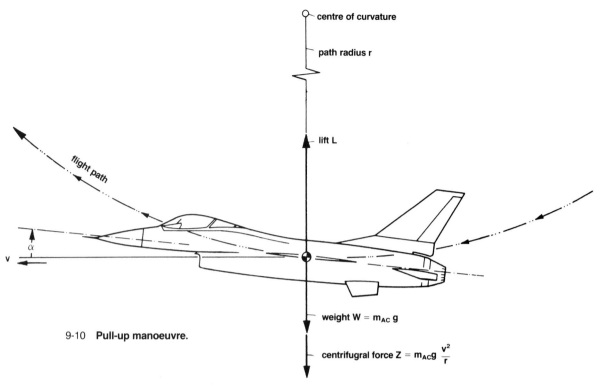

centre of curvature

path radius r

lift L

flight path

α

v

weight $W = m_{AC}\, g$

9-10 **Pull-up manoeuvre.**

centrifugal force $Z = m_{AC}g\, \dfrac{v^2}{r}$

$$C_L = \frac{nW}{qS} \qquad (9.7)$$

The limiting curves of the flight envelope ($P_s = 0$) can be determined with this equation for any arbitrary load factor, as was shown previously (see Chapter 9.2.3) for n = 1.

Of course, today this work is carried out by computer. The drag behaviour of the aircraft and the thrust characteristic of the engine are fed into the computer in analytical form or point-by-point.

The pull-up radius r is derived from the definition of the load factor and is given by the relation

$$r = \frac{v^2}{g\,(n-1)} \qquad (9.8)$$

The radius increases with the square of speed and becomes less with an increasing load factor. At an airspeed of 300 m/s (540 knots), a radius of 9.2 km (5 nm) results for n = 2, while for n = 5 the radius is 2.3 km (1.25 nm) large. This shows that at a given speed a certain

minimum altitude is required in order to be able to pull out at all.

Contour diagrams with lines of constant specific excess power (P_s = constant) reveal where a combat aircraft has excellent manoeuvring properties (Fig. 9-11). The line $P_s = 0$ forms the boundary at which the aircraft, at the stated load factor of 3, can maintain constant altitude and Mach number (see Fig. 9-11a). The lines $P_s > 0$ identify the latent thrust potential, which can be used to alter the flight path, for example by climbing, accelerating or increasing the load factor.

If two combat aircraft designs are compared at the same load factor in a diagram of this kind, then the aircraft which possesses the greater specific excess power has a decisive combat advantage at the same Mach number and altitude.

The method of representation of excess power can also be used to compare lines $P_s = 0$, i.e. limiting curves of the flight envelope, with each other for various load factors (see Fig. 9-11b). It can be seen that with an increasing load factor manoeuvrability is considerably re-

stricted. The aircraft which can tolerate a higher 'g' than the opponent at a particular point in the curves has a significant manoeuvre advantage.

In combat aircraft design the wing loading is a decisive design parameter (see Fig. 9-11c). If two combat aircraft with different wing loadings but with the same thrust/weight ratio are compared, it is clear that the lighter aircraft has the advantage in the lower Mach number range. This advantage can be used to fly tighter turns and outmanoeuvre an opponent.

The significant influence of thrust/weight ratio also becomes clear from a comparison of the load factors (see Fig. 9-11d). The aircraft with the greater thrust/weight ratio has a considerably extended operating envelope compared with another aircraft and is still manoeuvrable whereas the other aircraft barely manages level flight.

These descriptions show why a low wing loading and a high thrust/weight ratio are aimed at for an air superiority fighter.

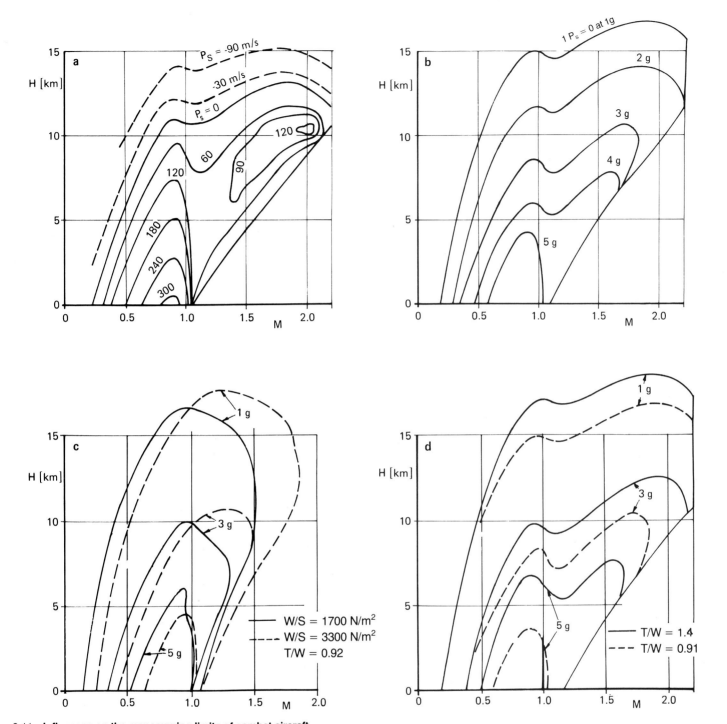

9-11 **Influences on the manoeuvring limits of combat aircraft.**

205

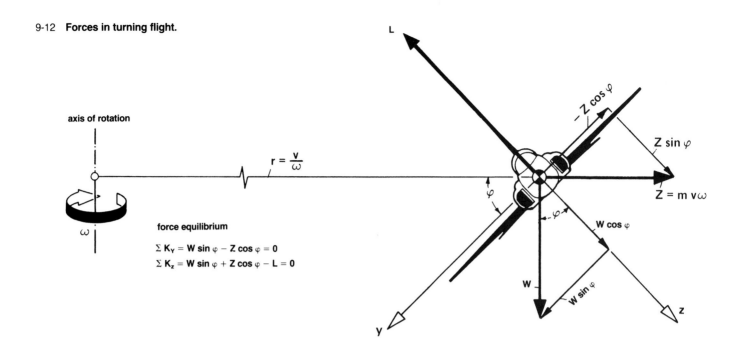

9-12 **Forces in turning flight.**

$r = \dfrac{v}{\omega}$

force equilibrium

$\Sigma K_Y = W \sin\varphi - Z \cos\varphi = 0$

$\Sigma K_z = W \sin\varphi + Z \cos\varphi - L = 0$

9.3.3 Turning Flight

Doubtless the most important property a combat aircraft must have is the ability to turn.

Forces acting on the aircraft in the x-y plane are lift, weight and centrifugal force (Fig. 9-12). To allow level turning flight – without altitude loss or gain – the forces K_y and K_z, with reference to the y-axis and z-axis, must be in equilibrium:

$$\Sigma K_y = W \sin\gamma - Z \cos\gamma = 0 \quad (9.9)$$

$$\Sigma K_z = W \cos\gamma + Z \sin\gamma - L = 0 \quad (9.10)$$

Weight W and centrifugal force Z are so-called mass forces which are determined by the mass of the aircraft, i.e. mainly by its size; via the lift L the relationship with the aerodynamic properties is established. By means of relatively simple mathematical operations the turning flight performance can be determined from these initial conditions, for example as turn rate ω [45] versus Mach number for one particular flight altitude.

---
[45] ω = omega

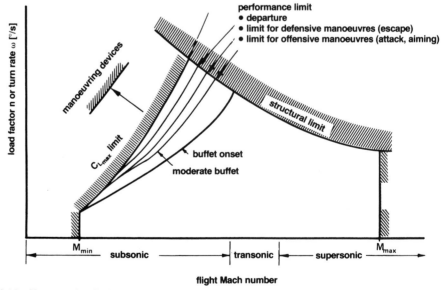

9-13 **Manoeuvring limits of combat aircraft.**

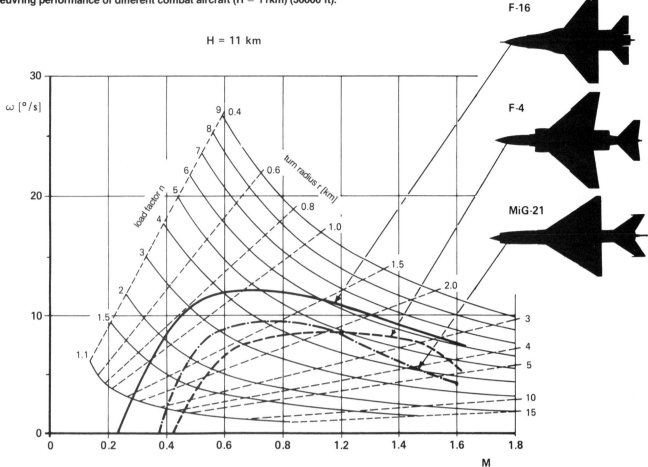

By **turn rate** is meant the angle through which the turn radius sweeps in a unit of time. Between turn rate, load factor, Mach number and flight altitude exists the relation

$$\omega = \frac{g}{M \cdot a} \sqrt{n^2 - 1} \qquad (9.11)$$

In order to achieve maximum manoeuvring performance, the load factor must therefore be made as large as possible by means of the aerodynamic design of the aircraft. The potential influence of this factor can be seen from the definition of load factor and the load equation:

$$n = \frac{L}{W} = q \frac{C_L}{W/S} \qquad (9-12)$$

Consequently high load factors can be attained by means of a low wing loading

W/S as well as a high usable lift coefficient C_L. The attainment of high lift coefficients is generally limited at a given thrust by induced and trim drag, unless the aircraft is dived, which is not desirable in aerial combat.

The high thrust/weight ratios of modern combat aircraft increasingly allow penetration into flight regimes which are less limited by the available thrust than by aerodynamics. Thus the manoeuvrability in turning flight is often limited by the fact that wing buffeting makes it difficult or impossible to continue combat (Fig. 9-13).

Equation (9.11) can be used to calculate[46], for one particular flight altitude, a whole set of curves, in which the load

_____
[46] The interested reader may calculate this himself.

factor n appears as the parameter (Fig. 9-14). With the relation

$$r = \frac{M^2 a^2}{g \sqrt{n^2-1}} \qquad (9.13)$$

the turn radius can be determined. From this is derived a grid of realistic combinations of turn radii and load factors for acceptable turning flight manoeuvres. In this diagram limiting curves $P_s = 0$ can be entered for various aircraft designs and compared with each other. Those shown are the F-16, F-4 and MiG-21. It shows that low wing loading in connection with the most advanced aerodynamics, as shown in the F-16, leads to superior manoeuvring performance for a particular altitude over the entire Mach number range. This need not apply for all altitudes, however. Thus a low wing loading at low

Comparing the turn performance of the F-4 and F-16. Both aircraft began the turn simultaneously and with a flight Mach number of 1.2, altitude 10 km (32000 ft). The F-16 (inner condensation trail) demonstrates its superior turn potential.

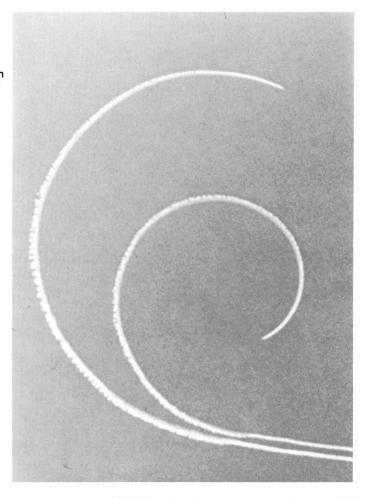

altitudes is less suitable for combat manoeuvring because of gust sensitivity.

A vivid illustration of the turning flight potential of modern combat aircraft comes from a comparison between the F-16 and F-4 (Fig. 9-15). The turning manoeuvre, initiated at the same time and with the same Mach number, shows that the F-16 achieves practically double the turn rate of the F-4 but needs only half the turn radius. It is easy to imagine the moment when the F-16 gets behind the F-4 in a firing position.

9.4
Variables Influencing Manoeuvring Performance

Climb performance and turning flight capability are the essential attributes of a combat aircraft. However, the other factors which determine flight performance cannot be dealt with in the limitations of this description.

Among these are, for example:
- calculation of the flight profile (flight duration, range);
- climb behaviour (optimum climbing time, optimum-fuel climbing flight, for minimum fuel consumption, altitude factors);
- take-off and landing (take-off and landing distance, engine failure).

Fig. 9-16 shows those design parameters which are of particular importance during individual phases of a mission.

			performance requirements				
			take-off and landing	combat manoeu-vres	maximum Mach number	specific excess power	operational radius
design	design parameters	wing loading W/F	●	●		●	●
		thrust/weight ratio T/W	●	●	●	●	
		lift/drag ratio		●		●	●
		$C_{L_{max}}$	●	●			
		specific fuel consumption					●
	aero-dynamics	wing geometry	●	●		●	●
		high-lift system	●	●			
	engine	bypass ratio					●
		pressure ratio				●	
		afterburning		●	●	●	
		integration		●	●		●

The influence of specific performance requirements on essential design parameters.

10 Aircraft Armament

10.1 **The Range of Weapons**

Only by integrating the weapons system with aerodynamics, propulsion and avionics is a successful combat aircraft developed. Essentially, the weapon load determines the combat value of the aircraft. The types of weapons are determined by the particular operational task, and those for air-to-air operations are different from air-to-ground operations. Long range, accuracy of fire, freedom from interference, and all-weather capability are general requirements for all weapon system.

10.1.1 **Air-to-Air Armament**

The experience gained from past air wars emphasises that the most effective armament for air-to-air combat consists of:
- a gun
- at least two missiles for short range (up to 2.5 km) (1.3 nm) and
- at least two missiles for the ranges out to 8 km (4.2 nm).

The gun is the best weapon for short range up to a distance of 1 km (Fig. 10-1). It is equally suitable for air-to-air and air-to-ground operation.

The high rate of fire required for combat is obtained with modern 're-volver' guns; for example, the 30-mm Oerlikon KCA (Fig. 10-2, top). This type of gun is, however, smaller and lighter than the the 20 mm calibre multi-barrelled M 61A "Gatling" used as a standard in the USA (Fig. 10-2, bottom).

Improved effectiveness is achieved only with larger calibre (25-30 mm) as well as by suitable fuses which act in proximity to the target (proximity fuses), as well as at small angles of impact.

The biggest disadvantage of the gun is its short range. Up to distances of 1 km (3300 ft) it is very accurate, but at ranges above 2 km (6600 ft) it is of little use. The most favourable weapon turns out to be the infrared target seeking missile. This responds to the hot parts of the target (exhaust nozzle, jet) (see Fig. 10-1). The standard weapon of this kind in NATO is the **Sidewinder** AIM-9, originally developed for the US Navy. This is employed in a number of different versions. It is also used as a ground-to-air missile (Fig. 10-3). In addition, other states also develop and manufacture modern aerial combat missiles. With the **Matra Magic R550** France has developed a very successful missile, while SAAB has planned the type 372 for the fighter version of the Viggen. Comparable Israeli missiles with manoeuvring capability are the Python and Shafrir.

Infra-red target seeking missiles have

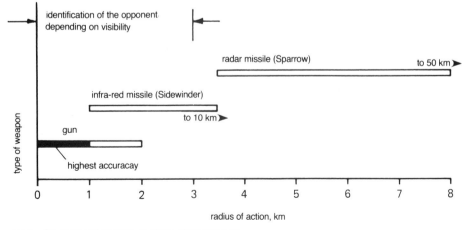

10-1 **Operational ranges of air-to-air armament.**

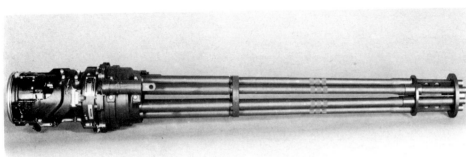

10-2 **Aircraft gun**
Top: 30 mm Oerlikon KCA revolver gun
Below: M 61A-1 Gatling gun, 20 mm calibre, made by General Electric.

the advantage that they automatically head for the target after release and cannot easily be interfered with by electronics. The relatively low price per unit is also significant. However, a disadvantage is their inability to differentiate between hostile and friendly aircraft so that special firing procedures must be used.

Air-to-air missiles designed for the medium and longer range are those with a semi-active, radar target-seeking head, such as the American **Sparrow** AIM-7 (Fig. 10-4), the British **Sky Flash** (a derivative version of the Sparrow), the Italian **Aspide** and the French **Matra Super** 530. Compared with infra-red missiles radar-controlled missiles are suitable for all weathers because their radar beams are not affected by meteorological factors. However, a big disadvantage turns out to be their high susceptibility to interference by electronic countermeasures (ECM). A further drawback is that throughout their flight the fighter must keep flying towards the enemy, "illuminating" him with a radar beam.

Another type which uses radar is the Hughes **Phoenix** long-range, guided missile carried by the F-14. This missile has an active (i.e. self-emissive) radar target-seeking head for terminal guidance to the target.

10-3 **Bottom left: infra-red guided AIM-9 Sidewinder missile at the underwing stations of an F-15; at the fuselage stations four radar-controlled AIM-7 Sparrow missiles.**

10-4 **Right: release of a radar-controlled AIM-7 Sparrow missile from an F-16 prototype; a Sidewinder missile is at ▶ each wingtip.**

211

10-5　**F-15 during bomb release.**

10.1.2 **Air-to-Ground Armament**

In this case the distinction between weapons relates to whether they are directed against area targets or against pin-point targets.

WEAPONS AGAINST AREA TARGETS

The simplest way of achieving an area effect is by the release of a carpet of bombs. For this purpose it is usual to use free-falling weapon types. It has become apparent that this task can also be carried out by those aircraft originally designed for air-to-air operation (Fig. 10-5).

If bombs are to be released at low-level, then built-in braking devices (brake parachutes, brake flaps) must be used to delay their fall so that the aircraft releasing the weapons is not affected by their explosions.

An area effect can also be achieved with **scatter bombs,** where the external casing – the drop canister – opens after release. This ejects a large number of small bombs (submunitions). The BL-755 weapon developed in Great Britain is an example of this type.

A good area effect on a suspected target at close range can be achieved by releasing a large number of non-guided rockets (Fig. 10-6).

WEAPONS AGAINST PIN-POINT TARGETS

Pin-point targets may be moving or stationary. Moving pin-point targets are, for example, tanks, motor vehicles and ships; stationary pin-point targets are bridges, defences and radar targets.

The classic weapon for pin-point target attack is the gun. It has been developed to such an extent that today it is even effective against tanks. Thus the A-10 is equipped with the General Electric GAU-8/A 30mm gun (Fig. 10-7).

10-6　**Producing an area effect by releasing numerous non-guided rockets from a BAe Buccaneer aircraft.**

The increasing effectiveness of air defences means that attacking aircraft venture close to the target only when absolutely necessary.

Modern weapon technology makes it possible to keep to a safe stand-off distance and still attack the target effectively. Guided weapons have been developed for this purpose having high accuracy. They are either ballistic such as glide bombs, or have a propulsion system such as air-to-ground missiles. Because of their small dimensions they are very difficult to counter.

A prerequisite for the effective employment of these relatively expensive weapons is an exact knowledge of the target. The target has to be found by the aircraft even in bad weather. This requires corresponding avionic equipment for guiding the weapons to the target. Three procedures are available for this:
- infra-red (IR)
- TV
- laser.

With the IR procedure the infra-red radiation from the target is used to guide the missile. The picture obtained with an IR camera built into the target-seeking head is transmitted to the cockpit. After that the lock-on to the target phase is initiated. This process permits versatile employment, particularly at night.

With the TV technique, a TV camera built into the guided missile transmits its picture to a monitor screen in the cockpit. With the aid of the TV display the observer or pilot guides the weapon to the target which is visible on the screen. This type can also be guided automatically after lock-on, such as with the Maverick (Fig. 10-8) and some GBU-15

10-7 **Top: GAU-8/A 30 mm "Gatling" gun, manufactured by General Electric, used for attacks on pin-point targets. Below: firing the GAU-8/A from an A-10.**

10-8 **Below: A-10 with Maverick laser-controlled air-to-ground missiles carried below the wings.**

fighter-bomber with search
and tracking equipment

loiter position for new
attack or return flight

airborne target designator

navigation to target area

co-ordination with target
designator on the ground

target acquisition
and tracking

target approach using
decoy manoeuvres

breakaway

probing

release

target designator on the ground

10-9 **Principle of laser target marking.**

types. In spite of high-resolution cameras, which see more than the pilot's eyes, a TV target-seeking head does not have an all-weather capability.

With the laser technique the target is irradiated – 'illuminated' – by a laser device. This is carried either in the aircraft or is aimed from another position by an observer on the ground or from another aircraft with the specific task of designating the target (Fig. 10-9). The reflected energy is picked up by the laser target-seeking head, after which the missile heads for the target automatically. If the target is moving, it must be continuously irradiated. The distance between the 'illuminating source' and the target is limited by the usual energy-distance law, as the laser target-seeking head in the weapon must receive sufficient reflected energy. Because of the scattering effect only a very small part of the energy transmitted by the illuminating source in a target-seeking head reaches the target.

Some American 'smart' bombs, glide bombs and guided missiles are equipped with laser target-seeking heads.

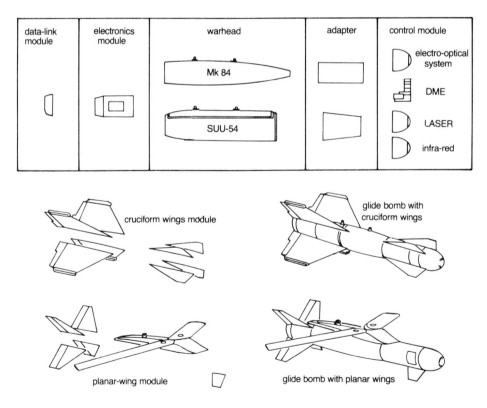

data-link module	electronics module	warhead	adapter	control module
		Mk 84		electro-optical system
		SUU-54		DME
				LASER
				infra-red

cruciform wings module

glide bomb with cruciform wings

planar-wing module

glide bomb with planar wings

10-10 **GBU-15 glide bomb for precision target attack**

Smart bombs (Homing Bomb System, HOBOS) were developed from conventional bombs of the types

Mk 82, 2.2 kN (500 lb)
Mk 83, 4.4 kN (1000 lb)
Mk 84, 8.9 kN (2000 lb)
M 118, 13.3 kN (3000 lb)

and equipped with a laser or TV target-seeking head as well as additional control surfaces. This type of bomb is suitable for precision attack on weakly defended or undefended targets, because the aircraft must approach relatively close. The range is relatively short because of the poor lift/drag ratio.

In order to increase the range, guided bombs were given plain wings without twist and camber (planar wing). By using the three target-seeking head types a modular glide-bomb family was developed with the designation GBU-15 (Fig. 10-10). One version had two wing halves which extended after the bomb was released to assume a slightly swept-back angle; the other version had a cruciform tail and small control surfaces at the nose. Glide bombs equipped with folding wings, released at great altitude, can achieve ranges of up to 100 km (54 nm). However, this requires a flight control system and distance measuring equipment.

An example of a guided missile with its own propulsion system is the Hughes AGM-65 **Maverick.** This was initially equipped with a TV target-seeking head (Fig. 10-11). The use of a laser or infra-red seeking head is also possible. The Maverick allows the carrier aircraft to break away immediately after weapon release and thus stay outside the air defence zone.

With weapons of this kind battlefield interdiction (see Chapter 2) appears in a new light. If these weapons can be successfully provided with adequate range, then targets in the enemy's interior can be attacked from one's own area of operations.

10-11 **The Maverick guided missile-carried on an A-10 can be equipped with a TV, laser or infra-red target-seeking head.**

215

10.2 **Influence of External Stores**

10-12 **Modern combat aircraft can carry a diverse load of weapons (top: A-10, bottom: F-16).**

The extremely high cost of modern combat aircraft makes it absolutely necessary to have maximum versatility in the deployment of such an expensive machine. This is met by carrying a number of different external stores (Fig. 10-12).

The positioning of external store stations depends largely on the strength of the aircraft and accessibility for loading. In many examples, aerodynamic reasons play only a minor part here, although an effort has to be made to keep the drag increments caused by external stores within limits. Nevertheless, a considerable performance loss is unavoidable, as a comparison of the flight envelope of the F-4 with and without weapon load shows (Fig. 10-13). For this reason exact information on the influence of external stores on the flight performance, particularly on drag, must be obtained: wind-tunnel experiments are usually conducted for this purpose, because theoretical procedures do not provide useful predictions. This is because there are difficulties in determining interference effects between external store, pylon and wing or fuselage.

Wind tunnel experiments of this kind constitute a relatively large proportion of an experimental programme. They are intended to provide evidence on **which,** and **how many,** external loads can be carried, and where these can best be mounted. At the same time the release characteristics of numerous external stores combinations are determined, not only with regard to static but also with regard to dynamic behaviour. Aircraft which can accommodate large weapon loads under the wings, such as the A-7, must, in addition, be investigated regarding their aeroelastic behaviour. The procedure here is to use miniature wire strain-gauges on the external store models and at the pylons to measure the aerodynamic forces both individually and together as total force. In order to determine the manoeuvring margins the effectiveness of the rudder must also be determined.

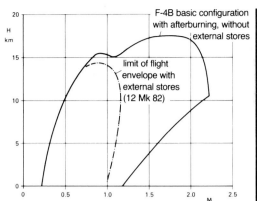

10-13 **When carrying external stores the flight envelope is considerably restricted (F-4B flight envelope with and without external stores).**

The wind-tunnel experiments are distinguished by two types:
a) the external stores remain attached to the aircraft during the entire period of measurement (flight simulation);
b) when simulating release the reactions of the separating external stores on the aircraft are determined (separation simulation).

In the first example, the aerodynamic forces are measured at the loads themselves and at the pylons. In addition the aerodynamic forces of the entire configuration are measured. These provide the input variables for the determination of flight performance. Inteference effects can be determined from the forces acting at the individual stores, pylons and as the total configuration by establishing difference values.

In order to enhance the force measurements, pressure distribution measurements and wake measurements of the external stores can be carried out (wake survey). However this involves considerable time and expense. On the contrary, an easier solution as a basis for analysis is the use of oil-film coatings which make the flow visible at the stores and the wing. At supersonic Mach numbers the Schlieren optical procedure can be applied to obtain information about shock formation.

Investigations of weapon release are conducted in such a way that a dummy

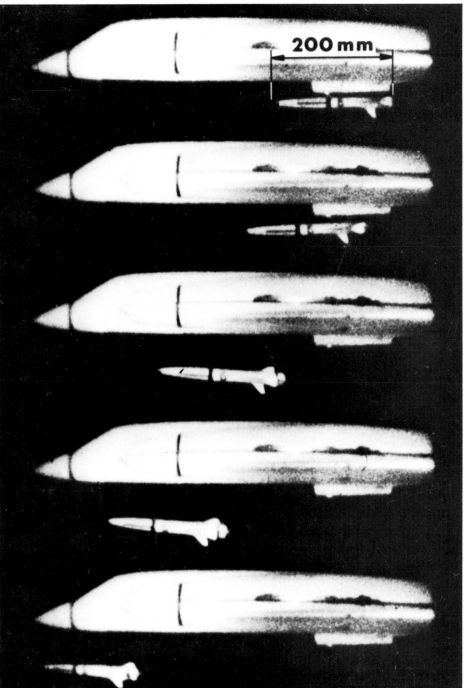

10-14 **Investigation of weapon launch in the wind tunnel using a high-speed camera at a Mach number of 2 (ONERA, France).**

or model body is released or launched and the resultant flight path is recorded with high-speed cameras (Fig. 10-14). After the release the dummy weapon is in free flight until it strikes against the wind-tunnel walls or the model. At lower Mach numbers the model is caught by a net at the end of the test section. High speed

217

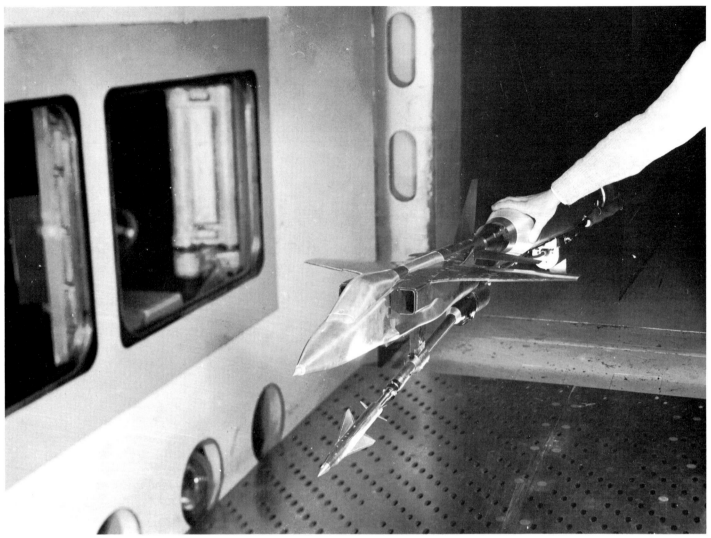

10-15 The missile model can be dealt with independently of the aircraft model so as to allow the simulation of all trajectories and flight attitudes. Strips affixed in the area of the leading edges and tips are intended to induce turbulent boundary-layer and thus lead to realistic flow conditions (model of a Jaguar combat aircraft and a Kormoran in the S3 wind tunnel of ONERA, France).

experiments can be conducted only in blow-down tunnels, because the model is destroyed at the end of the experiment. (In blow-down tunnels the flow is conducted behind the test section into the free atmosphere, so that the models cannot cause any damage to the propulsion system of the tunnel).

Dynamic release experiments of the kind described above are suitable mainly for propulsionless, free-falling weapons (bombs), but are less suitable for missiles, as the scaling of the thrust is difficult with models of this kind. Here a different technique is used. The missile is on a separate mounting which can usually be dealt with independently of the aircraft (Fig. 10-15). By this means all trajectories and flight attitudes of the guided weapon can be simulated in continuous wind-tunnel operation. The specific difficulties of the gravity model, such as scaling the mass, the thrust, the separation forces and the drags at the launching rails, can be avoided.

11 Avionics

According to its definition avionics means the application of electronics in aviation equipment and systems. The efficiency and reliability of military and civil aircraft is based increasingly on avionic systems. These have become more and more complex with the advance of technology. Some avionic devices are used to give the pilot information and thereby reduce workload. Other devices take over the automatic control of the aircraft. This can go so far that the aircraft cannot be flown without them (for example: control configured vehicles (CCV)). On the other hand, other avionic devices make communication with the outside world possible. Among these is, for example, radar.

In Fig. 11-1 avionics systems for combat aircraft are listed according to their categories
– information and display
– control
– communication and radar.

The unit price of a modern combat aircraft is roughly made up of one third propulsion, one third avionics and one third airframe. As the avionics amount to a considerable proportion of the total cost, an effort is made to restrict this to what is absolutely necessary; however, the possibility is always kept open of extending the avionics as needed.

Certain avionics devices, such as jamming transmitters, can be carried in easily mounted external containers. When complex devices are permanently

Information and display systems

Flight attitude: artificial horizon
Air-data computer
Engine: speed, temperature,
        pressure ratio
Radar screen
Head-up display
Map display

Control systems

Inertial navigation
Tacan
Electric and hydraulic powered flight control systems
Aircraft electrical power operation
Engine control
Nozzle power setting

Communication and Radar

Radio
Radar altimeter
Radar transmitter/receiver and
        scanner

11-1 **Avionics for combat aircraft.**

built in, they are wasted if the aircraft remains on the ground. Thus, for example, USAF combat aircraft usually carry their laser systems in external removable containers. This allows a smaller stock of laser systems. In contrast, the laser system of the RAF's Jaguar is an integral part of the aircraft's wedge shaped nose and is, therefore, an aerodynamically favourable solution (Fig. 11-2).

To fulfil the basic combat task a certain fit of avionics is absolutely necessary. This might be as follows:

1. **Flight management**
   – autopilot
   – gyro platform
   – air-data computer
   – crash recorder
2. **Navigation**
   – Tacan
   – VOR/ILS
3. **Communication**
   – VHF/UHF – receivers and transmitters
4. **Weapon aiming and management**
   – Radar (forward looking Radar)
   – head-up display (HUD)
   – guided weapons control unit
   – potential data-link
   – (missiles, guns, bombs)
5. **Identification**
   – identification friend or foe (IFF)

However, depending on the role and costs, the following additional avionics devices may be carried:

11-2 **Left: receiver for laser radiation in an external container on an A-10 (Pave Penny detector from Martin Marietta). Right: active laser and detector behind the glazed nose of the Jaguar.**

Navigation
- inertial navigation, coupled with weapon aiming computer
- radar altimeter
- terrain-following radar with map display.

Weapon-aiming system
- moving target indicator (MTI)
- air-to-ground radar.

Other equipment
- radar warning system (in the tail)
- self-defence capability using jamming transmitter units
- escort capability due to jamming transmitter pod.

An important task is to assemble the different systems into a functioning avionics system. The way this is done will be described using the example of the Tornado's navigation and weapon aiming system (Fig. 11-3). The radar system has search, target acquisition, ground mapping, distance measurement and terrain-following modes. It supplies data to the central digital computer, which also uses the data from the inertial platform, Doppler radar and the angle-of-attack

probe. Pressure and temperature values go via the air-data computer to both the central computer and to the head-up display and weapon-aiming system. The central computer outputs to the flight-control system, the moving-map display and the head-up display and weapon-aiming system.

11.1 **Radar**

Most (about 60%) modern combat aircraft are equipped with efficient and versatile radar systems. The considerable progress made in electronics by the introduction of miniature circuits has made possible highly-developed systems hav-

ing a multitude of functions in the most confined spaces of an aircraft.

The word 'radar' comes from England and is an abbreviation of 'radio detection and ranging'. **Radar** is a method for measuring direction and distance whereby a transmitter emits electromagnetic waves (radio waves). These strike an object, are reflected and travel back to the transmitter. When the wave propagation velocity is known, the travel time is a measure of the distance to the object being irradiated. In fact the measurement of distance is thereby reduced to a measurement of time as a function of the property of electromagnetic waves. The advantage of radar is that the location of a target in space is possible from one position, such as an aircraft.

11.1.1 **Pulse-radar**

The earliest radar systems emitted a continuous signal from a transmitter and used a separate aerial for the reception

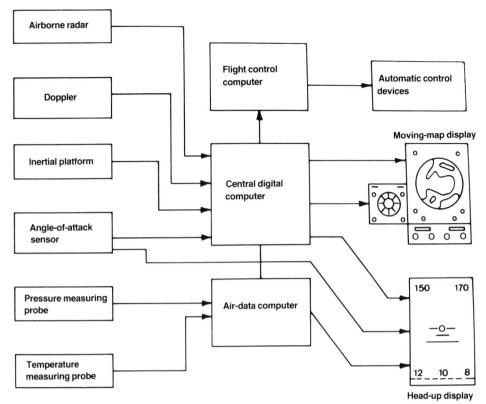

11-3 **Navigation and fire control system of the Tornado.**

of the echo. Systems in use today are are distinguished by the use of a transmitter which emits intermittently in pulses and has a single aerial (antenna) system for both transmission and reception. A schematic of such a system is shown in Fig. 11-4.

In the **transmitter** electro-magnetic oscillations at a very high frequency are generated, usually in the range of 10^{10} Hz (10 GHz). The transmitter is not switched on continuously, however, but for only a brief period, by the pulse triggering circuit. Only during this period is a pulse emitted via a directional aerial. Afterwards the transmitter is switched off, and in the transmission intervals the echo is received. As the same aerial is used for both processes, to save space, an electronic switch is required to ensure that the high-energy transmission pulse is not short-circuited to the highly sensitive receiver. The transmission pulse is conducted to the aerial, while the considerably weaker echo arriving at the aerial goes only to the receiver.

The transmitted pulse is propagated at the speed of light (300,000 km/s) in accordance with the laws of propagation of radiation. On impact with a solid body reflection, refraction or diffraction takes place, depending on the properties of the body, and a greater or smaller proportion of the energy radiated returns to the radar aerial system. There it is received by the dual-purpose aerial, amplified and either displayed on a cathode-ray tube or immediately processed in a weapon-aiming computer.

This process is repeated, depending on the system, 1000 to 300,000 times per second. This emphasises that the duration of a pulse is extremely short; a typical value is a millionth of a second (one microsecond, abbreviated to μs).

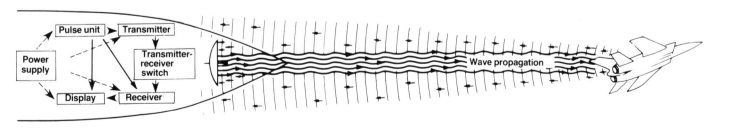

11-4 **Schematic of a pulse-radar system.**

221

There is a simple relation between frequency f and wavelength λ:

$$f \cdot \lambda = c$$

f = cycles per second, unit of measurement Hertz, abbreviated to Hz
λ = wavelength, unit of measurement usually in metres
c = speed of light = 300,000 km/s, a constant.

This means that the product of frequency and wavelength is always constant and equal to the speed of light; therefore long waves have low frequencies and short waves have high frequencies. In this way a complete system of electromagnetic waves is established, which also includes visible light (Fig. 11-5). The difference between the regions of the spectrum is only in the frequency or in the wavelength. This alone is the basis of the different effects of waves and their application.

The frequencies used in radar technology lie in the wavelength band between radio and infra-red. The reason for preferring this range is that emissions can be relatively easily focused to a sharp beam.

It is usual to subdivide the range of radar waves into individual sub-ranges, so-called **wavebands** (see Fig. 11-5, bottom right). The classification formerly used today originated from the Second World War, but a more modern classification is in common use.

Most aircraft radar devices transmit in the X-band between 8.5 GHz and 10.7 GHz. Until recently the generation of these high frequencies took place in a magnetron, but was limited to about 40 MHz.

Higher frequencies have to be generated in a multiplier circuit. Today the frequencies in the Gigahertz range are directly generated by the so-called **Gunn** diode. This permits simplified circuits and gives considerably higher reliability in operation. It is basically possible either to transmit this high-frequency wave train continuously (continuous wave transmission, CW), or only parts of it as **pulses.**

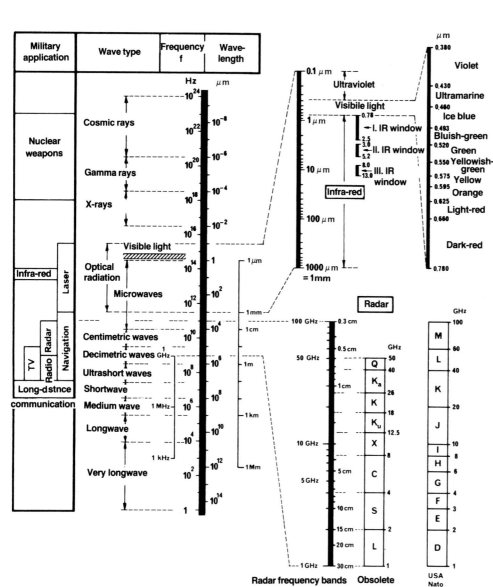

11-5 The electromagnetic wave spectrum.

11.1.2 Waves and Pulses

All sensors employed in avionics make use of the properties of electromagnetic waves. The notion 'wave' generally means a propagation process which is characterized by recurrent periodic motions. The description of a wave includes the terms **amplitude** (= intensity of oscil-lation), **frequency** (= number of oscillations per second) and **wavelength** (= distance between the same points in a cycle). The period of oscillation T, as the reciprocal value of frequency, is also used.

The velocity of propagation is the same for all electromagnetic waves and is about 300,000 km/s (speed of light).

The transmitting of a continuous signal makes a separate receiving aerial necessary, which is unsuitable when there is limited space. For this reason the technique is used for transmitting only a part of the wave train as an extremely short pulse, and in the interval between receiving the echo of the reflected signal.

The advantage of this technique is emphasised by an example. Let us assume that after every thousandth of a second (10^{-3}s) a pulse with the duration of a millionth of a second (microsecond, 10^{-6}s) is transmitted. The transmitter accordingly oscillates for only a microsecond (1 μs), followed by a 999 μs interval before the cycle begins again. In this time the transmitted pulse travels to the target, is reflected and received again by the radar aerial as a signal, albeit somewhat weaker. For example, if the echo reaches the aerial after 60 μs ($60 \cdot 10^{-6}$s), then the target is located at a distance of 4.8nm, as is shown by a simple calculation (Fig. 11-6):

distance = speed of light · half the travel time

$$\text{distance} = 3 \cdot 10^5 \text{ km/s} \cdot 30 \cdot 10^{-6}\text{s} =$$
$$9 \text{ km} = 4.8 \text{ nm}$$

A further advantage of pulse radar is that the transmitter can be highly overloaded for the period of a pulse, i.e. for a very short period. In this way high radiated powers during the pulse periods can be produced. Substantial distances can be spanned in this way, because the intensity of the reflected wave is considerably greater than in the case of continuous-wave transmission. The powers which can be taken from the relatively small transmitters in this way reach peak values of up to 10 MW which are 1,000 to 10,000 times greater than in continuous-wave operation, which allows only medium power of some kW at the most.

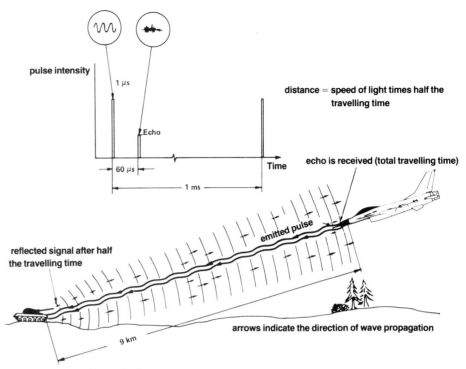

11-6   **Example of rangefinding.**

11.1.3 Doppler-radar

For optimum air-to-air weapon use it is important to know not only the position of the hostile aircraft but also its speed and direction relative to one's own aircraft. Radar can be used to solve this task also.

If the beam of an airborne radar detects another aircraft whose track forms an angle with one's own aircraft, then the reflected beam from the target is altered in its frequency. If the aircraft are moving towards one another, the frequency increases; if they are moving away from one another, the frequency decreases (Fig. 11-7). This is the Doppler effect, discovered by the Austrian physicist Christian Doppler as early as 1842 in experiments with sound and light waves.

The effect can be observed frequently and impressively by sound waves in the air, because the ear reacts very sensitively to changes of frequency. Thus, for example, the sound waves generated by the engine of an approaching car are perceived as a relatively high note which decreases noticeably in frequency (pitch) as the car passes.

In comparison to the initial frequency the size of the frequency alteration Δf_D caused by the Doppler effect is very small and is mathematically determined by the equation

$$\Delta f_D = \frac{2\,v\,f}{c}\cos\delta$$

v = relative velocity between two aircraft, m/s
c = speed of signal propagation, m/s (in the case of electromagnetic waves the speed of light, in the case of acoustic waves the speed of sound)
f = transmission frequency, Hz
δ = angle between the direction of the transmitted beam and the track of the target aircraft.

223

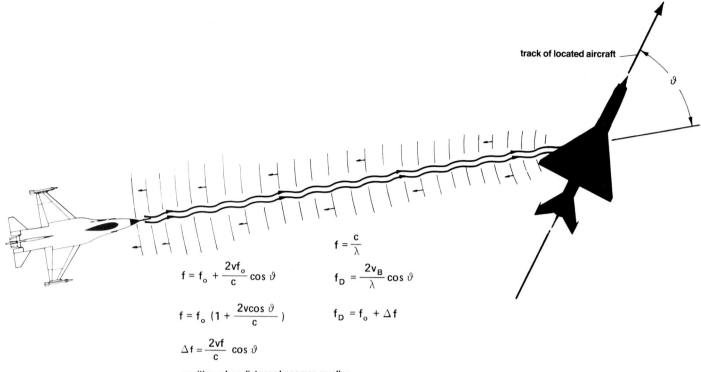

$$f = \frac{c}{\lambda}$$

$$f = f_o + \frac{2vf_o}{c} \cos \vartheta \qquad f_D = \frac{2v_B}{\lambda} \cos \vartheta$$

$$f = f_o \left(1 + \frac{2v\cos \vartheta}{c}\right) \qquad f_D = f_o + \Delta f$$

$$\Delta f = \frac{2vf}{c} \cos \vartheta$$

positive, when distance becomes smaller

11-7 **Mode of operation of Doppler radar.**

Accordingly, two cases are possible, although rare, in which a Doppler measure cannot be obtained. These are:

1. The aircraft being tracked is flying on the same heading and exactly at the same speed, i.e. the relative velocity v between both aircraft is zero, and thereby Δf is also zero.
2. The aircraft being tracked crosses the radar beam at a right-angle, hence $\delta = 90°$, $\cos\delta = 0$.

In order to understand the frequency alterations of the Doppler effect, here is an example. An aircraft flying at a speed of 2000 km/h tracks a hostile aircraft whose speed is 1840 km/h. Both aircraft use the same heading, so that the angle of intersection ϑ is zero and the $\cos\vartheta = 1$. The speed difference of the two aircraft is consequently 360 km/h = 100 m/s. The radar of the pursuing aircraft transmits in the X-band at 10 Ghz = 10^{10} Hz. These values produce a frequency difference

$$\Delta f = \frac{2 \cdot 100 \cdot 10^{10}}{3 \cdot 10^8} = 6667 \text{ Hz}$$

This apparently quite high value must, however, be seen in relation to the transmitted signal. An oscillation at 10 GHz (10,000,000,000 Hz) was transmitted, while 10,000,006,667 Hz was received. The difference between the two signals is relatively so small that it requires a considerable amount of electronics in order to find the Doppler frequency. An added difficulty is that the reflected signal is very weak and subject to strong noise, and therefore has to be processed first. The measurement process, moreover, does not take place in a still atmosphere, but in an aircraft which is subject to strong buffeting arising from gust effects.

Nevertheless, the Doppler radar has proved a success in modern combat aircraft. Its great advantage is that a moving hostile aircraft can also be recognized at night against the ground and

in all meteorological conditions. The **ground clutter** reflected from the landscape can be suppressed by relatively easy methods. In addition, modern radar systems offer the possibility of choosing from several modes, for example switching over from Doppler to normal pulse radar (Fig. 11-8).

11.1.4 Terrain-following Radar

The relative ease with which an aircraft flying at medium or high altitude can be detected is, at present, renewing interest in an operational altitude which until recently could not be used. This is extreme low-level, 'nap of the Earth', high-speed flight. By 'low-level' is meant between 100 and 150 metres (320 and 500 ft). At these heights there is a good chance of escaping detection by enemy radar and carrying out attacks with minimum risk. However the requirements for this are the ability to fly in almost any type of weather and at any time of day close to the speed of sound close to the ground. While altitude can remain unchanged over flat terrain and above the sea, the contours of the Earth's surface in hilly or mountainous country predicate extremely quick control reactions.

From these problems arose an entirely new radar technology, with radar providing the input variables for fully automatic flight control. Systems of this kind, known as **terrain-following radar** (TFR), are seen as crucial for high-speed, low-level flight. The technique is based on the fact that the contours of the Earth's surface in the area of interest (i.e. in front of and below the aircraft) are scanned by radar and the data obtained provide inputs, via a computer, to the flight control system (Fig. 11-9). As a potential failure can have disastrous consequences for crew and aircraft, the system must have maximum reliability. This includes automatic fault detection and location of failed units and components. Built-in test equipment (BITE) locates, records and bypasses failed elements of a system. In the event of complete or partial breakdown, a standy-by system must automatically take over the function of a defective element. Only in this way can the crew be given the necessary confidence to fly 'nap of the Earth' missions.

11.1.5 The Radar of the F-16

Maximum use is made of the F-16's aerodynamic performance by the APG-66 multi-purpose radar from the Westinghouse company (Fig. 11-10). This radar system, which is of the pulse-Doppler type in the X-band, is able to detect and track low-flying aircraft in spite of background noise just as well as high-flying aircraft. The weight of the system (without cockpit display) is about 1.3 kN (288 lb).

11-8 **Modern radar systems offer a choice of several modes (Ericsson PS-/46A radar device for the AJ37 Viggen).**

One of the outstanding features of the system is a mode for aerial combat; if there are several hostile aircraft the system automatically locks onto the nearest target when the pilot operates the push-button 'DOGFIGHT' on his manual control (Fig. 11-10, bottom left). A diamond-shaped mark then appears

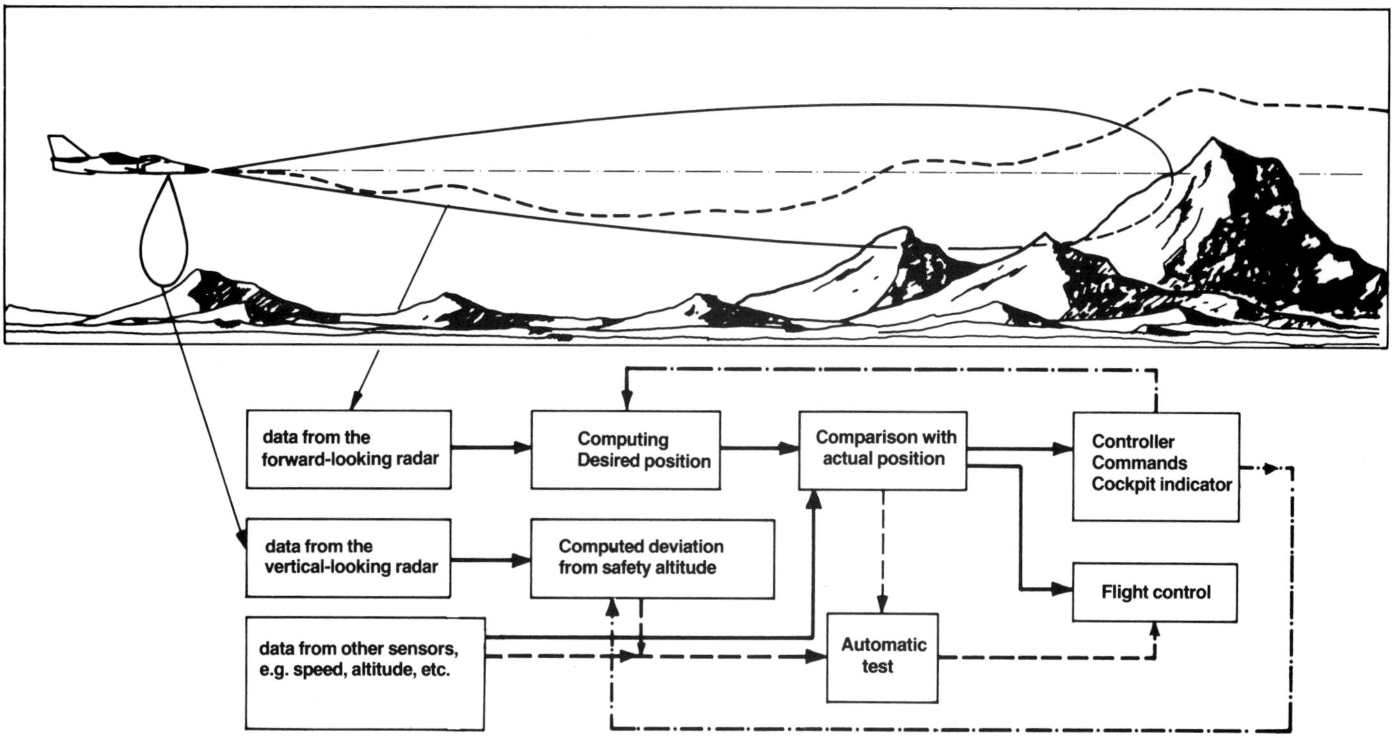
data from the forward-looking radar
Computing Desired position
Comparison with actual position
Controller Commands Cockpit indicator
data from the vertical-looking radar
Computed deviation from safety altitude
Flight control
data from other sensors, e.g. speed, altitude, etc.
Automatic test

11-9 **Terrain-following radar.**

on the head-up display combining glass which shows continuously the position of the target. Therefore, if several hostile aircraft are encountered, a new target can be selected without losing the first.

The display in the 'combat' mode, for which the radar system is primarily designed, is generated synthetically – similar to a TV picture – by the radar computer and is, therefore, completely free of noise.

Several modes are available for air-to-ground operations:

1. Conventional ground scanning is by pulse radar. This generates a weather-independent picture of the terrain in front of the aircraft. By switching, a part of the picture can be enlarged four times.
2. Should the pilot desire higher resolution of the terrain picture, for example in order to identify the target, the system can be switched over to operate in the pulse-Doppler mode (Doppler beam sharpening). This makes it possible to enlarge the picture eight times. The ground scan mode does not give a display of the terrain immediately forward of the aircraft but only to each side.
3. The radar picture can also be 'frozen', like a still picture with the transmitter generating no further signals and retaining the last indication. However a mark controlled by the inertial navigation system continues to move, and this indicates the position of the aircraft on the terrain picture.
4. Marine targets can be located by means of rapid change of frequencies so as to improve the signal/noise ratio when over the sea.
5. For weapon release, the position of an enemy target is fed to the computer and flown towards with the aid of a transmitter on the ground. This beacon can be positioned by troops on the ground. This procedure ('beacon mode') is also used for air-to-air refuelling when the beacon is carried on the tanker aircraft.

In spite of the numerous functions and modes, operating the system is very simple: there are only four control knobs and three toggle switches (see Fig. 11-10, centre left).

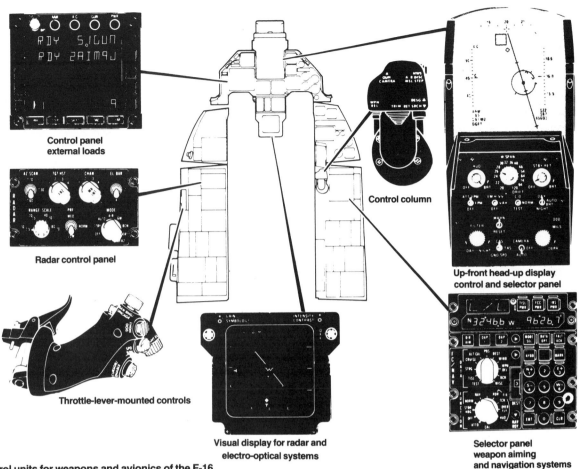

Control panel
external loads

Radar control panel

Throttle-lever-mounted controls

Control column

Visual display for radar and
electro-optical systems

Up-front head-up display
control and selector panel

Selector panel
weapon aiming
and navigation systems

11-10   **Control units for weapons and avionics of the F-16.**

11.2 **Head-up Display**

The severe strain on the pilot in critical phases of combat has led to the development of electro-optical equipment which superimposes flight information into the pilot's field of vision. This permits continuous monitoring of the outside view without looking at the cockpit instruments. Such head-up display systems (HUD), so-called because the head need no longer be lowered to obtain flight information, are principally used for target acquisition. Today they are generally regarded as essential for combat aircraft. Their continuous improvement has been accelerated by the increasing effectiveness of modern anti-aircraft systems, which have forced fighter-bombers to adopt new attack techniques. Among these are, in particular, low-level flight at high speed, as well as one pass over the target in order to keep the time in the target area to a minimum and to make detection by the enemy air defences more difficult.

Systems which make it possible to carry out such a difficult task, i.e. target acquisition in fast low-level flight yet still achieving acceptable accuracy, must necessarily be of a high technical standard. In addition, the pilot who operates this system also has to fly the aircraft. In combat this imposes an enormous physical and mental strain.

11.2.1 **Mode of Operation**

A crucially important factor for the success of a mission is the display unit as link between the target/navigation computer and pilot. This display unit, part of the head-up display system, contains

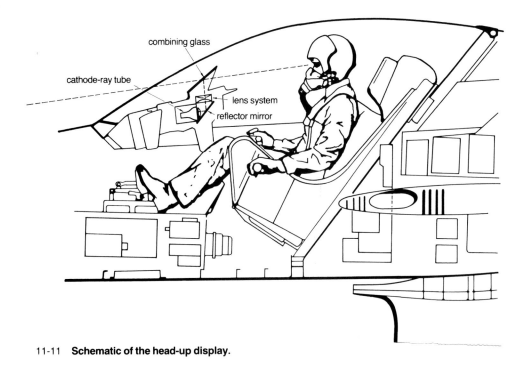

11-11 **Schematic of the head-up display.**

a cathode-ray tube (CRT), on whose face the various symbols for the representation of information are generated by the electronics (Fig. 11-11). From the CRT, the light rays travel through a system of lenses onto a combining glass, lying in the pilot's field of vision, which transmits a proportion of the light into his eyes. Thus, on the one hand the pilot looks at the screen, which optically is focused at infinity; on the other hand, he sees the landscape through the combining glass. The superimposition of the two pictures, the real world and the electronically generated symbology, enable the pilot's eyes simultaneously to assimilate pictorial information from the outside world — for example, the position of the landing strip during the approach, an obstacle during low-level flight or a target when weapons are employed. Particularly in bad weather, this can result in lifesaving seconds. Measurements have shown that up to two seconds are needed to direct one's gaze from the outside world, turn to the instrument panels, adjust the

eyes to the closer focus and less brightness, read an instrument and direct the eyes back, with renewed adjustment of focus to the outside world. In this time the aircraft may have flown 1500 feet in which the pilot receives no information of any kind. Incidentally, HUDs have a potential application for civil aviation.

11.2.2 Representation of Information

Depending on the flight mode, the pilot can select various modes on the head-up display system, so that only those graphics, symbols and alphanumerics needed in each are displayed, such as, for example, landing, weapon release and navigation. The symbology used cannot be standardised, because improved displays are being continually developed from practical experience.

GENERAL MODE

The mode suitable for the representation of information is the **general mode.** This reproduces the indications of the most important flight instruments in compact form, and in this format can also be of interest to civil aviation (Fig. 11-12). The symbols have the following meaning:

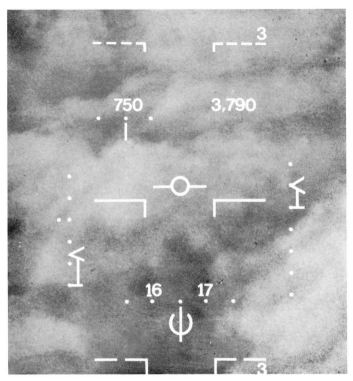

11-12   Indication of primary flight instruments in symbolic form; typical symbology for navigation mode.

11-13   PLF-mode for increasing accuracy of fire when attacking ground target.

1. Airspeed
Indicated airspeed (IAS) in knots (1 knot = 1.853 km/h) indicates the uncorrected airspeed (Fig. 11-12, 750 knots = 1390 km/h). Alternatively the Mach number can be displayed instead. Continuous re-calculation takes place at intervals of half a second.

2. Speed error
The central point (below the number 750) symbolizes the nominal speed, while the points to each side indicate speed deviations, usually ± 20 knots (± 37 km/h). The line below is movable and indicates the deviation of the actual speed from the datum speed.

3. Altitude
Indication of barometric altitude in feet (1 ft = 0.3048 m, here: 3790 ft = (1155 m). By switching on the control system at altitudes below 5000 ft (1500 m) the radar altitude can be option-

ally displayed. In this case the altitude indication includes an R, followed by the altitude in feet.

4. Angle-of-attack
Angle-of-attack is displayed on the left-hand side. With increasing angle-of-attack the < symbol moves upwards. At the same time the vertical line extends. Critical angles-of-attack can be indicated on the scale as double dots.

5. Vertical speed (climb, descent)
Vertical speed is indicated on the right-hand side of the display. The short horizontal line marks the zero position, while upward or downward movement of the < symbol indicates rate of climb or descent. The scale range can be extended if necessary.

6. Heading
The **heading** appears as a moving tape scale consisting of indices as well as numbers from 1 to 36, which correspond

to a compass card. It is read against the fixed lubber line (in the example shown a heading of 165 degrees is shown).

7. Cross-track distance (symbol for radio compass)
Permits homing on UHF/VHF radio beacons.

8. Artificial horizon
The horizontal bars are controlled by a gyro platform and correspond to the actual horizon.

9. Flight Director
The aircraft symbol (centre of picture, circle with two horizontal lines) indicates, together with the artificial horizon, the instantaneous flight attitude. The upward and downward movement between the strokes of the artificial horizon indicate the degree of pitch. If the aircraft symbol and the artificial horizon are in alignment, then the aircraft is in level flight.

229

AIR-TO-GROUND OPERATION

From the numerous possibilities with this mode only those will be mentioned in which the pilot can correct a determined position (Fig. 11-13). In the example a bearing is taken on a familiar waypoint, such as a chimney, outbound to the target. The co-ordinates of this point are keyed into the navigation computer. The computer makes a comparison between the desired position and the actual position. Using the corrected data the target point is recalculated.

In order to carry out this task the pilot has to bring the marker on the head-up display system into coincidence with the point referred to, by manual adjustment. The symbols represented have the following meaning: the two diagonal strokes on the aircraft symbol indicate that the mode chosen for correction of position has been selected (this is called the PLF mode; PLF = precise local fix).

The marker cross (plus sign) corresponds to the fixed point on the ground. In order to increase the accuracy, a laser or radar beam can be coupled with the cross.

The (long) target line indicates the track over the ground. The airspeed is 425 kt (788 km/h), the radar altitude 825 ft (251 m). The other general mode symbols (see Fig. 11-12) are not needed for this flight task and therefore are not displayed.

AIR-TO-AIR OPERATION

The head-up display is equally suited for air-to-ground and air-to-air operations. In the latter case two modes are available, in which on the one hand the computed lead angle is calculated and on the other hand the trajectory.

In determining the **computed lead angle,** a circular symbol of strokes with a point in the centre is displayed (Fig. 11-14). The pilot sets the estimated wing span of the target aircraft on the control unit (this is not difficult, because only a few types are involved, and, moreover,

their dimensions are known). Using the control grip on the control column, the circle's diameter is adjusted until the target is exactly encircled. The position of the point in the centre then takes into account the lead angle determined by the computer. As long as the point is located on the target, the aircraft is always in the best possible firing position.

The alternative mode for aerial combat computes the trajectories which would result due to the assumed characteristics of the gun (computed shell trace). This takes into account the laws of ballistics as well as the speed of the aircraft. This provides the pilot with information about the theoretical shell impacts if the guns were fired at that moment (Fig. 11-15). This is comparable to the use of tracer bullets, without a single shot having to be fired. Conversely, the required lead angle can be derived by this means. The pilot manoeuvres the aircraft in such a way that the shell line goes through the target. In practice the guns are fired shortly before the range circle moves onto the target in order to take into account the flight time of the shells.

The symbols shown have the following meaning (see Fig. 11-15):

The symbol of one's own aircraft (circle with dot and two horizontal strokes) coincides with the bore axis of the gun, and stays in this position. The artificially generated shell line (sequence of dots) reproduces the computed hit position of the shells, when fired at equal intervals. The range marking (circle with dot) appears as soon as the target is within range. It is always used in conjunction with a range-finding system (laser, infra-red, radar). The target marker (a square standing on its tip) works together with one of the rangefinding techniques and can be locked onto the target after one setting. The HUD weapon-aiming system continually updates the position of the marker. The horizontal bars make it easier to estimate the range. This is especially important when no range-finding system is available. The strokes are located at selected points on the artificial shell line and make it possible to estimate the shell flight time.

11.3 Other Avionics

The head-up display and weapon aiming system of the type described, can be used only if the target is visible to the pilot. This is a major disadvantage of an expensive system in that it is dependent on visual meteorological flight conditions (VMC). There has, therefore, been no lack of effort to make the head-up display system compatible with visibility conditions in which the human eye can perceive only very little or nothing at all.

The current solution to this problem is based on the use of electro-optical sensors for which either the low light level still

available is sufficient (low light level enhancement), or to radiation in the infra-red range (i.e. to heat radiation).

The low-light television (LLTV) enables the pilot to perceive the outside world even at night, the degree of illumination is dependent on various factors, such as weather, moonlight and starlight. This makes it possible to fly combat missions at virtually any time of day and in almost any weather.

In the same way infra-red sensors (Forward looking Infra-Red, FLIR) are even able to assimilate information and

11-14 **Determining the lead angle.**

11-15 **Continuously computed trajectories.**

convey it to the human eye when it is completely dark. Thus it is possible not only to locate vehicles with engines running but also to detect these even when the engines have been switched off some hours before, solely on the basis of the heat still being emitted.

In principle, the information gained in this way can be integrated into the existing head-up display system, so that an attack can be completed as if the visibility conditions were in daylight. The pilot has to become accustomed to trusting an artificially produced TV picture in order to complete the sortie.

12 Cockpit

The cockpit of an aircraft is the control centre of a complicated machine which is the interface between man and technology (Fig. 12-1). Commands are conveyed from the cockpit to the individual subsystems (such as flight control system, engine system); these 'report' back to the cockpit. Incorrect information or false reactions may have disastrous consequences.

INSTRUMENTATION OF A MODERN COMBAT AIRCRAFT

An important factor in the design and equipment of the cockpit is the amount and quality of information needed by the pilot in order to carry out the mission of the aircraft.

When the cockpit is being designed, the following questions arise:
1. What is really necessary?
2. How can necessary data be clearly conveyed to the pilot in the simplest way?
3. What can the pilot do with the information?

The F-15 cockpit is studied as an example of solutions to the problems of design.

The limited space in the aircraft and the number of instruments needed for control make it essential that all available cockpit surfaces be used. In a combat aircraft – as with the F-15 – this has led to a solution in which the most important instruments and control switches are arranged on the conventional central **cockpit panel,** whereas the secondary – but equally necessary – control equipment is accommodated on the side consoles.

Among the information absolutely essential for piloting an aircraft – no matter whether military or civil – are data on attitude, altitude, speed and vertical speed. The instruments for these are located in a central position in the cockpit. In the centre is the attitude indicator. A gyrostabilized artificial horizon indicates the attitude of the aircraft, represented by a fixed symbol, relative to the Earth's surface. The circle with horizontal lines, moving in all axes, indicates pitching attitude and thereby the angle of climb or descent. The angular position of the artificial horizon with respect to the horizontal indicates bank. The position of the horizontal and vertical lines relative to the aircraft symbol shows the deviation from a pre-selected or computed heading, which can be the radial of a VOR. The aircraft is steered in the direction indicated (command display) or until the lines intersect with the centre of the aircraft symbol. Moreover, this instrument, also known as a 'flight director', offers further indications, such as **turn and slip** for establishing the correct angle of bank; an indication of deviation from the datum speed during landing approach and others.

Below the attitude director (AD) is the **horizontal situation indicator** (HSI) which displays headings and distances. It has a rotating azimuth card, divided into 360° and, displays the indication of the **gyro-magnetic compass.** The system consists of an electrically-powered directional gyroscope, a magnetic master compass and the HSI. The magnetic compass measures the terrestrial magnetic field, thereby providing the input to the directional gyroscope. The directional gyroscope is mounted on gimbals with three axes of freedom and a horizontal datum axis. As a consequence of its high rpm the attitude of the datum axis is maintained. Frequent monitoring and correction are needed to allow for the tendency for a gyro to precess, and to allow for manufacturing inaccuracies.

This instrument displays the following:
– course deviation;
– a numeric course readout to enhance reading accuracy;
– a numeric distance measurement to or from a transmitter (distance measuring equipment, DME);
– a 'To-From' display to indicate whether the aircraft is moving to or from a radio beacon.

To the left of the flight director is the combined Mach-airspeed indicator. The speed is indicated, as is usual, in knots (= nautical miles per hour). To the right of the flight detector is the altimeter, whose indication is calibrated in feet, and below that the vertical speed indicator of

12-1 **In the cockpit: the interface between man and complicated systems (McDonnell Douglas F-15).**

climb and descent speed (in feet per minute).

The following instruments for monitoring the propulsion systems are on the right of the cockpit:
- engine tachometer for indicating rpm in per cent of the rated speed,
- exhaust gas temperature (EGT) in degrees Celsius, as measured behind the turbine,
- hydraulic and oil pressures,
- fuel consumption and quantity,

- nozzle position,
- finally the gas turbine starter control handle. The starting process takes place automatically.

These instruments essentially correspond both in their type and in their arrangement to the instruments in a commercial aircraft. On the other hand there are some which are peculiar to combat aircraft, such as the display screens for the electronic combat systems and the radar. The electronic

combat display gives the pilot information on a possible enemy attack on the aircraft, so that avoiding action can be taken or countermeasures initiated.

The radar screen to the left in the cockpit provides a multi-function display, such as attack symbols for ground targets, a radar map picture of the terrain flown over, as well as displays of attacking missiles or aircraft. The control and display panel for operation of the weapon systems is located on the left. The head-

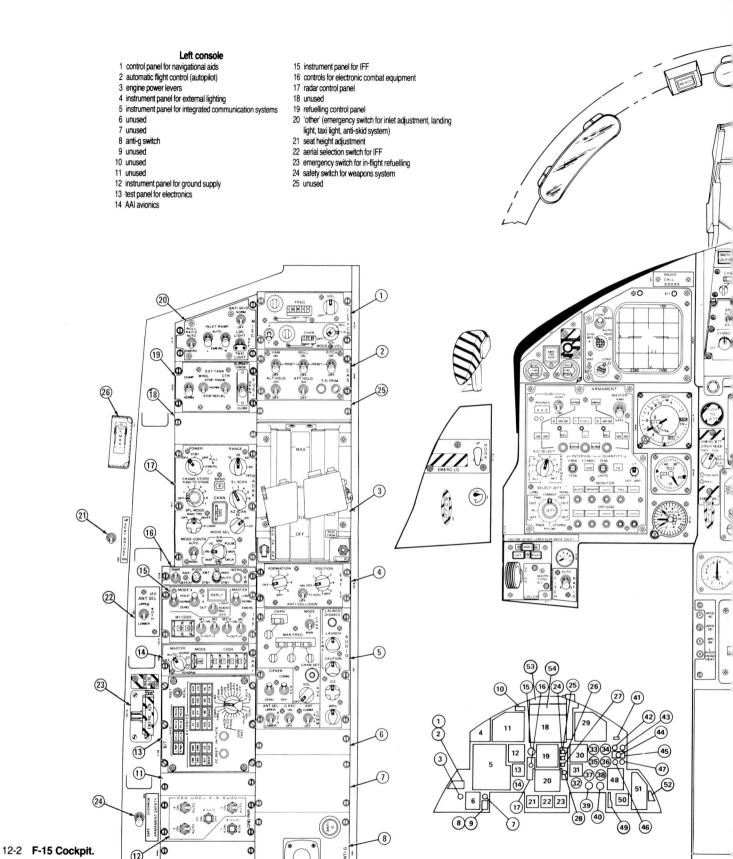

Left console

1 control panel for navigational aids
2 automatic flight control (autopilot)
3 engine power levers
4 instrument panel for external lighting
5 instrument panel for integrated communication systems
6 unused
7 unused
8 anti-g switch
9 unused
10 unused
11 unused
12 instrument panel for ground supply
13 test panel for electronics
14 AAI avionics

15 instrument panel for IFF
16 controls for electronic combat equipment
17 radar control panel
18 unused
19 refuelling control panel
20 'other' (emergency switch for inlet adjustment, landing
      light, taxi light, anti-skid system)
21 seat height adjustment
22 aerial selection switch for IFF
23 emergency switch for in-flight refuelling
24 safety switch for weapons system
25 unused

WARNING
LANDING GEAR CONTROL
HANDLE MUST BE IN
DOWN POSITION BEFORE
OPERATING THIS SWITCH

12-2 **F-15 Cockpit.**

234

F-15A

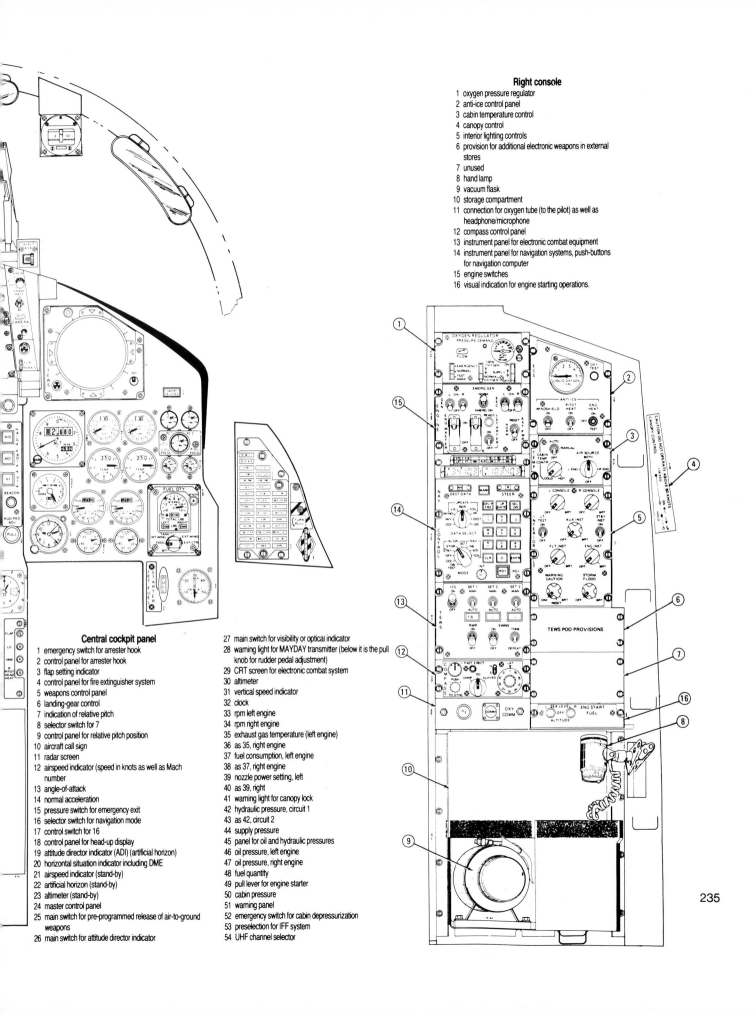

Right console

1 oxygen pressure regulator
2 anti-ice control panel
3 cabin temperature control
4 canopy control
5 interior lighting controls
6 provision for additional electronic weapons in external stores
7 unused
8 hand lamp
9 vacuum flask
10 storage compartment
11 connection for oxygen tube (to the pilot) as well as headphone/microphone
12 compass control panel
13 instrument panel for electronic combat equipment
14 instrument panel for navigation systems, push-buttons for navigation computer
15 engine switches
16 visual indication for engine starting operations.

Central cockpit panel

1 emergency switch for arrester hook
2 control panel for arrester hook
3 flap setting indicator
4 control panel for fire extinguisher system
5 weapons control panel
6 landing-gear control
7 indication of relative pitch
8 selector switch for 7
9 control panel for relative pitch position
10 aircraft call sign
11 radar screen
12 airspeed indicator (speed in knots as well as Mach number
13 angle-of-attack
14 normal acceleration
15 pressure switch for emergency exit
16 selector switch for navigation mode
17 control switch for 16
18 control panel for head-up display
19 attitude director indicator (ADI) (artificial horizon)
20 horizontal situation indicator including DME
21 airspeed indicator (stand-by)
22 artificial horizon (stand-by)
23 altimeter (stand-by)
24 master control panel
25 main switch for pre-programmed release of air-to-ground weapons
26 main switch for attitude director indicator

27 main switch for visibility or optical indicator
28 warning light for MAYDAY transmitter (below it is the pull knob for rudder pedal adjustment)
29 CRT screen for electronic combat system
30 altimeter
31 vertical speed indicator
32 clock
33 rpm left engine
34 rpm right engine
35 exhaust gas temperature (left engine)
36 as 35, right engine
37 fuel consumption, left engine
38 as 37, right engine
39 nozzle power setting, left
40 as 39, right
41 warning light for canopy lock
42 hydraulic pressure, circuit 1
43 as 42, circuit 2
44 supply pressure
45 panel for oil and hydraulic pressures
46 oil pressure, left engine
47 oil pressure, right engine
48 fuel quantity
49 pull lever for engine starter
50 cabin pressure
51 warning panel
52 emergency switch for cabin depressurization
53 preselection for IFF system
54 UHF channel selector

235

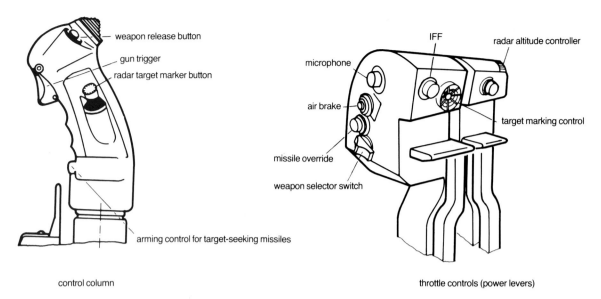

weapon release button
gun trigger
radar target marker button

arming control for target-seeking missiles

control column

IFF
radar altitude controller
microphone
air brake
target marking control
missile override
weapon selector switch

throttle controls (power levers)

12-3   **The control column carries a number of controls (F-15).**

up display with up-front controls is mounted in the upper area of the central cockpit panel.

The most important controls on the left hand console are the engine power levers, each of which carries a number of control buttons (Fig. 12-3).

Also on the left-hand console are the autopilot controls, all the radio controls, and the controls for radar and identification friend or foe (IFF). The right-hand console is used for the inertial navigation system controls, engine starting controls, as well as instruments for monitoring the environmental conditions in the cockpit.

This brief survey is intended to show that, in the cockpit of the modern combat aircraft of the 80s and 90s, a large number of indicators and controls is needed, in spite of their being restricted to essential equipment. However, the present trend is towards reducing the number of discrete instruments. To achieve this, however, a new approach to cockpit equipment needs to be adopted. The cockpit of the future will be distinguished by colour CRT screen displays with extensive automatic operation of the operating sequences, so that the pilot can concentrate still more on the flying tasks. The head-up display has already shown the way toward this new concept.

13 The Combat Aircraft of the Future

In previous chapters the technology and function of the modern combat aircraft have been described. Many of the aircraft types mentioned represent the latest state of technological development. These aircraft will still be seen in operation after the year 2000.

Nevertheless, it is a fact that technological progress renders many designs to a large extent obsolete, even before they have entered squadron service. This is because of the long development periods from five to ten years.

By designing variants of a basic design, an attempt is frequently made to improve the performance of a combat aircraft and so prolong its operating life. Advances in avionics and in weapon technology enable current aircraft to be updated. However, these will have to be replaced at some time. It will now be shown where substantial advances are to be expected in future combat aircraft design.

costs could be 14% lower. Gains for payload or range can be directly derived from this. Additional advantages are to be expected from a shorter period of development.

The beginnings of electrical control systems date back to the early 1950s, when the search was made in Britain for ways of improving flight performance and reducing the vulnerability of combat aircraft. For manned space travel in the early 1960s, electric controls offered the most elegant solutions from the beginning – in particular because of the weight advantage, which pays off even more in space travel than in aviation.

With the increasing performance potential of modern combat aircraft, the development of electrically signalled flight control systems turned out to be an absolute necessity. The first step in this direction was **hydraulic boost,** in which hydraulical control units generate additional 'muscular strength' for operating the aerodynamic control surfaces (Fig. 13-1). In motor vehicles similar devices are in use for power steering and power brakes.

13.1 **Advanced Control Concepts**

The control of present-day civil and military aircraft is effected primarily in the following way: hydraulic control elements at the control surfaces are actuated by the control unit in the cockpit (for example, by the control stick) through a direct mechanical link. The pilot is not able to generate the necessary forces; with the control stick he actuates only servo systems, mostly of the hydraulic type. These provide the necessary control forces. The mechanical parts of a control system — pushrods, levers, cable controls – may become extremely complex.

The advantage of a mechanical control system is its high reliability. However, there is the disadvantage, of complexity, weight and space.

Advanced control concepts for future aircraft are based on the idea – which at first appears simple – of replacing **mechanical** controls by an **electrical** signalling line (fly-by-wire, FBW). The advantages are greater simplicity, lower weight and lower costs. For the F-111, for example, FBW would be 45% more favourable with regard to weight and the space required than the comparable mechanical system, while the production

The simple hydraulic system leads to the pure **fully powered control,** in which hydraulic units alone are actuated by the pilot's control commands (see Fig. 13-1). By adding sensors the simple open-loop control can be changed to a closed-loop system. This can be used to fly an aircraft automatically as well as damping out control fluctuations in turbulent conditions. This is a stability augmentation

237

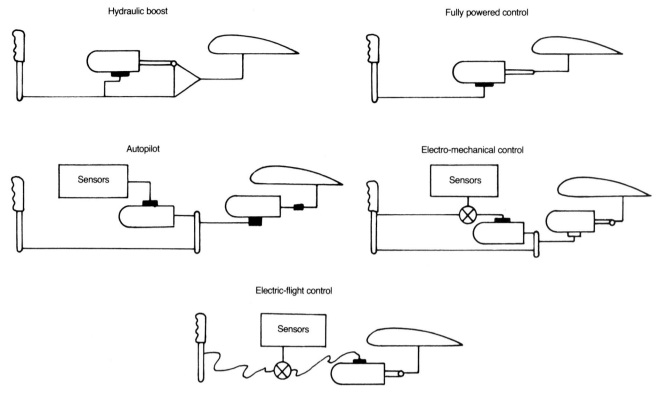

Hydraulic boost

Fully powered control

Autopilot

Sensors

Electro-mechanical control

Sensors

Electric-flight control

Sensors

13-1 **The development to electrically signalled flight control.**

system (SAS). Control systems of this type are called 'autopilots'.

The next step led to a control system in which direct mechanical controls are in parallel with electrical signals (control augmentation system, CAS). By removing the mechanical elements, as with the CAS principle, a pure electric control is obtained.

Electric flight control is being introduced gradually. It is universal in all the latest combat aircraft, and is also a feature of the newest commercial jetliners.

The first production aircraft with pure electrically signalled control was the Tornado; although the F-18 has a system of this kind, a standby mechanical system is also provided.

The use of electrically signalled flight control systems significantly influences aircraft design. The possible control con-

cepts open up entirely new ways of improving flight performance. The **control-configured vehicle** (CCV) concept predicates that advanced control concepts must be taken into account in the earliest stage of design.

Up until now aircraft designers have limited the application of control systems to improving flight characteristics. In practice, this has meant at best the control of longitudinal motion as well as the damping of lateral and directional motion. On the contrary, a CCV design permits novel aerodynamic solutions and improvement in airframe design. It can lead to considerable improvement in performance with positive benefits to weight and cost. At present numerous CCV designs are at an advanced stage of development.

These are categorized as follows:
1. Relaxed static stability (RSS)

2. Direct lift control (DLC)
3. Direct sideforce control (DSC)
4. Manoeuvre load control (MLC)
5. Gust alleviation
6. Active flutter suppression.

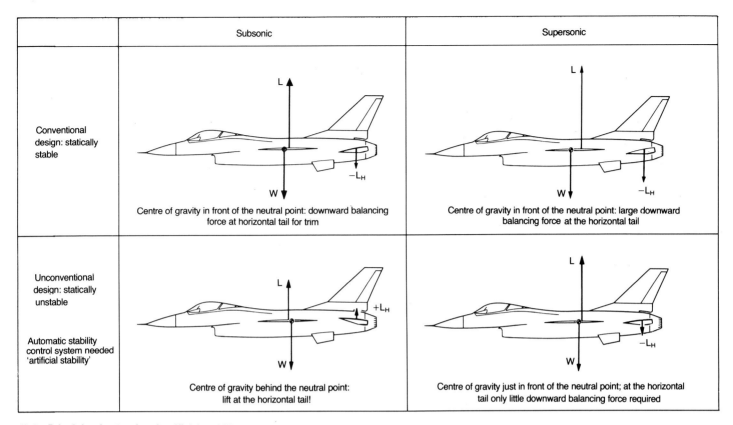

	Subsonic	Supersonic
Conventional design: statically stable	Centre of gravity in front of the neutral point: downward balancing force at horizontal tail for trim	Centre of gravity in front of the neutral point: large downward balancing force at the horizontal tail
Unconventional design: statically unstable Automatic stability control system needed 'artificial stability'	Centre of gravity behind the neutral point: lift at the horizontal tail!	Centre of gravity just in front of the neutral point; at the horizontal tail only little downward balancing force required

13-2 **Principle of natural and artificial stability.**

13.2 **CCV: Artificial Stability**

13.2.1 **Reduced Static Stability**

By the concept **artificial stability** is understood:
a) that the moment equilibrium of an aircraft will be produced in such a way that the manoeuvring performance is optimised;
b) that a sufficient margin of control must be present even in extreme attitudes;
c) that the flight control system ensures optimum flight characteristics over the entire flight range and makes the aircraft easy to control.

Fig. 13-2 shows the principles of operation of statically stable and statically unstable designs. At supersonic speeds the resultant aerodynamic force L lies, in the stable design, somewhat **behind** the centre-of-gravity of the aircraft, causing a nose-down moment (see Chapter 5). The moment equilibrium is generated by a force $-L_H$ directed downwards at the tail plane (downward balancing force). This force is at the expense of the lift generated by the wing.

In contrast with an unstable aircraft, the lift generated by wing and fuselage acts somewhat **in front of** the centre-of-gravity (see Fig. 13-3, bottom left). By this means the tailplane must now, in order to produce the moment equilibrium, generate a lift force $+L_H$ which is up-wards and therefore appears as a gain in the lift sum.

At supersonic Mach numbers the resultant aerodynamic force moves downstream, as described in Chapter 4, and is located in both cases behind the centre-of-gravity, so that a nose-down moment always arises. As in the case of an unstable design aircraft the centre-of-gravity lies further back, however, the nose-down moment is less, and consequently the downward balancing force to be generated by the tailplane also decreases (see Fig. 11-3, bottom right). From this it follows that, even in the supersonic regime, the unstable aircraft makes greater lift possible.

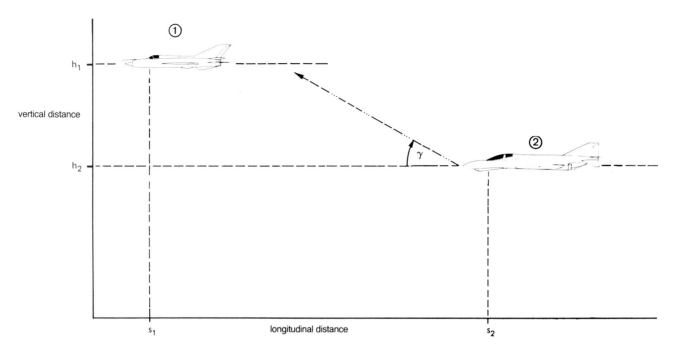

13-3 The conventionally designed aircraft is not suitable for particular combat manoeuvres. In order to achieve a favourable firing position, the aircraft must first go to altitude h, along with rotation about the lateral axis.

The advantages can, on the one hand, be used to improve flight performance; on the other hand, with the **same** performance the aircraft can be smaller. In the latter case the same effective lift is available and the aircraft is lighter and produces less drag. It is even possible that this will allow the use of a less powerful engine with better specific fuel consumption. This leads in turn to increased range or to a reduction in fuel carried. For a typical fighter-bomber theoretical weight savings of up to 10% can be demonstrated on paper.

THE SIGNIFICANCE OF THE AFCS

An unstable design aircraft cannot be flown without an all-axes fully automatic flight control system (AFCS). The missing 'natural' stability must be generated artificially (hence the term 'artificial stabil-ity'). As long as the AFCS works, the pilot does not notice the missing stability and the aircraft can be flown conventionally.

When the AFCS fails, however, an aircraft of this configuration can no longer be controlled. This then imposes stringent reliability and fail-safe requirements on the AFCS. As an electrical flight control system must also have high reliability, the CCV concept and electric control can be integrated.

The necessary safety and reliability can be achieved by means of **redundancy,** in other words multiplexed control paths and individual elements including power supply.

One of the critical points of a redundant multiplex automatic control system is design logic of the redundancy itself. This covers the selection of signals, the detection and isolation of faults and the provision of alternative paths.

DESIGN OF THE CONTROL COLUMN

The use of an electrical automatic flight control system permits the use of a novel form of control column, which in the example of the F-16 is fixed. The manual forces produced by the pilot are converted through sensors into electrical signals and transmitted to the AFCS.

As there are no moving parts, friction and hysteresis effects are eliminated. Moreover, this system shows better survival capability in combat and gives the designer greater freedom in designing the cockpit as a whole.

13.2.2 Direct Lift Control

Since the beginning of aviation, the configuration of aircraft has, in principle, scarcely changed; practically all aircraft have standard arrangements of the control surfaces with elevator, rudder and

240

ailerons. This design has considerable disadvantages for particular combat manoeuvres, however, as will be shown using a simple example (Fig. 13-3).

The pursuing aircraft 2 flies on a straight track behind aircraft 1. In addition to the longitudinal distance, the two aircraft are at a vertical separation from each other. In order to be able to aim the gun at the pursued aircraft, aircraft 2 must either go up to altitude h or pitch by the angle γ.

A conventional aircraft must first of all use the elevator for this, after which a rotation about the lateral axis is initiated; only then can the required movement in the vertical direction be carried out. The path alteration takes the form of an oscillation.

If the combined rotational and translational motion could be successfully uncoupled, aircraft 2 would have an invaluable manoeuvring advantage. In this example three possibilities can be chosen from (Fig. 13-4):

a) the pilot commands an alteration of fuselage longitudinal position angle, without the fight path changing (independent fuselage control, see Fig. 13-4, centre);

b) the pilot commands a load factor n_z; a path alteration results without changing the fuselage attitude (vertical translation control, see Fig. 13-4, bottom);

c) the pilot commands a load factor n_z **and** angle-of-attack alteration by means of simultaneous translation and rotation of the fuselage; the advantage is that conventional manoeuvres can be flown more quickly and with smaller turn radii (see Fig. 13-4, top).

The uncoupled motions can be equally used for evading manoeuvres and air-to-ground attacks. However, the question is still open of how these procedures are to be technically realized. The aim is a change of flight path without rotation and by directly influencing lift. The most suitable solution for this seems to be control surfaces, among which are elevator, flaps, spoilers and canard foreplanes

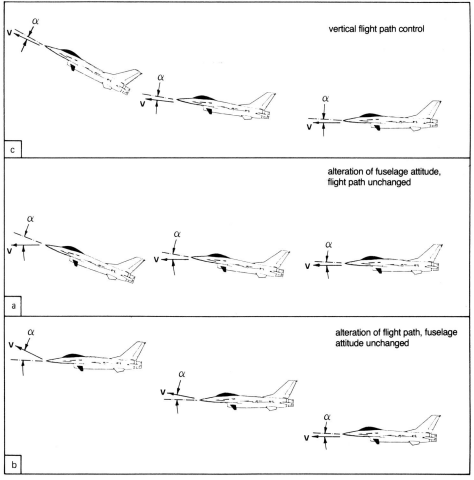

direct lift control

vertical flight path control

alteration of fuselage attitude, flight path unchanged

alteration of flight path, fuselage attitude unchanged

13-4 **CCV configuration for the uncoupling of the longitudinal motions.**
a) Pitch attitude control at constant flight path angle (middle illustration).
b) Vertical velocity control at constant pitch attitude (bottom).
c) Vertical flight path control at constant angle-of-attack (top).

(these being smaller, however, than those on the Viggen).

A computer-based automatic flight control system is required for the co-ordinated actuation of the control elements.

13.2.3 **Direct Sideforce Control**

Analogous to Fig. 13-3, is combat in the horizontal plane. In order to initiate a turn, the pilot must operate rudder and

ailerons simultaneously and in the same sense. Every turn requires, at the same time, a rotation about the longitudinal axis (roll).

In this case, too, advantages are to be expected from an uncoupling of the two forms of motion, as will be shown from examples (Fig. 13-5):

a) the pilot commands a sideslip angle β while maintaining the flight path (independent fuselage azimuth control, see Fig. 13-5, centre);

b) the pilot commands an additional acceleration n_y while maintaining

241

flight direction (lateral translation control, see Fig. 13-5, bottom);

c) the pilot commands a load factor n_y **and** a yawing motion by means of simultaneous fuselage translation and rotation (direct side force, see Fig. 13-5, top).

Improving manoeuvring performance by using sideforce control is even more promising than direct lift control. Wind tunnel experiments have demonstrated that considerable side forces can be achieved by differential deflection of inclined canard surfaces. These forces arise due to different pressure distributions on the left and right fuselage sides. In addition to canard foreplanes vertical auxiliary fins may also be used. The co-ordinated deflections of the control surfaces concerned are again possible only with the aid of an automatic flight control system. This particular technology, however, is only in its infancy.

13.2.4 Manoeuvre Load Control (MLC)

The object of manoeuvre load control for combat aircraft differs from that for transport aircraft. With combat aircraft the improvement of manoeuvring performance is paramount: it is characterized by specific excess power and maximum load factor.

With manoeuvring load control, control surfaces and manoeuvring devices are automatically adjusted in order to generate a desired load distribution for manoeuvring flight. Adjustments are initiated by a control system.

A transport aircraft is designed in such a way that the lift distribution of the wing in steady level flight produces minimum drag. As aircraft of this kind normally fly with a load factor $n = 1$, it makes little sense to improve the drag in manoeuvres (turning, take-off, landing) by means of MLC. Instead an attempt is made to reduce the root bending moment at the

direct sideforce control

lateral acceleration without sideslip, simultaneous translation and rotation

alteration of the sideslip angle, flight path unchanged

lateral acceleration at a constant sideslip angle, flight azimuth heading unchanged

13-5 **CCV configuration for the uncoupling of lateral motion.**
a) Directional attitude control at constant flight path angle (middle illustration).
b) Lateral velocity control at constant yaw attitude (bottom).
c) Directional flight path control at zero sideslip angle (top).

wing/fuselage junction by shifting the lift distribution inwards.

Moreover, corresponding leading-edge flaps are extended in the inner area of the wing; they increase the lift here, while, if necessary, spoilers in the outer area reduce lift (Fig. 13-6). This concept can lead to savings in structural weight.

In contrast to the transport aircraft, it is when manoeuvring that a combat aircraft has to produce maximum performance. An MLC concept must therefore provide for high-lift devices – leading-edge flaps,

trailing-edge flaps, and canards. In this way drag can be reduced and buffet onset delayed to higher Mach numbers.

The greatest advantages of manoeuvre load control are to be expected when the aircraft is designed to be unstable because the drag-increasing downward balancing forces of the horizontal tail are eliminated.

13.2.5 Gust Alleviation

Attack missions force combat aircraft to operate mainly in the high-speed, low-altitude mode in order to fly under enemy radar and evade air defences.

Flying in this mode exposes aircraft and crew to extremely heavy stresses, resulting primarily from atmospheric turbulence. The turbulence may become so severe that the operation has to be aborted.

Those aircraft whose wings have a relatively steep lift slope C_{L_α} with simultaneously lower wing loading (see Chapter 4) are particularly susceptible to the effects of turbulence. On the other hand, wings with flat lift gradients and high wing loading are more suitable for such missions; for example, thin delta wings. These configurations are, however, characterized by large concentrations of mass in the fuselage which unfavourably affect the rotational behaviour about the lateral axis (short-period mode).

The aim of CCV designs for gust alleviation is to damp the additional lift and side forces caused by vertical and horizontal gusts. For this, there must be a way of immediately influencing the lift gradient and the sideslip angle behaviour.

The lift gradient can be influenced within certain limits by rapid adjustment of swivelling wing tips. The angle-of-attack range is very small because of the low gust speed in comparison with the flight speed.

The damping of lateral gusts requires additional vertical control surfaces at the fuselage nose which are adjusted in the same direction as the rudder in order to counteract lateral acceleration.

The use of gust alleviation improves crew comfort and reduces airframe fatigue stress. Weight savings may also result from this technique.

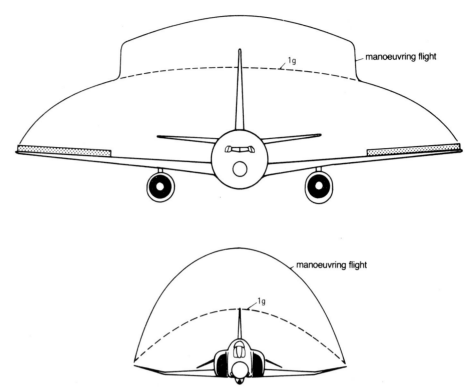

13-6 **Manoeuvre load control (MLC).**
a) Transport aircraft: displacement of the lift distribution inwards reduces the root bending moment and permits a lighter type of construction.
b) Combat aircraft: increase of total lift distribution by adjusting the high-lift devices: application in manoeuvring flight.

13.2.6 Active Flutter Damping

Carrying underwing stores favours flutter of the wing (transport aircraft whose engines are mounted under the wing are faced with similar problems).

Flutter is a type of oscillation – frequently with increasing amplitude – which develops from the interaction between aerodynamic, elastic and inertial forces. In conventional aircraft flutter is countered by increased structural rigidity, which leads to greater weight.

Flutter in combat aircraft is expressed by oscillations of the weapon stores. A way of damping flutter is demonstrated by the stores themselves which can have adjustable aerodynamic surfaces controlled by an internal sensor.

It must be said, however, that not everything which seems technically feasible has a chance of being realized. The more complex a system becomes, the greater the probability of failure.

243

13.3 Cockpit Design

The aim of this technology is the advanced design of the cockpit and ensuring that the pilot will be capable of acting even under high acceleration forces (high acceleration cockpit, HAC). Its realization is seen in the introduction of cockpits with an all-round view as well as in the installation of an inclined seat for the pilot. Investigations in a centrifuge have shown that the human pilot, in a particular seating position, is capable of withstanding normal accelerations of 10 g for up to two minutes.

A favourable solution turns out to be a seat which can be inclined by 60 degrees backwards and simultaneously raises the pilot's legs to prevent the blood from flowing into the lower parts of the body (Fig. 13-7). If the pilot is compelled to bale out, a pressure-loaded spring erects the ejector seat within 0.3 seconds before the propelling charge ignites. This time is needed in any event for the release of the cockpit canopy.

13.4 New Materials

The introduction of fibre-reinforced materials promises a considerable saving in weight with future combat aircraft. This method of construction, developed for space flight is even now at a level of technology which raises expectations of revolutionary methods of airframe construction. In contrast to present aircraft construction techniques, where the material is processed as a semi-finished product by shaping, the final structure is created during the production process. The fibre reinforcements can be designed exactly according to the computed stress curve.

The structure weight of future aircraft can be considerably reduced by this technology, which will, in turn, have an effect on airframe design. Present-day modern combat aircraft, such as the F-14, F-15 and F-16 contain 5% of the new composite materials. In later fighters the percentage can be as high as 34%.

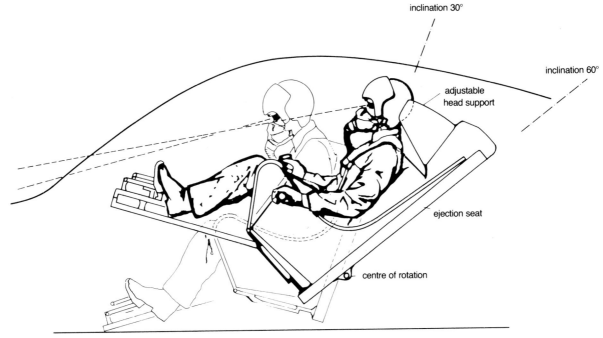

13-7 **Inclining seat for acceleration to 10 g.**

13.5 **Towards the Combat Aircraft of Tomorrow**

The next generation of combat aircraft, of which the first outlines are appearing, will be operational in the 1990s. Combat performances may be expected which will considerably exceed the potential of most present-day equipment. The appearance and combat performance of these new fighters can be gleaned from current directions of development, above all in the USA, where the Air Force and NASA are jointly working on advanced combat aircraft technologies. These are being carried out within the so-called AFTI (Advanced Fighter Technology Integration) programme. AFTI is a continuous programme which, basically, pursues the following goals:

- new kinds of manoeuvre at supersonic and transonic speeds,
- increasing target acquisition and weapons capacities in air-to-air and air-to-ground operations,
- improved survival capability.

The technologies required for these goals are to be defined and made ready for use.

The first phase (AFTI 1), which ran until 1975, was devoted to the definition of a suitable technology demonstrator incorporating a maximum of the already available technological knowledge. The areas under consideration included:

- aerodynamics,
- flight controls,
- materials and
- cockpit design (high-acceleration cockpit).

The goal of the AFTI programme is that flightworthy aircraft should be built as test carriers in the 80s. Certain groups of functions in the total programme were assigned to individual programme sections (AFTI Tech Set = Set of Technology) and worked on.

Within the investigation section, termed Tech Set I, a modified F-15 and F-16 are to be used to test respectively increased survival capability and the firing of air-to-air and air-to-ground weapons (Fig. 13-8). The aircraft are equipped with electronic flight control systems and artificial stability, and are intended to establish the applicability of the CCV concept in aerial combat (see Chapter 13.2). With the aid of direct lift and sideforce control the flight path can be altered in a horizontal and vertical direction without the need for rotation about the particular axis. This makes continuous aim at air or ground targets possible while maintaining full manoeuvrability.

Apart from the uncoupled motion sequences the following points are to be investigated within this programme section:

- coupled weapon-aiming and flight control;
- improved aerodynamics and methods of construction;
- high-acceleration cockpit.

The purpose of phase Tech Set II, which is being mainly carried out by Boeing, General Dynamics and Grumman, is primarily an investigation of the transonic range. For this purpose, among other things, an F-111 was fitted with a supercritical wing. It is known that cruising flight can be carried out at high subsonic speeds with considerably less drag by this means. As transonic profiles react very sensitively to deviations from the design Mach number, ways are also being studied, by altering the profile geometry, of achieving optimum matching to the particular flight Mach number.

A further part of this programme section is the investigation of the rectangular nozzle (2-D nozzle). This type can be easily integrated into the tail contours and with the swivelling design, permits direct lift control (see Chapters 6 and 8). A lift increase is expected from this, as well as reduced take-off and landing runs, and an improvement of manoeuvring performance (Fig. 13-9).

If the investigations show that considerable improvements of combat per-

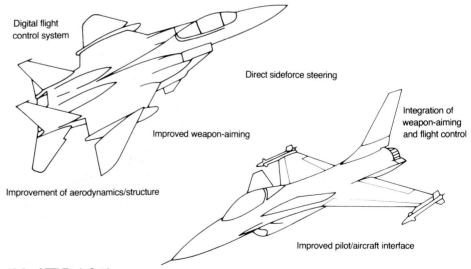

Digital flight control system

Direct sideforce steering

Improved weapon-aiming

Integration of weapon-aiming and flight control

Improvement of aerodynamics/structure

Improved pilot/aircraft interface

13-8 **AFTI Tech Set I**
A modified F-15 and F-16 are intended to furnish evidence respectively of a higher survival probability and improved techniques of weapon-aiming.

formances are to be expected, then the subsequent phase Tech Set III is intended to lead to a completely new type of combat aircraft configuration (Fig. 13-10). This aircraft would be a signpost to a future generation of combat aircraft which will be in production from the year 2000 on and could give the armed services an unparalleled combat strength.

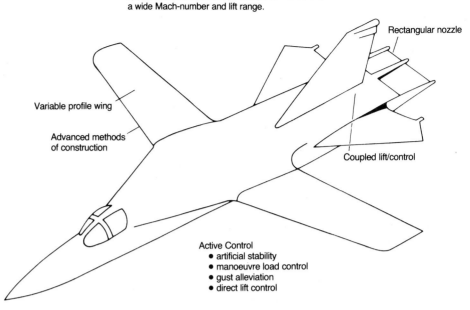

Improvement of the aerodynamic performance over a wide Mach-number and lift range.

Rectangular nozzle

Variable profile wing

Advanced methods of construction

Coupled lift/control

Active Control
● artificial stability
● manoeuvre load control
● gust alleviation
● direct lift control

13-9 AFTI Tech Set II
Improved flight performances in an extended Mach number range.

13-10 AFTI Tech Set III
Application of the latest technologies to a high-performance combat aircraft for the year 2000.

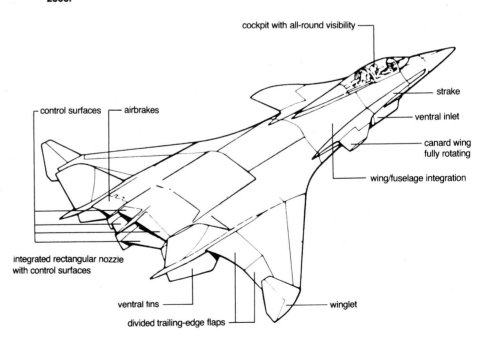

cockpit with all-round visibility

control surfaces   airbrakes

strake

ventral inlet

canard wing fully rotating

wing/fuselage integration

integrated rectangular nozzle with control surfaces

ventral fins

winglet

divided trailing-edge flaps

Appendix

Systems of Units

In practical use there are at present three systems of units:
1. the International System of Units (SI)
2. the Technical System of Units
3. the UK/US System of Units.

An attempt is being made to replace the other systems by degrees. Accordingly, the International System of Units is generally used in this book, although the other two systems are also frequently used.

The International System of Units uses six basic quantities, of which four are important in aeronautics:
- the metre (m) as unit of length
- the kilogram (kg) as unit of mass
- the second (s) as unit of time and
- the degree Kelvin (K) as unit of temperature.

All other units, such as force, energy, pressure, power are derived from them and are listed in the following table.

Type of Quantity	Unit	Definition (SI)	Conversion
Force	Newton N	$1\,N = 1\,\dfrac{m\,kg}{s^2}$	$1\,lb = 4.45\,N$
Energy	Joule J	$1\,J = 1\,N_m = 1\,\dfrac{m^2\,kg}{s^2}$	$1\,ft\,lb = 1.356\,J$
Pressure	Bar	$1\,bar = 10^5\,\dfrac{N}{m^2}$	$1\,lb/sq\,in = 6895\,\dfrac{N}{m^2}$ 1 bar = 750.08 mm (29.53 in.) Hg
	Pascal Pa $1\,Pa = \dfrac{N}{m^2}$		
Power	Watt W	$1\,W = 1\,\dfrac{J}{s} = 1\,\dfrac{m^2\,kg}{s^3}$	$1\,h.p. = 0.74567\,kW,$ $1\,ft\,lb/s = 1.356\,W$

CONVERSION OF IMPORTANT QUANTITIES

Quantity	UK/US System	Conversion
length	inch (in)	1 in = 2.54 cm
	foot (ft)	1 ft = 0.3048 m
	statute mile	1 mile = 1.609 km
	nautical mile	1 nm = 1.853 km
mass	pound (lb)	1 lb = 0.4536 kg
pressure	pound/square inch (lb/sq in)	1 lb/sq in = 0.068948 bar = 0.0703 daN/cm^2
power	horse-power (h.p.)	1 h.p. = 0.7457 kW = 1.0139 PS
speed	knot (kt) = nm/hr	1 kt = 1,853 km/h
	foot/minute (ft/min)	1 ft/min = 0.00508 m/s
temperature	absolute temperature in degrees Rankine (R)	$1\,R = \dfrac{5}{9}\,K$

Greek Symbols

Mathematical or physical quantities are frequently labelled with letters of the Greek alphabet, either alone (e.g. α for the angle-of-attack) or in combination with a Latin letter (e.g. μs for a millionth of a second). In the following all the Greek symbols and symbol combinations with pronunciation and meaning (also multiple meaning) are compiled in tabular form.

Symbol	Pronunciation	Meaning
α	alpha	angle-of-attack
β	beta	sideslip angle
γ	gamma	radio of specific heat capacities (Anglo-American) Mach angle inclination of flight path
Δ	(capital) delta	for the indication of differences
δ	(small) delta	rudder angle
ϵ	epsilon	lift/drag ratio
η	eta	efficiency
ϑ	theta	for the indication of angle
κ	kappa	ratio of specific heat capacities
Λ	(capital) lambda	aspect ratio (A.R.)
λ	(small) lambda	taper ratio (wing) wavelength (radiation) total pressure loss (inlet)

Symbol	Pronunciation	Meaning
μ	mu	combined with Latin letters as unit symbol of the millionth part of this unit
μs	mu-s	a millionth of a second, microsecond
μm	mu-metre	a millionth of a metre = a thousandth of a millimetre, micrometre
Π	(capital) pi	pressure ratio pressure recovery
ρ	rho	air density
Σ	(capital) sigma	mathematical sign for sum
φ	phi	for the labelling of angles frequently with an index
φ_v	phi-vee	leading edge sweep angle (English $\Lambda_{L.E.}$ = lambda leading edge)
φ_{25}		sweepback at 25% angle
ω	omega	turn rate, angular velocity
ν	nu	kinematic viscosity

Ideal Gas

The relationship between density ρ, pressure p and absolute temperature t is given by the thermal equation of state for ideal gases:

$$p = \rho \, Rt$$

In the International System of Units the gas constant R has the value 287 J/kg K or 8314.34 J/kmol/K.

Reynolds Number

There is mechanical similarity between two flows if the Reynolds number is equally large in both cases. The Re number is dimensionless and defined as follows

$$Re = \frac{c \cdot l}{\nu}$$

c = flow velocity (m/s)
l = characteristic length (m)
ν = kinematic viscosity (m^2/s)
(for air $\nu = 14.4 \cdot 10^{-6}$ m^2/s under standard conditions).

In the case of incompressible flows (M < 0.4) the condition of equal Reynolds numbers is sufficient; in the case of compressible flows Mach number equality must be additionally required.

The production of mechanical similarity generally breaks down with small models imposed by the dimensions of some wind tunnels. At Re numbers which are too small the flow has, however, a different character; it is **laminar** and causes less – and thereby false – drag than in the case of turbulent flow which arises at the Re numbers of the full-scale model.

As, with given wind-tunnel measurements, the Re number cannot be influenced, an attempt is made artificially to force the boundary layer transition by means of so-called **transition strips** on the model (see Figs. 4-65 and 10-15).

Standard Atmosphere

For aeronautical applications the change of air density and air pressure with altitude is important. Both are dependent on the vertical temperature distribution t(H) in the atmosphere. Because of the continual variations in the atmosphere a so-called **standard atmosphere** was created by international agreement; fixed values for pressure p_0, density ρ_0 and temperature t_0 at seal level and the temperature decrease dt/dH with altitude were established:

$p_0 = 1.01325$ bar $= 101{,}325$ N/m^2
$\rho_0 = 1.225$ kg/m^3
$t_0 = 288$ K (15C)
dt/dH $= -6.5$ degrees/kilometre

With these the variables of state can be computed as follows:

temperature $t = t_0 - \text{dt/dH} \cdot H$ (H in km, t in K)

pressure: $p = p_0 \left(1 + \dfrac{dt}{dH} \dfrac{H}{t_0} \right)^{\frac{n}{n-1}}$

density: $\rho = \rho_0 \left(1 + \dfrac{dt}{dH} \dfrac{H}{t_0} \right)^{\frac{1}{n-1}}$

$n = 1.235$ as so-called polytropic exponent

Acknowledgements

The pictures and information contained in this book have been gathered from many sources. I would like to take this opportunity to thank the following companies and institutions for their support:

General Dynamics Corp., Ft. Worth, Texas, USA
General Electric Co., Cincinnati, Ohio
Grumman Aerospace Corp., Bethpage, New York, USA
Lockheed Aircraft Corp., Burbank, Calif., USA
McDonnell Aircraft Co., St. Louis, Missouri, USA
Northrop Corp., Los Angeles, Calif., USA
Office National d'Études et de Recherches Aérospatiales
   (ONERA), Chatillon, France
Saab Scania AB, Linköping, Sweden
Telefonaktiebolaget LM Ericsson, Mölndal, Sweden
Martin Marietta Aerospace, Orlando, Florida, USA
Smiths Industries Ltd, London, UK
MBB, Ottobrunn, West Germany
MTU, Munich, West Germany
Avions Marcel Dassault, Vaucresson, France
British Aerospace, London, UK
Ministry of Defence, London, UK
Israel Aircraft Industries Ltd., Israel

North American Rockwell, El Segundo, Calif., USA
Fairchild Industries Inc., Farmingdale, New York, USA
Vought Aeronautical Co., Dallas, Texas, USA
Raytheon Co., Lexington, Mass., USA
Westinghouse Electric Corp., Washington D.C., USA

Special thanks to Mrs. Alexandra Oertel (General Electric), Mr Porter L. Woolsey (McDonnell Aircraft), Mr. Benjamin S. Park (McDonnell Aircraft), Mr. Harry S. Gann (Douglas Aircraft Co.), Mr. George A. Lutz (Martin Marietta), Mr. Walter A. Barron (Grumman), Herr Dipl.-Ing. Richard Stieb (MBB), Herr Dipl.-Ing. Hans-Joachim Knupper (MBB Bremen), Monsieur Jean-Paul Ledy (ONERA), Mr. Roy E. Wendell (Fairchild) and Mr. Rob Mack (then at General Dynamics).

Thanks to my colleagues, Herr Dipl.-Ing. Rolf Banning and Herr Dipl.-Ing. Manfred Schalk (MBB, Bremen), for their advice. My wife gave me active support in preparing the numerous drawings. I received a great deal of help with the captions to the drawings from Frau Höhne and Frau Stättel. Finally, thanks to Fräulein Maren Gießen for conscientiously preparing the manuscript.

(Klaus Huenecke)

Bibliography

Jane's All the World's Aircraft
Jane's Yearbooks, London

Jane's Weapon Systems
Jane's Yearbooks London

The Observer's Basic Military Aircraft Directory
London, 197e

M. E. Brazier, W. H. Ball – Accounting of Aerodynamic Forces on Airframe/Propulsion Systems
in: AGARD CP-150, Airframe/Propulsion Interference

Schlichting/Truckenbrodt – Aerodynamik des Flugzeuges, Bd. I u. II,
Berlin/Göttingen/Heidelberg, 1960

F. Dubs – Aerodynamik der reinen Unterschallströmung
Basel/Stuttgart, 1954

F. Dubs – Hochgeschwindigkeits-Aerodynamik
Basel/Stuttgart, 1961

J. Barche – Aerodynamik des Flugzeuges
Vorlesung an der TU Berlin, WS 1968/1969

W. R. Burris, J. T. Lawrence – Aerodynamic Design and Flight Test of U.S. Navy Aircraft at High Angles of Attack
in: Fluid Dynamics of Aircraft Stalling AGARD-CP-102, 1972

D. E. Johnston, J. R. Hogge – Nonsymmetric Flight Influence on High-Angle-of-Attack Handling and Departure
AIAA Paper 74-834, 1974

– The Effects of Buffeting and other Transsonic Phenomena on Maneuvering Combat Aircraft
AGARD-AR-82, 1975

A. H. Shapiro – Compressible Fluid Flow,
Bd. I u. II
New York, 1954

– Stall/Spin Problems of Military Aircraft
AGARD-CP-199, 1976

– Aircraft Stalling und Buffeting
AGARD-LS-74, 1975

– Aerodynamic Drag
AGARD-CP-124, 1973

– Aerodynamic Interference
AGARD-CP-71-71, 1971

– Fighter Aircraft Design
AGARD-CP-241, 1978

G. J. Hancock – Problems of Aircraft Behaviour at High Angles of Attack
AGARDograph 136, 1969

H. Behrbohm – Basic Low-Speed Aerodynamics of the Short-Coupled Canard Configuration of Small Aspect Ratio
SAAB TN 60, 1965

– Stability and Control
AGARD-CP-119, 1972

J. Barche – Offene Probleme der Flugzeug-Aerodynamik
Vortrag 71-105, 4. DGLR-Jahrestagung, 1971

The Aerodynamics of V/STOL Aircraft
AGARDograph 126, 1968

Prediction Methods for Jet V/STOL Propulsion Aerodynamics Vol. 1 und 2
Naval Air Command, Research and Technology Group, 1975

B. Etkin – Flugmechanik und Flugregelung, 1966

W. Richter – Flugmechanik
Leipzig, 1959

W. Pollitt – Der Flug, Start–Flug-Landung
Braunschweig–Berlin

C. D. Perkins/R. E. Hage – Airplane Performance Stability and Control
New York, London, Sydney, 1967

B. R. A. Burns – Design Considerations for the Satisfactory Stability and Control of Military Aeroplanes – in: Stability and Control
AGARD-CP-119, 1972

Stability and Control USAF Aerospace Research Pilot School
FTC-TIH-68-1002, 1968

H. G. Münzberg – Flugantriebe
Berlin – Heidelberg – New York

– The Jet Engine
Rolls-Royce Publication,
Ref. T.S.D. 1302

– Theorie der Flugzeugtriebwerke, Band I Grundlagen der Thermodynamik und Gasdynamik, Band II Theorie der Strahltriebwerke
Berlin (DDR)

H. H. Ellerbrock, R. P. Cochran – Turbine Cooling Research
in: Aircraft Propulsion, NASA SP-259, 1971

M. J. Zucrow – Aircraft and Missile Propulsion
New York

K. Hünecke – Flugtriebwerke – Ihre Technik und Funktion
Stuttgart, 1978

Airframe/Engine Integration
AGARD-LS-53, 1972

J. E. Hawkins – YF-16 Inlet Design and Performance
AIAA Paper 74-1062, 1974

J. F. Mello – Testing for Design – F-15 Powerplant Integration
AIAA Paper 75-328, 1975

W. F. Imfeld – Development Program for the F-15 Inlet
AIAA Paper 74-1061, 1974

W. H. Ball and P. A. Ross – Experimental Correlation of Installation Effects on Inlet Pressure Recovery
AIAA Paper 71-759, 1971

Inlets and Nozzles for Aerospace Engines
AGARD-CP-91-71, 1971

Supersonic Inlets
AGARDograph 102, 1965

Airframe/Propulsion Interference
AGARD-CP-150

Exhaust System Interaction Program
D162-10467-11, 1973

Program for Experimental and Analytical Determination for Integrated Airframe-Nozzle Performance
LR 24830, 1972

E. R. Glasgow, D. M. Santman – Aft-End Design Techniques for Twin-Engine Fighters
AIAA Paper 72-1111, 1972

B. L. Berrier – Effect of Empennage Interference on Single-Engine Afterbody/Nozzle Drag
AIAA Paper 75-1296, 1975

W. B. Compton – An Experimental Study of Jet Exhaust Simulation
in: Airframe/Propulsion Interference AGARD CP-150, 1974

H. McDonald, P. F. Hughes – A Correlation of High Subsonic Afterbody Drag in the Presence of a Propulsive Jet or Supporting Sting,
in: Journal of Aircraft, Vol. 2, No. 3, May-June 1965

F. Aulehla, K. Lotter – Nozzle/Airframe Interference and Integration
in: Airframe/Engine Integration AGARD LS-53, 1972

E. R. Glasgow, D. M. Santman, L. D. Miller, et al – Experimental and Analytical Determination of Integrated Airframe-Nozzle Performance
AFFDL-TR-72-101, Oct. 1972

R. E. Martens – F-15 Nozzle/Afterbody Integration
AIAA Paper 74-1100 San Diego, Oct. 1974

Abbott/v. Doenhoff – Theory of Wing Sections
New York

H. Friedel – Flight-Maneuvre and Climb-Performance Prediction
in: Aircraft Performance-Prediction Methods and Optimization AGARD-LS-56, 1972

W. H. Ball – Rapid Calculation of Propulsion System Installation Corrections,
in: Journal of Aircraft, Vol. 13, No. 7, July 1976

W. Herbst, B. Krogull - Design for Air Combat
AIAA-Paper 72-749, 1972

X. Hafer – Flugleistungen
Vorlesung an der T. H. Darmstadt

C. D. Perkins, R. E. Hage – Airplane Performance Stability and Control
New York, London, Sydney, 1967

R. H. Klepinger, J. W. Carlson, W. M. Stout – Future Advances in the Aerodynamics of Military Strike Aircraft
in: Preliminary Design Aspects of Military Aircraft AGARD-CP-62. 1969

S. B. Moore – Wind-Tunnel Systems and Techniques for Aircraft/Stores Compatibility Studies,
in: J. Aircraft, Vol. 8, No. 12, Dec. 1971

Prediction of Aerodynamic Loading
AGARD-CP-204, 1976

L. H. Schindel – Store Separation
AGARDograph 202, 1975

Opto-Electronics
AGARD-LS-71
Sept. 1974

D. C. Fraser, P. G. Felleman – Digital Fly-By-Wire,
in: Astronautics & Aeronautics, July/August 1974

B. R. A. Burns – Fly-by-wire and control configured vehicles – rewards and risks,
in: Aeronautical Journal, Februar 1975

M. A. Ostgaard, F. R. Swortzel – CCVs Active Control Technology Creating New Military Aircraft Design Potential,
in: Astronautics & Aeronautics, Februar 1977

A. Simpson, H. P. Y. Hitch – Active Control Technology,
in: Aeronautical Journal, Juni 1977

J. A. Baudrean – Impact of CCV Requirements on Flight Control System Design
AIAA Paper 76-941, 1976

D. C. Anderson, R. L. Berger, J. R. Hess Jr. – Maneuver Load Control and Relaxed Static Stability Applied to a Contemporary Fighter Aircraft,
in: J. Aircraft, Vol. 10, No. 2, Februar 1973

A. E. Preyss, W. G. Williams – AFTI-Advanced Fighter Technology Integration
AIAA Paper 76-888, 1976

– US-Kampfflugzeuge für das Jahr 2000,
in: Flug-Revue + flugwelt, 1/1978 und 2/1978

G. Rosenthal – Faichild Republic Fighter Technology Integrator (AFTI)-Phase 1 Program Review
SAE Paper 751077, 1975

Index